I'll See You
in the
Morning

Front cover photo:
The Petoskey, Michigan breakwater,
where Marty and Norma often walked.

One girl's choices
made all the difference

Patty Martin

ISBN: 978-1-933753-80-5

Text design by Larisa Yoder
Art by Ruth Martin: pages viii, 11, 23, 39, 47, 70, 83, 89, 131, 179, 205, 279, 299, 351, 361,
367, 375, 387
Art by Christopher Martin: pages 17, 33, 57, 65, 73, 101, 111, 119, 125, 147, 165, 217, 225,
259, 307, 323
Art by Ann Marie Johns: pages 139, 155, 191, 237, 287, 317, 335, 343
Art by Edith Burkholder: girl on front cover, page 55

2673 Township Road 421
Sugarcreek, Ohio 44681

Carlisle Press   800.852.4482
WALNUT CREEK

Acknowledgments

Many thanks to the friends and family who helped to make this book possible—my husband David for his editorial work; my sons Ernest and Jay Paul for typing and for editing photos; Christopher Martin, Edith Burkholder, Ruth Martin, and AnnMarie Johns for their artwork; and Louise Martin (Mandy's daughter) for her encouragement and the helps from her book *Aaron and Amanda Shirk of Laurel Hill*. Thanks to my brothers and sisters, my cousins, Aunt Esther Nelson, Paul Brubacher, Bill and Ila Gregory, and many others for contributing memories and photos. Thanks to God for His help and inspiration in this project. Most of all I thank God for His guiding hand in my mother Norma's life and her influence and her inspiration to me.

Introduction

Abandoned by her parents at a tender age, Norma Brenneman Reed found her way through life. At thirteen, she was on her own with no one to guide her decisions.

For over fifty years, starting in 1956, she kept a diary. Tucked in among her diaries throughout the years were memories of her childhood on which this story is based. It was her prayer that someday her story would be written so it could be a help to others.

Marty and Norma Reed

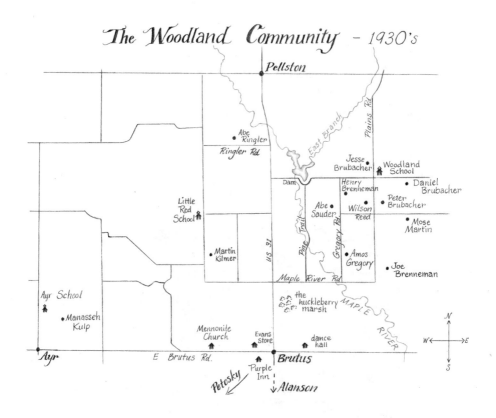

Table of Contents

chapter one

The Paper on the Door

Brutus, Michigan: September 1925

"**C**ome on, Norma, let's go!" Arthur shouted.

Norma raced across the grassy field with her older brothers. The sun shone hot on her face. The empty molasses pail she was carrying clanged against her side. With one hand she pushed a tangle of dark curls out of her face.

"I'm going to pick the most blackberries," Arthur panted.

"But I'm going to beat you there," Walter responded, adding a burst of speed to his already flying feet.

Just then Norma heard a sad cry. "Me too! Me too!" It was Raymond. She looked back and saw him struggling through the tall grass, his pail dragging and his blue eyes filled with tears.

"Oh, how could I have forgotten him," she thought. Quickly she hurried back to him. She set her pail down and with five-year-old motherliness gently dried his tears with her skirt. "Come," she coaxed, taking his hand. "I'll help you." He smiled at her tearfully. She led him over to the berry patch. "Here, Raymond, you can reach these branches." She popped a juicy berry into his mouth. Then she wandered toward Walter and Arthur, picking and eating as she went.

It was unusual for Mom to tell them they could eat all the berries they wanted. Usually she at least wanted enough brought back for some pies, but Mom didn't have time to bake right now because Elenora was sick. Elenora had always been such a happy baby, but now she just coughed and coughed. It was scary when she coughed so hard that she could hardly get her breath. Even Mom looked scared sometimes.

Norma was used to Mom counting on her to keep Raymond and Elenora happy, and she didn't mind. She had no doll of her own, but five-month-old Elenora was better than a doll. She smiled and cooed and played with toys. "I hope she's better soon," Norma thought.

Oh, dear, Raymond was crying again! She hurried to where he sat beside his empty pail. Big tears streamed over his berry-stained face.

"My head hurts!" he sobbed. Then his sobs turned to a fit of coughing. Norma put her arm around him as he struggled to catch his breath.

"He coughs kind of like Elenora," Norma thought. She glanced across the grassy field to the forlorn-looking shanty by the big pine tree. "Maybe we better go to Mom," she said.

Arthur poked his head up from the middle of the berry patch. "I'm going to put some more berries in my pail first," he stated as he glanced anxiously at Walter's half-full pail. "I'm going to have the most!"

Norma took Raymond's pail. "Come, Raymond, let's go find Mom," she encouraged him. Taking his hand in hers, she helped him stumble toward the house.

Neighbor Lovina met them at the door. She had come to help Mom. "Here, let's wash your faces at the pump in the yard. We must be quiet. The baby is sleeping now." She glanced sharply at Raymond as he started coughing. "Oh, no! Not you too!" She gathered him up in her arms and headed for the house.

Norma was ready to follow them when she heard the rattle of a horse and wagon coming closer. She waited. Who could it be? The wagon stopped by their house. Curiously she watched as Dad and another man got down from the wagon and went into the house. The other man carried a little black bag.

Walter and Arthur came hurrying from the berry patch. Arthur lagged a bit behind, carrying his pail carefully. He had indeed filled his pail the fullest.

"Who came with Dad?" Walter questioned.

"I don't know," Norma answered. "He had a black bag."

"Oh, that's the doctor, I think," Walter stated with seven-year-old authority. "I wonder why he came."

Arthur ran over and peeked into the kitchen window. "He's looking at the baby. Now he's looking at Raymond too. Let's stay out here. I don't want him to check me! Now he's coming to the door. Let's hide!"

"No, look," Walter said. "He's putting a paper on our door. I wonder why. Now they're leaving. Dad's probably taking him back to Brutus. Let's go look at the paper. That's a big word—"

Just then the door opened, and Mom stood there. Her face looked tired and sad.

"Mom, what's this paper?" Walter questioned. "What does it say?"

"Look, Mom, I brought you some blackberries," Arthur interrupted.

"Quiet! Don't wake the baby," Mom said wearily. "Arthur, don't touch that paper. The doctor put it there. It says, 'Quarantine.'"

"What's that?" Walter asked.

"It's because we have whooping cough at our house. No one is allowed to come into our house so they don't get the sickness."

Norma's eyes were serious. "Where will we sleep?"

"But Lovina's here," Arthur objected.

"For how long?" Walter wondered. "Can Dad come home? How will we get food?"

"We will sleep in our house, but other visitors may not come. It will be that way until no one is sick anymore. Lovina can come and help us, and Dad can go to the store, but they will need to be careful about washing their hands and changing their clothes."

Mom turned quickly to go back into the house when she heard a fit of coughing behind her. Norma followed her mother to where baby Elenora lay in her little bed made from a wooden box. Mom picked up the baby as she struggled for breath.

Raymond lay on a blanket close to the woodstove. Norma did not know what to do. Her little brother and sister both needed help that she could not give.

"Mom, I'm scared. Will Elenora get better?"

"The doctor doesn't know," Mom answered shortly.

"Oh, Mom!" Norma said. Elenora was her special baby sister. "May I hold her?" Mom looked like she was going to say "no," but then she carefully put the now-sleeping baby in Norma's arms. Gently Norma stroked the baby's soft hair and touched her warm cheek.

The door burst open, and Arthur came in, followed closely by Walter. "I don't feel good," Arthur said, sitting down cross-legged on the floor and propping his head in his hands.

Mom looked up in alarm. "What is wrong with you?"

"My belly hurts," Arthur groaned.

"Huh—that's 'cause he ate his whole pail of blackberries," Walter informed her.

"Oh, Arthur," Mom sighed.

The next morning when Norma woke up, something seemed wrong, but she didn't know what. Raymond coughed fitfully from his corner close to the stove. Everything else was quiet. Elenora wasn't coughing. Oh, maybe that meant she was better.

She raised her head and saw Mom sitting by the stove. Her arms were empty, and her head was down. Was—was—*Mom* crying? Mom never cried.

Then she heard Walter and Arthur whispering in their bed. "The baby died last night. Dad went to get somebody."

No! No! Not her only little baby sister! Norma leaped out of bed and ran to the baby's bed. There she was, but she was not crying or coughing—she was very still.

Norma looked at Mom in alarm. The sound of sniffling came from the boys' bed. "Mom!" Norma said, panic edging her voice.

"She's gone, Norma," Mom said dully. "She died in the night." Norma stood in shock. It couldn't be true!

There was a sound at the front door. Dad came in. His face looked very stern. His blue eyes looked straight ahead.

"They're here," he said.

Slowly Mom came over and pulled the cover over little Elenora's face. Then she helped Dad pick up the baby's bed. Norma watched. What were they going to do? They carried the little wooden box bed to the front kitchen window. Dad opened the window and carefully handed the baby through the window to someone outside. Then he closed the window.

"No! No! Mom!" Norma felt Mom's arms around her.

"Hush, baby Elenora is gone. They will take care of her. We can't go because of the quarantine."

"I want my baby," Norma sobbed. She felt Dad's hand on her shoulder. More sobbing came from the boys' bed.

"Why did baby Elenora die? Where did she go?"

Dad turned away. Mom bent to straighten Raymond's cover. No one answered Norma's questions. A deep, dark sadness settled over the little family.

Then there was a knock at the door. Dad glanced out the front window to see Elsie Gregory, the neighbor lady, walking away from the house. On the stoop sat a big box. Dad opened the door and carried the box to the table. Drying her tears on her sleeve, Norma climbed up on a chair to look into the box.

Her eyes opened wide. "Mom, look!" Inside was food—more food than Norma had seen in quite a while—bread, jars of soup, and a pie. Way down in the corner of the box, Norma spied four pieces of maple sugar candy! Elsie was a true friend!

Mom moved about the house caring for Raymond and saying nothing. Dad went outside to chop wood. Norma forgot Elsie's wonderful box and stood looking out the window where they had taken Elenora. What did they do with Elenora? Was she all right now? Norma's arms felt so empty. A tear rolled down her cheek.

chapter two

The Best Birthday

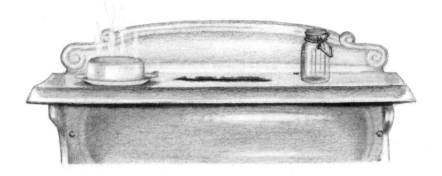

Petoskey, Michigan: June 1926

Norma carefully smoothed the sandy soil at her favorite spot under the birch tree. Taking several small sticks, she made the outline of a house. Inside the house, she put her pinecone people. Sprigs of long-needle pine made little trees around her house. Raymond sat nearby, busily digging a hole with a broken stick.

"Norma, where's Lovina? I like Lovina. Where is she?" Raymond piped up.

"Lovina's at Brutus," Norma explained. "Remember when we came to our new house in Petoskey? Lovina lives back by our old house."

"But I want to see her!" Raymond protested.

"Lovina's nice. She helped Mom a lot. She helped us when you were sick. I'm so glad you got better. But we can't go back there now.

"Look, here come Walter and Arthur. Don't bump my house!" Norma warned as the two boys came and sprawled out in the shade.

"It's hot!" Arthur announced, pushing his thick, black hair off his forehead. "I wish we could go to the lake. I liked when Mom took us there. Lake Michigan is so-o-o big! It even has ships on it sometimes."

"It was fun at the lake, but if I had a bike to ride, I could cool off whenever I want to," Walter replied. "I wish I could have gotten one on my birthday like the neighbor boy did."

"I'm going to have a birthday soon. I can hardly wait," Norma said excitedly. "Maybe if Mom can get some eggs, she'll bake a cake."

"I like cake, but I wish we would get toys for our birthdays," Arthur said wistfully. "I'd pick a wagon."

"I'd like a doll—a doll of my very own that I can play house with," Norma dreamed. "I miss baby Elenora. If I had a doll, I would name her Elenora. Oh, Mom's calling." Jumping up, Norma brushed the sand from her skirt and sped to the house.

"Here, Norma, I need you to stir this for me," Mom said. Pushing a block of wood over to the cookstove, Norma stood on it and took the big spoon from Mom.

"Mom, how soon will my birthday be? Will you make a cake?"

"It's just three days yet. I'll make a cake if Dad can buy some eggs."

"Mom, I wish I had a sister. If I can't have a sister, then I wish I had a doll. Mom, did you ever have a sister?"

A faraway look crossed Mom's face. "Yes, I have five sisters."

Norma's eyes widened. "*Five* sisters! Where are they, Mom? I never saw them."

"They live far away in Mayton, Alberta. That's where I lived when I was a girl."

"Did you have brothers too, and a mom and dad?"

"Yes, I have four brothers and a mom. I had a dad too, but he died."

"Tell me some more, Mom."

"Well, we lived in a house with a long lane. The house had a big, rounded window. My mom always had pretty red flowers called geraniums blooming inside the windows."

"Was I there too?"

"Well, no. First I grew up and met your dad. Then we moved to a place called Redcliff, Alberta. That's when we got you. We already had Walter and Arthur."

"I don't remember that!"

"No, you were just a six-month-old baby when we brought you to Brutus."

"Can I go now, Mom? Look, here comes Dad. Do you think he got eggs?"

"Yes, you may go, but don't talk about a cake now," Mom said.

"Why, Mom?"

"Hush!"

Norma watched eagerly as Dad set a small basket of eggs on the table. Glancing up, she saw Mom's warning look. Quietly she slipped out of the kitchen, but there was a puzzled frown on her face. Why couldn't she talk about a cake?

The next morning, sunshine streamed across Norma's little cot in the corner of the kitchen. She stretched and yawned. Then she sniffed. What was that good smell? Peeking over the covers, she looked around the room.

There—there on the shelf above the cookstove sat a small, round cake! Tomorrow was her birthday. Mom had made a cake! Norma was just ready to jump out of bed when she heard Mom's and Dad's voices.

Dad sounded angry. "You wasted those eggs on a *cake*? But I brought them for breakfast. Don't you know how hard I work just to get enough to keep us from starving? We're living in hard times, Alzina. We don't need a cake!"

"But, John," Mom replied sounding determined. "It's Norma's sixth birthday tomorrow. She wants a cake, and she deserves a cake. She won't get much else. There are still four eggs left. You and the boys can each have one. Norma and I will eat porridge again."

Norma pulled the covers up over her ears. It always made her afraid when Mom and Dad argued.

The door slammed. Dad must have gone outside. Jumping out of bed, Norma pulled her dress on and went over to the window. Pressing her nose against the glass, she looked out at the sunny day. She could see Dad chopping wood by the corner of the house. Soon a horse-drawn carriage went past. The neighbors' whole family was in it. They looked all dressed up. Soon another carriage went by, and another. Turning from the window, Norma asked, "Mom, why is everyone going away? It looks like they are all dressed up."

"They're probably going to church," Mom answered shortly.

"What's church, Mom?" Norma wondered.

Mom sighed. "Oh, it's a place where people go to sing and pray and read the Bible."

"What's the Bible, Mom? Did you ever—"

"Come, Norma, put the bowls on the table. Don't talk about church. Dad won't like it."

Slowly Norma turned to do her job. She thought about the people in the carriages. Those people looked so happy!

It was late afternoon when Arthur and Walter burst into the kitchen. "Lovina's here! Lovina's here!"

"You mean *our* Lovina from Brutus?" Norma responded unbelievingly.

Raymond raced to the window. Soon he was dancing up and down, his blue eyes shining. "Lovina did come!"

Mom wiped her hands on her apron and went to the door. "You made it," she said. Lovina gave her a smile. The children crowded around.

When Norma had a chance, she whispered shyly to Lovina, "I'm going to have a birthday tomorrow. See, Mom made a cake," she added, pointing to the cake on the shelf. Lovina smiled and gave her a little squeeze.

Tomorrow would be June 26. Norma was almost too excited to sleep. She would be six years old!

"Happy birthday, Norma!" Norma rubbed the sleep from her eyes. Lovina was still here. Norma heard Mom and Dad talking in the bedroom. This time they sounded happy.

"Come, Norma," Mom called. "Come see what you got for your birthday." Quickly Lovina helped her slip on her dress. Taking Lovina's hand, Norma followed her to the bedroom.

What was she seeing? Norma rubbed her eyes again. "Look, Norma," Mom said. "You have a new baby sister. Her name is Erma."

"Oh, Mom!" Then Norma was speechless.

"She came right on your birthday, and she looks just like you," Mom

Norma holding Erma

said.

The baby's little hand waved in the air. Norma reached out and carefully touched the soft cheek. "Oh, Mom!"

Just then the baby let out a wail. There was the sound of pounding feet. Walter and Arthur poked their heads in the open door. "What do we hear?"

"Come, see," Dad responded.

"A baby!" they both said together.

"Yes, our baby," Mom said happily. "Her name is Erma."

"I wanna hold her," Arthur begged.

"Lovina will help you have a turn," Dad said. "But the first turn is Norma's. It's her birthday, you know."

Norma settled happily into the chair. Lovina carefully lifted baby Erma into her arms, keeping a protective hand nearby. Baby Erma opened her eyes and looked at Norma. Norma touched the little hand, and the tiny fingers quickly closed around her finger.

Looking up with shining eyes, Norma said, "This is my best birthday ever! Mom, I don't need a doll. We have a real baby—a baby sister. I'm going to take care of her always."

chapter three

School Days and Tattered Shoes

Grand Rapids, Michigan: 1927-1929

Norma sat rocking baby Erma, waiting for her eyes to close. Mom was busy making supper. She looked down at her little sister. How sweet and chubby baby Erma looked! Norma just loved her, even though she was always busy looking after her—feeding her, changing her, pulling her back from the cookstove, and keeping her from crawling out the open door. Norma could hear the boys outside playing tag. Just as little Erma's eyes closed, Arthur shouted, "I got you! Yes, I did!"

The baby's eyes jerked open again. Finally she slept. Mom quickly wiped her hands and came to lay her down. "Tell the boys to bring some wood in, Norma. Then you put the plates on the table."

Walter came in carrying an armful of wood. "Where's Dad?" he asked.

"Oh, he's out looking for a job again," Mom answered. "He thought it wouldn't be so hard to get a job when we moved here to Grand Rapids, but so far he's had no luck. I hope he finds something so we can get you children some warm clothes for school."

Just then Norma heard someone whistling outside. She hurried to the window. Dad was coming down Mason Street. He looked happy.

"I got a job, Alzina," he announced as soon as he was inside the door.

Dad with delivery wagon

"Oh, good! Where?" Mom asked.

"Well, I tramped around town all day. There just aren't many jobs to be had. You know there are lots of vegetable growers around here. Someone suggested I try the greenhouses since they are in their busy season. Sure enough, they needed help. It's a little ways to work, though. I hitched a ride today, but I'm afraid we're going to have to keep on scraping like we've been doing so I can get myself some transportation. Maybe an old Model T that needs tinkering."

Norma saw Walter and Arthur exchange happy grins. A car of their own!

Excitement ran high when Dad brought home a rather dilapidated Model T. The boys hung over Dad as he spent several days tinkering until the old car sounded much better. Dad explained to the boys that lots of people were buying the new Chevrolets, and Model Ts weren't being made anymore, so he got a really good deal.

Norma wasn't interested in how cars work. She had found a new friend. The neighbor girl, Lillian Crab, was teaching her to skip rope. She and Lillian thought it would be fun to sit in Dad's car and pretend they were fancy ladies going on a long trip, but Dad was very particular with his car. He said, "No playing in the car." Neither did Dad take them all for rides just for fun. Gas was just too expensive.

Mom scrimped and saved and made do, so when school started, the children had reasonably warm clothes for the two-mile walk. Norma wasn't quite sure—was she mostly excited, or a little scared? She was going to be in the first grade. What would school be like? She grabbed her first reader and the molasses pail that Mom had put her lunch in and hurried after the boys.

The boys didn't seem to be in much of a hurry. A small creek ran alongside the gravel road where they walked.

"Look, Art, there's lots of frogs in here!" Walter shouted. The boys dropped their books and lunch pails in the tall grass and squatted by the creek. Norma stood by the road waiting.

With a quick swipe of his hand, Arthur shouted, "I got one!"

"Come on, boys," Norma begged. "We're going to be late for school!"

"Hey, I got one too!" Walter exclaimed. "Look how their eyes bug out. Wow, he's a big one!"

"Aw, mine got away," Arthur cried.

"Boys," Norma pleaded.

Snatching up their books, the boys started down the road again.

"Oh, no!" Norma said. "Now I have to take a stone out of my shoe. Wait, boys!" Sitting down in the grass, she stuck her finger in the toe of her high-topped shoes. Dad hadn't been able to find new shoes for her yet. She was wearing her only pair, and they had a big hole in the toe.

"Hurry yourself," Arthur said impatiently. "Let's just go, Walt. She'll catch up."

"No," Walter replied. "Mom said we mustn't run ahead of Norma. Come now, Norma, let's run. Watch out! Get to the side of the road. Here comes a horse and wagon."

After a while, the boys slowed to a walk again. Plucky little Norma had kept right up with them. Norma was learning to keep to the side of the road so her torn shoe was mostly in the grass.

Just as they walked onto the schoolyard, a bell clanged. All the students dropped their playing and ran to the door. Norma and the boys slipped in along with the other children. The teacher was a big, stout lady. Norma wondered if she should be afraid of her until she saw the good-natured look on her face. It didn't take Norma long to decide that she liked school, especially recess and skipping rope with the other girls.

One day when she came home from school, Norma didn't see Mom anywhere. Peeking into the bedroom, she saw baby Erma sleeping in her little bed. Mom was bent over the chest that she used to store clothes. "What are you doing, Mom?" Norma whispered.

"I'm getting some of your outgrown clothes for baby Erma. She is growing so fast. Here are some dresses that I think will fit her. I wonder if I can find a coat for her—"

"Oh, Mom!" Norma interrupted. "What is that at the bottom of the chest? It looks like a doll. Is it? Can I play with it, Mom? Please?"

"No," Mom said, putting some tiny baby clothes on top of the doll. "Not that doll."

"Why, Mom? I'll be careful."

"That's a very old doll. Its head would break easily. Then you would be disappointed again. Someday I hope you can have a doll," Mom said with a sigh. "Go now, baby Erma is crying."

Disappointed, Norma went to get her little sister. It would have been fun to cuddle a doll. Baby Erma was getting bigger. She didn't always want to be cuddled. She was walking now, and she wanted to run everywhere.

The weather turned chilly. The children were tramping through fallen leaves on their way to school. Norma was glad that her seat at school was close to the woodstove so she could warm her toes. Dad still hadn't been able to get new shoes for her. The hole in the toe kept getting bigger.

One day there was a knock at the door. Mom answered the door with Erma in one arm and Raymond clinging to her skirt. Norma followed behind Mom to see who would be knocking at their door. There stood neighbor Hattie with a big smile. In her hands was a beautiful red geranium plant. Mom's mouth fell open in surprise as Hattie handed the flower to her. "I started a bunch of these from slips off my plants. I thought you might like one."

"Why, thank you!" Mom gasped. "How did you know geraniums are special to me? My mom always grew them. Hers were red too."

"I didn't know," Hattie replied. "But I had so many, and I just wanted to share."

"Thank you again," Mom said as Hattie turned to leave. Norma knew Mom loved pretty things. Mom set the geranium in the kitchen window. What a bright, cheery spot it made in the otherwise drab room. Mom looked so pleased.

But when Dad came home, he wasn't in the door long until he asked sternly, "Where did you get that flower? You know we can hardly keep these children fed and clothed. How dare you waste money on something like that?"

Mom's lips tightened. "Well, John, I'll have you know I didn't waste any money. That flower was given to me."

"And who would bring you something like that? I'll have you know, woman, if you ever have other men in here—"

Norma ran to the bedroom and buried her face under the covers. She didn't want to hear more.

The next morning when Mom woke Norma, she said, "Norma, come and see what else Hattie brought to our house when you were sleeping." Norma threw the covers back and jumped out of bed. Mom was holding something out to her. It was—could it be—a pair of shoes?

Mom smiled and said, "Put them on, Norma. I think they will fit you. Then you will have warm feet for school."

Happily, Norma slipped her feet into the shoes. They were not new, but they had no holes, and they were only a little bit too big. "I'm so glad, Mom!" Norma rubbed her hand over the smooth toes.

"So am I," said Mom. "Come now, let's get the porridge on so you're not late for school."

When she came home from school, Norma asked Mom, "May I go over to Lillian's house and show her my new shoes?"

"Sure," Mom answered.

Norma found Lillian behind her house, playing on the porch. "Look, Lillian! I'm so happy I got new shoes—no more cold toes. No more stones in my shoes. I'm so happy I could dance."

"Let's," Lillian responded. "Let's get up on this old table here on the porch, and I'll show you how to dance the Charleston."

Soon the girls were kicking their feet and trying to imitate the popular fast dance. Finally they collapsed, exhausted and giggling. They sat on the table, swinging their feet.

"Your dad's really nice," Lillian said. "He was over talking to my mom last evening. I kind of like when he comes, 'cause my mom always acts so nice then."

Norma didn't answer. She felt troubled, but she didn't really know why. "I think I better go now. Mom's going to need me."

Walter and Lillian's brother Ronald were coming out of the woods along the road. The two boys followed Norma into the kitchen. Something about Ronald made her feel uncomfortable.

The two boys were sitting at the table talking. Norma heard Ronald say, "You see that kerosene can over there by the stove? I can make that handle jump without touching it."

Norma looked at the kerosene can. Sure enough, the handle went up and down. No one was near it. But Mom had heard too. Turning quickly to Ronald, she said, "You get out! You get out right now, and stay out!" Mom was angry.

Ronald lost no time getting out the door.

Mom looked at Walter sternly. "Don't you ever bring that boy in here again! You stay away from him! He's a bad boy!"

Norma was scared. Raymond and Erma were too. They crowded up against her. She hugged them tightly to herself.

"Mom, why did the handle do that?" Norma wondered.

"He's a bad boy, and he's playing with the devil," Mom answered. "Just stay away from him."

"Can I still play with Lillian? Please, Mom. She's nice."

"Yes," Mom answered. "Lillian's a nice girl. I'm glad you have her for a friend."

Walking home from school one day, the boys were kicking an old tin can in front of them. Suddenly Walter stopped. "Hey, Art, do you know what's growing in that field? I think it's turnips. Let's pull one up and find out. I'm hungry! That bread and butter Mom put in our lunch pails didn't fill me up. I don't think anyone would care if we helped ourselves to some turnips."

"Turnips! Yum!" Arthur shouted, dropping his lunch pail. "I'm hungry too. I'm always hungry." Carefully the children pulled some of the smaller turnips from here and there along the road. Then, after wash-

Mom holding Erma, Arthur, Raymond, and Norma (Walter ran away from the picture)

ing them off in the creek, they munched happily as they walked along.

Dad's Model T was parked beside the house when they got home, so he must have come home early. Raymond sat on the doorstep, watching down the road for them. When he saw Norma, he ran quickly to her. Angry voices came from inside. The children looked at each other in dismay. Why did Mom and Dad argue so much?

"Let's just stay outside," Arthur suggested. Soon the children were playing a halfhearted game of tag. Norma was standing close to the house when she heard Mom say loudly, "Move again? This is the nicest house we've ever lived in. How are we going to crowd into a two-room shack?"

She couldn't hear Dad's answer. Then she heard Mom say, "That's too far away. How do you know they will take the boys?"

Norma stood frozen at the side of the house. She didn't hear any more. Take the boys? Who? Where? Move? Leave Lillian? No!

"Hey, I caught Norma!" Raymond said gleefully. "You're 'it,' Norma. You didn't see me come. I caught you!"

Dad came out. "Boys, time to bring in some wood," he said. "You too, Raymond. You're big enough to help."

"Hey, Dad! I caught Norma!" Raymond said happily. But Dad didn't seem to hear. He walked down the road without looking back.

Norma was afraid to ask Mom any questions, but the next morning before they left for school, Mom said, "I guess we're moving again. Dad doesn't have much work, so we have to move to a smaller house."

The children didn't say much, but Norma lingered after the boys were out the door. "Are the boys going with us, Mom?"

Mom looked up quickly and studied Norma's face. "Yes," she said. "Of course. We're all going."

I'LL SEE YOU IN THE MORNING

chapter four

Tarpaper Shack

Grand Rapids, Michigan:1929-1930

"Here, Raymond; here's one for you," Norma said, carefully breaking a thick icicle off the wire fence. "And here's one for you, Erma." Pulling another icicle off the fence for herself, Norma settled down next to the other children.

Arthur had a big icicle in each hand. He was licking back and forth between the two icicles. "I wanna see which one gets gone first," he said between licks. Happily the children sat on the hillside beside the fence that separated their yard from the neighbors and licked their icicles.

Walter was at the woodpile, trying his hand at splitting wood. Dad said he was big enough to do it, but Mom wanted the other children to stay out of the way while he learned.

Norma looked around at the new neighborhood with interest. Nearby she could see the hospital. She liked to watch the cars come and go there, and she wondered about the sick people that might be inside.

The closest neighbor's house made their own little tarpaper shack look pretty small. Even Norma realized how small it was. Mom had hung a curtain in the bedroom in order to turn it into two rooms. On their side of the curtain, Norma slept in the same bed with Erma. Raymond and Arthur shared the other. Walter had to sleep on the kitchen floor. It was no secret that Mom wasn't very happy about the move from Mason Street, but she kept the house clean and made do the best she could.

Their hands red with cold, the children continued to break off icicles and lick them. Little Erma started to whimper. "I'm cold," she said. Norma snatched her up and took her into the house. Mom was busy rolling pie dough at the table. Spicy smells came from the cookstove.

"Tell Arthur and Raymond to come in, Norma," Mom said. "It's time to go sell pies."

Reluctantly the boys came into the kitchen. "Do we have to, Mom?" Arthur pleaded. "I don't like to go up to other people's houses and knock on their doors."

"Yes, Arthur. Dad doesn't have so much work right now. You are eleven years old, and that's plenty big enough to do your part. Here," Mom instructed. "You take this big box of pies, Arthur. Raymond, you knock on the doors. And carry the bag for money. Put it in your pocket and be careful. Here, Norma, you can carry this smaller box of pies. Erma, you must stay here with me until you get bigger. Come back as soon as you sell them. I'll have more pies ready then."

Down the street the children trudged. "I don't like this!" Arthur grumbled. "I don't even know these neighbors, since we just moved here." Then he said in a new tone of voice, "Yum! These pies smell so good! Do you think if we sort of dropped a pie or smashed one somehow, that we could eat it for supper? Mom wouldn't want us to sell it that way, would she?"

"Watch out, Arthur!" Norma protested. "Don't you bump me. I'm going to tell Mom on you if you do!"

Mom's pies looked nice and sold quickly. Soon the children were back for more. Up and down the street they went until all their pies were gone.

"I wish we could have a pie too!" Raymond begged Mom.

"I made some baked apples for us. We need to save the flour and lard to make more pies," Mom answered. "I'm just glad Dad found that store where he could get the food they wanted to throw out. The apples were still good enough for pies, even if they were wrinkly and spotted."

Arthur made a face at Raymond. Norma knew that he was remembering the brown bananas and wilted lettuce that Dad brought home. Mom said, "Eat it or go without."

But one day when Mom called the children for supper, they ran into the kitchen and stopped in surprise. Norma could hardly believe her eyes! The table was covered with a pretty new oilcloth. It was white with little blue flowers. Supper was set out on the table, and Norma smelled meat! Mom had made beef gravy to go over their potatoes. There were actually big chunks of beef in the gravy!

"Meat!" Arthur cheered.

"How did we get meat?" Walter wondered.

Dad said, "The grocery store had some meat that needed to go, so I brought it home. Mom had to trim it a bit, but it sure looks good, doesn't it?"

Norma ran her fingers over the pretty blue and white tablecloth. Everything looked so nice and so good. She glanced at Dad. Was he unhappy about the tablecloth? Where did it come from? No, Dad didn't seem unhappy. Norma felt relieved. She looked around the table. Mom seemed happy too. Why couldn't they always be happy like this?

One sunny day, Norma ran outside to skip rope. Mom had given her a bit of old clothesline. Skipping rope made her think of Lillian. She missed Lillian.

Walter and Arthur came walking around the corner of the house. They were talking quietly. "Dad told me we don't have any choice. We are going, and that's it."

"Just you and me? Will we be at the same place?"

"We won't be far apart. I'm supposed to be at Grandpa's and you with Uncle Joe. Do you remember Dad's brother Joe?"

Norma's rope dangled on the ground. "Boys! What are you talking about? Where are you going? Who is Grandpa, and who is Uncle Joe?"

The boys stopped and looked at her soberly. Walter spoke up. "Sorry, Sis, but I guess Dad's taking Art and me back to Brutus. He says lots of boys eleven and twelve years old work out on farms. He says we are big enough to earn our own keep."

"I don't really remember Uncle Joe," Arthur said anxiously. "I do remember Grandpa a little, but I was just six then. Maybe it will be fun if they have good food to eat."

"But when will you come back? Who will help sell pies?" Norma asked, looking worried. "What will we do without you?"

"Dad didn't say when we'd come back. We'll probably be gone a long time. You'll make it." Walter gave Norma a sympathetic pat on the back. "Maybe sometimes you'll get to come visit us."

Norma didn't feel like skipping rope anymore. Brutus—Lovina, baby Elenora, a blackberry patch—it all seemed so happy and long ago. The little tarpaper shack would seem empty—much too empty.

When Dad left several days later with Walter and Arthur in the Model T, Norma waved sadly from the front yard. Then she turned to Raymond and Erma. At least she still had them. She was glad she didn't have to go off to a strange place by herself.

That night, snuggled up to Erma in bed, Norma heard sobbing coming from the boys' bed. How Raymond missed his big brothers! Slipping away from Erma, who was sound asleep, Norma crawled in beside Raymond and put her arm around him. "Don't cry, Raymond. I'm still here."

"You know what?" she whispered. "Walter said maybe sometime we can come to visit them. Wouldn't that be fun! I think we'd have to take a long ride in the Model T." Raymond was listening quietly with only an occasional sniff. "I don't know how far, but we would see lots of things." Norma talked on and on. "Maybe tomorrow I can teach you how to skip rope like Lillian taught me. Would you like that?" Raymond didn't answer—he was sound asleep.

Carefully and quietly, Norma slipped back to her own bed. She felt like crying too. But no, she had better not. She would just pretend she was riding on a long trip away, away to Brutus, where there was someone called Grandpa and someone called Uncle Joe, and most of all, two grinning dark-haired boys.

Norma and Raymond learned to sell pies by themselves. Sometimes little Erma went along, but she was only three—pretty small for a seven- and nine-year-old to keep track of while they sold pies. Mom didn't always have apples to make pies, but the children weren't sorry. Norma didn't like selling pies any better than Arthur had liked it.

Coming home one day, Norma spied a little snake slithering in the grass at the side of the road. "Look, Raymond, it's a garter snake. That's what Walter called it. Isn't it fun to watch? It won't hurt us. I wish I could have it for a pet. We never had any pets."

Carefully she picked up the little snake. It curled up tightly in her cupped hands. "Poor little snake," she crooned. "You don't have to crawl in the dirt. You can live in my pocket. It's nice and cozy in there. I'm going to call you Sadie."

Slipping the snake into her skirt pocket, she said, "Come on, Raymond. I wonder what I should feed Sadie? I wish we could ask Walter. It will be fun to have a pet."

Later, Norma sat at the table eating supper. Gently she patted her pocket. Sadie was still there, but she was wiggling. Suddenly Erma's eyes got big. "Norma has a worm in her pocket. I see its head!"

Norma looked down. Sure enough, Sadie was peeking out.

Dad saw Sadie too. "What are you doing with a garter snake in your pocket, Norma?"

Mom got up quickly and backed to the other side of the room.

"Oh, that's Sadie. She's my pet," Norma answered. "I found her beside the road." She looked at Dad to see if he was upset. She thought she saw a little twinkle in his eye. "Do you know what I should feed her, Dad?"

"You must take her outside and let her feed herself," Dad said. "No pet snakes."

Mom was still standing by the far wall. Norma took Sadie outside and put her down on the ground. "Bye, Sadie," she whispered sadly as Sadie slithered away into the grass.

When she came back in, Dad said, "Now, Norma, I know you want a pet. But snakes won't do, and any other pet would cost money. We need all our money to feed you children."

Dad was at work one day when Mom brought a brown bag out of the bedroom. "Here, Norma, I have a surprise for you. I decided that you waited long enough." Curiously, Norma looked into the bag that Mom held out. Suddenly her eyes got big and her mouth fell open. "A doll?" she gasped.

"It's for you, Norma," Mom said with a smile. "You can take it out."

Slowly Norma reached into the bag and pulled the doll to herself. "Oh, Mom! Is it really mine?" Carefully Norma cradled the doll, looking into its face. Gently she touched its cheek and smoothed its dress. "Mom, where did you get it? Can I really keep it for my own?"

"Yes," Mom answered happily. "It's yours. I took some of the money from selling pies and bought it in town. I decided it's time for you to finally have a doll."

"Oh, thank you, Mom!" Norma put her cheek against the doll's smooth head. "I'm going to call her Lillian, just like Lillian at Mason Street."

Norma cared tenderly for Lillian. She wrapped her up in an old baby blanket that Mom found in the clothes chest. At night she tucked her into bed. Erma slept on one side of her, and Lillian slept on the other.

chapter five

Something's Wrong!

Grand Rapids, Michigan: 1930

Several days passed until Dad came home from work and spied Lillian. His face got red. He looked at Mom. "What does this mean?"

Mom said nothing. Dad walked over to the stove where Mom was working. Norma quickly grabbed Lillian and slipped into the bedroom. She hid Lillian way down under a pile of covers on the bed.

"I said, what does this mean?" Dad shouted.

Norma threw herself on the bed and covered her ears with her hands. Still she could hear angry words. Dad wouldn't take Lillian from her, would he? Why did Dad get so angry? Tears slid down Norma's cheeks onto the covers. After a while, Norma heard the door slam. Slowly she uncovered her ears. It was quiet. Dad must have gone out.

Nothing more was said, but after that, Norma always tried to have Lillian tucked safely into bed before Dad came home.

Norma came out of the bedroom one morning holding Lillian. Dad wasn't around. He worked at night now, so the children didn't see him much. Norma looked at Mom. Mom looked different this morning. What was it?

Ohh—it was Mom's hair. Usually Mom had her hair done up in a bun, but this morning Mom had it hanging down, and it was shorter. Mom had cut her hair! What would Dad say? Norma hoped she wasn't there when Dad found out.

"Mom, I thought I heard a car stop here after we were in bed. Did we get company?" Norma wondered.

Mom didn't answer. "Norma, go get me a couple pieces of wood. I sure miss the boys' help."

Several nights later, Norma came into the kitchen for one last drink before bedtime. Then she heard it again. A car had stopped out front. Glancing out the window, she saw a strange man sitting in the car.

"Go to bed, Norma," Mom said sharply. Quickly Norma slipped into the bedroom, but she listened. Soon she heard Mom go outside. She put one arm around Erma and one arm around Lillian. Something was wrong. Where was Mom?

After a while Norma heard the car door slam again. She thought she heard quiet voices. Dad was at work. Who was Mom talking to? She shut her eyes tightly and slid down under the covers.

Crash! Norma awoke with a start. She rubbed her eyes and looked around. Raymond and Erma were still sleeping. The sun shone in the window. Another crash. Angry voices. It was morning. Dad was home. A chair banged against the wall. Erma whimpered in her sleep. More angry voices. Kettles banged on the stove.

Norma turned on her side and put her pillow over her head. She thought about Walter and Arthur. Were they happy? Were Grandpa and Uncle Joe kind to them? How she missed them! She knew Raymond missed his big brothers too, even though Norma helped him carry wood and included him in her play as much as she could. Certainly Mom was not happy. She often talked to them sharply. Norma tried to keep the children out of her way. Why couldn't they all be happy?

One day Norma and Erma were playing on the bed with Lillian. "I'm going to see if I can find anything in the clothes chest that Mom won't care if I use for Lillian," Norma decided. Carefully she lifted the heavy lid of the chest. Inside was an old quilt. She knew that down under the quilt were old baby clothes, but probably Mom wouldn't let her have them. Maybe there was something else—just a scrap of cloth to make something for Lillian.

There—what was that white cloth sticking up in the back corner? Carefully Norma pulled on the cloth until it came out of the pile. It was nice and white, and it looked kind of like a hat. It might look like a shawl if it were wrapped around Lillian's shoulders.

Running to the kitchen with the white cloth, Norma begged, "Mom, please may I have this for Lillian?"

Turning from stirring a kettle on the cookstove, Mom gasped. She reached out and snatched the cloth from Norma. "No!" she said sharply. Quickly opening the woodstove, Mom threw the cloth into the fire.

"Mom!" Norma was shocked. Mom never wasted anything! Why did she throw that cloth away so quickly?

"I said 'no'! I don't want to hear any more about it!" Mom said sharply.

Sadly, Norma went back to the bedroom. She closed the chest and hugged Lillian to herself. Why did that cloth make Mom so angry?

It seemed like Dad missed Walter and Arthur too. One day, to the joy and delight of the children, Dad announced that they were all going to visit Walter and Arthur. "When will we leave?" "How long will it take?" "Will we go in the car?"

Everyone looked happy but Mom. "I'll ride along as far as Kingsley. I don't really want to visit your relatives anyway," Mom said, looking at Dad. "I want to help Minerva move. Kingsley's not that far out of the way. If you drop me off there, I'll help her."

"Whatever," Dad replied. "You just don't want my family to see that you cut your hair. I don't really care if you go along or not. I'm going to see the boys. If you want to go to Kingsley, fine." Norma was too excited to wonder long how Mom could miss the chance to see the boys.

At last they were all in the Model T and on their way. Mom and Dad sat in the front. They did not talk much. Norma, Erma, and Raymond sat in the back. Norma would have loved to bring Lillian along, but she didn't think Dad would like that, so she tucked her under the covers with a kiss and left her behind.

Erma soon fell asleep with her head on Norma's lap. Raymond and Norma were too excited to sleep. They were going on a long trip! There was so much to see, for Dad said it would take about five hours. But best of all, they would see Walter and Arthur!

By the time they got to Kingsley, Raymond had fallen asleep too. "Bye, Norma," Mom said, and then she was gone. Suddenly it dawned on Norma that Walter and Arthur weren't going to get to see Mom. Surely they would want to see her.

"It won't be much longer," Dad said. Raymond and Erma were waking up now.

"Where's Mom?" Raymond wondered.

"Mom?" Erma echoed.

"We left her at Kingsley," Norma explained. "Soon we will see Walter and Arthur."

"Dad, do the boys know we are coming?" Norma asked.

"No, I guess we'll surprise them," Dad answered.

Raymond wiggled with excitement. "I can hardly wait."

Soon the paved road gave way to gravel roads and farmlands. "Where did all the cars go?" Raymond asked. "There's lots of horses and wagons instead."

"Most of the people here at Brutus prefer horses instead of cars," Dad explained. "Your grandpa drives a horse too."

"Who is Grandpa?" Raymond wondered.

"His name is Henry Brenneman," Dad answered. "He's my dad, but you call him Grandpa."

"I didn't know you had a dad. Do you have a mom too?"

"My mom died when I was three. My dad has another wife now. You call her Grandma." Norma looked at Dad. She couldn't imagine him as a little boy whose mom died.

Soon the car turned into a lane that led to a farmhouse. A gray-haired man came out onto the porch and walked over to the car.

"Why, John, what a surprise! Come on in." Bending over, he peered into the back seat. "Well, who do we have here?"

"You may get out," Dad said to the children. "This is your grandpa."

Grandpa Brenneman took Norma's hand in both of his large, work-worn hands. "So this is Norma. It is so good to see you. How you have grown!" Norma looked up shyly and met Grandpa's blue eyes. Instantly she felt drawn to this kind, gentle man.

Now Grandpa was talking to Raymond and squatting down to take Erma's hand. The screen door slammed, and Norma looked up to see a lady with a long, dark dress and a white cap on her head, coming across the lane. This must be Grandma. "Lydia, come and meet John's children," Grandpa said.

Just then a barefoot boy came running around the corner of the house. "Walter!"

"Norma!" he said. For a little he seemed not to know what more to say. He just stood there grinning. Then he wondered, "But where's Mom?"

"She stayed at Kingsley to help Minerva move," Dad answered. "I thought it's time to come see how you boys are doing."

"Will you stay for lunch?" Grandma asked. When Dad gave his consent, she hurried off to the kitchen.

"May I show them the cow and horse and the chickens?" Walter asked. It was a whole new world to Norma, Raymond, and Erma as they toured Grandpa's farm with Walter. Raymond and Erma were busy looking at the fluffy little kittens when Walter turned to Norma. "How's it going, Sis?"

"We don't sell pies much anymore," Norma answered. "Mom doesn't have so many apples. I had a pet snake, but Dad said I must let it go. But something's wrong. Mom and Dad argue a lot. It makes me scared."

"I'm sorry," Walter sympathized. "I wish they could be happy like Grandpa and Grandma are. Art is happy at Uncle Joe's too. Uncle Joe isn't married, but his sister, Aunt Salome, lives there too. Hey, look, there comes Art now."

Norma looked up to see a rather funny-looking horse clip-clopping in the lane. On its back sat a dark-haired, tousle-headed boy, and he was grinning. Slipping quickly to the ground, he exclaimed, "Dad! Norma! When did you all get here?"

"We just came," Dad said. "So you learned to ride the mule."

"Yeah, that's Barney, but he doesn't always listen to me," Arthur answered.

"Where's Mom?" Arthur asked, looking around.

"She didn't come along," Walter answered. Clear disappointment showed on Arthur's face.

Just then Grandma called for lunch. "Come along, Arthur," Grandpa welcomed him. "Growing boys can always eat some more." Raymond stuck very close to his brothers as they all headed for the house. Norma took Erma's hand and helped her up onto the bench at the table. What a meal! They had homemade bread and strawberry jam, potatoes and ham, and pudding for dessert.

It seemed the children hardly played long at all after lunch until Dad said it was time to go. Raymond waved goodbye to Walter and Arthur with tear-filled eyes. Norma felt sad, but she knew now that Dad had chosen a good place for Walter and Arthur to work.

This time Norma rode in front. She watched the scenery, but her mind was back with the gentle couple called Grandpa and Grandma. She could still feel Grandpa's kind hand on her shoulder when he said goodbye. There was something very different about him compared to Dad. It was not just that Dad was short and wiry and Grandpa was taller. Norma couldn't really decide what it was, but she was glad to be his granddaughter.

Suddenly Norma spoke up, saying "Dad, don't forget to pick up Mom!" Dad said nothing.

Again Norma said, "Dad, don't forget to get Mom!" Dad drove on silently.

"Dad, isn't that the road we took to Kingsley?" Dad made no response.

Erma was sleeping, but Raymond whimpered, "I want Mom." Dad seemed to be far away. He drove on and on. Raymond finally fell asleep, but Norma was wide awake. A heavy feeling seemed to be pressing down on her. Something was wrong!

It was late when they arrived at the little tarpaper shack. Raymond rubbed sleepy eyes as he stumbled into the house. Dad carried Erma in and put her on the bed. The house was cold and empty.

Dad looked around the kitchen. "Well, it looks like your mom's not here."

Norma wanted to scream, "You didn't stop for her!" But you just didn't do that with Dad.

"I guess I'll have to take you back and see if Sarah will keep you."

Sarah who? Why? Raymond had crawled into bed, shoes and all. Norma went forlornly to the bedroom and curled up beside Erma under the covers. She shivered, and two tears rolled onto her pillow. She couldn't understand what was happening, but something was very wrong.

The next morning, Dad found some cold biscuits for their breakfast. "You finish eating," Dad said. "I'm putting some things in the car. We are going back up to Brutus."

"I want Mom!" Erma cried. Raymond rubbed his eyes hard.

"Now you be quiet," Dad said.

Soon they were all back in the car, headed for Brutus. This time, instead of having excited faces, Norma and Raymond looked sad. Where was Mom? What was happening?

chapter six

Buckets of Tears

Brutus, Michigan: 1930

After weary hours of driving, the old Model T turned off the main road onto the gravel roads of Brutus. Finally Dad spoke up. "We are going to your Uncle Peter and Aunt Sarah Brubacher's. Your Aunt Sarah is my sister. I want to see if she can keep you since your Mom's gone."

"How long, Dad?" Raymond asked. "When will Mom come back?"

"I don't know how long. Now you quit sniffling. You will be living close to Walter and Arthur. Your Aunt Sarah is a good woman."

The children said nothing. What could they say? Norma swallowed hard, but the lump in her throat just wouldn't go away. She had to be brave for Raymond and Erma's sake.

What was Aunt Sarah like? What if she didn't want them? What would Mom say when she found out they were gone? Would she know where they were? Would she be able to come way up here and get them? Norma swallowed hard again and rubbed her eyes.

Dad was turning into a lane now. A white house sat on a small hill. A big maple tree reached its branches over the front porch. A tall windmill lazily turned its arms behind the house. Beyond the windmill was a barn. Several children played on the barn hill with a wagon. Close to the house, a petite woman with long skirts and a white cap on her head was hanging up wash. She left the clothesline and came toward the car when Dad stopped.

"Well, John! Hello! I heard you were around, but I thought you had

Peter Brubacher's house and barn

gone home already." Norma watched her anxiously. This must be Aunt Sarah. She certainly looked like Dad. Aunt Sarah's face looked kind, and she was smiling.

Suddenly Norma realized that Dad and Aunt Sarah were talking in a language that she couldn't understand. She didn't know Dad could talk another language! Aunt Sarah turned and walked to the barn and disappeared inside. The children playing on the barn hill came close and stood looking shyly at Dad and the car.

"You may get out," Dad said to the children in the car. Norma got out and stood holding Erma's hand. Raymond crowded close to her. Seeing the children, Aunt Sarah's children came closer and, smiling, said something Norma couldn't understand.

"You have to talk English to my children," Dad explained. "They don't know Pennsylvania Dutch."

"I'm Katie," said the girl about Norma's size. "Do you want to go see the kittens in the barn?"

Norma looked at Dad. He nodded. "It's all right. You may go." Holding tightly to Erma's hand, Norma followed Katie.

The boy Raymond's age spoke to Raymond. "I'm Joshua. Do you want a wagon ride? We can both get in and go down the barn hill. It's fun!" Raymond hesitated only a bit and then ran off with Joshua to the wagon. Aunt Sarah had come out of the barn and stood talking with Dad again.

Erma was delighted with the kittens, but Norma found it hard to quit wondering what Dad and Aunt Sarah were saying. She could hear Joshua and Raymond's shouts of fun. Then she heard someone calling, "Ka-tie! Ka-tie!"

"Oh, that's Mandy calling us. The girls must have lunch ready." Katie took the kittens out of Erma's lap and reached for her hand. Erma stood up and reached her hand to Norma. Norma took Erma's one hand, and Katie took the other. The three girls headed for the house. Dad and Aunt Sarah were still talking by the lane. They came walking toward the girls.

"So this must be Norma and Erma," Aunt Sarah said pleasantly. "It looks like you found some friends, Katie." Bending down, Aunt Sarah gave Norma and Erma each a quick hug. "We are glad to have you at our house." Norma relaxed a bit. Aunt Sarah reminded her of Grandpa Brenneman. But what did Aunt Sarah and Dad decide?

Raymond and Joshua came running from the barn. "Dad, we rode in the wagon down the barn hill. It really goes fast!" Raymond's blue eyes sparkled.

Dad grinned at Aunt Sarah. "It sounds like old times, doesn't it?"

Aunt Sarah smiled back. "Joshua, you go make sure Dad and Silas know lunch is ready. They're working behind the barn."

"Come along, Raymond," Joshua invited him. The two boys raced toward the barn.

The girls followed Dad and Aunt Sarah up the board walk, through an enclosed back porch, and into a big kitchen. The kitchen was almost as big as their whole house at home, Norma thought. There was a cookstove just about like the one they had at home. But Mom wasn't at this cookstove. Instead there were two teenage girls bustling about. Suddenly Norma missed Mom badly. She blinked and swallowed hard. Aunt Sarah was telling Dad, "This is Lydia." She motioned to a light-haired girl several years older than Norma. "And this is Mandy." She motioned to a darker-haired girl who looked a bit older than Lydia. "Betsy and Mary are working for the neighbors."

"My, how time flies!" Dad responded.

The door burst open, and Raymond and Joshua came in, followed by a young boy and a man in overalls. "That must be Uncle Peter," Norma thought. Dad shook hands with Uncle Peter.

"This is Silas," Uncle Peter introduced the boy. They began speaking Pennsylvania Dutch again. Erma was tugging on Norma's hand. Norma bent over to her.

"Where's Mom?" she whispered, her eyes full of tears.

"Shh!" Norma answered quickly, drying Erma's tears with her sleeve.

"Come, girls," Aunt Sarah said, guiding them gently by the shoulders. "You can sit here on the bench with Katie." The homemade bread and soup looked good, but Norma ate very little. What *was* going to happen to them?

After lunch, the big girls cleared away the dishes, and the family scattered. "Come, Norma and Raymond," Dad said. "Bring Erma along. I want to talk with you." The children followed him outside. Aunt Sarah followed at a distance. Dad stopped by the Model T.

"Well," Dad said, "your Aunt Sarah said she will keep you. She will take good care of you, and I think you'll like it here. I brought your clothes along. I'll have to go now so I can get back to work."

The children looked at Dad soberly. "But Dad!" Raymond's chin quivered. "It's nice here, but—but Dad! When *will* you come back?" He dug his knuckles into his eyes. Norma swallowed and rubbed her own eyes quickly. Erma whimpered, sensing that something was wrong.

"I don't know," Dad answered, "but you be good for Sarah." Setting their bags on the grass, Dad got into the car. Aunt Sarah stood close behind them now. With tear-filled eyes, the children watched Dad drive away.

Suddenly the floodgates opened. Raymond sobbed uncontrollably. "I want Mom," Erma cried. Norma felt tears sliding down her own cheeks. Then they were in Aunt Sarah's arms. She encircled them all. They leaned against her apron and cried and cried. Aunt Sarah just let them cry.

Finally the sobbing lessened. "Come," Aunt Sarah said. "Let's wash your faces." She picked up the few bags of clothes from the grass and took Erma's hand. Slowly the children followed. With gentle hands, Aunt Sarah washed their faces. Mandy came into the kitchen carrying a kitten. Carefully she put it in Erma's arms. Erma smiled through her tears.

Just then Uncle Peter came to the kitchen door. "Raymond, would you like to help me feed the cows and horses?" With a tremulous smile, Raymond put his hand in Uncle Peter's outstretched one and followed him to the barn.

Aunt Sarah looked at Norma. "Norma, shall we take your things upstairs? Then maybe you can help Katie gather the eggs. I think you'll like the new little chicks."

Soberly Norma followed Aunt Sarah up the stairs. There was a hallway with three doors leading from it. "This is the boys' room," Aunt Sarah explained. "We'll put Raymond's things in here. Next is the big girls' room. And this is where you and Erma will sleep. This is Katie's and Lydia's room, but Lydia will go over with the big girls. I think you'd like to sleep with Erma for right now. Isn't that right?" Norma nodded, biting her lip to keep it from trembling.

"Let's put your and Erma's things here and go find Katie," Aunt Sarah said.

When they came downstairs, Mandy was holding Erma and rocking her. Erma's eyes were drooping. The kitten lay curled up in her lap.

"Come," Aunt Sarah said. "Let's go find Katie." Katie was swinging on a big swing hung from the maple tree beside the house. "Katie, you and Norma go get the eggs. I think Norma would like to see the new chicks."

Katie chattered on the way to the barn. "I'm ten. I just had a birthday. How old are you?"

"I'm nine, but I'll have a birthday before too long," Norma answered. "Erma's birthday is the same day as mine, but she's just three. Raymond is seven."

Katie chattered on. "Do you like to skip rope? I do. We have to go through the barn to get to the chickens. Dad made it that way to keep it warmer for the chickens in the winter."

Norma held the basket while Katie looked for eggs. Norma was not quite sure that she wanted to reach under the chickens for eggs. Their beaks looked sharp. But gathering eggs was fascinating. She had never done it before.

"Mom says to be careful not to crack eggs. She sells most of them when she sells butter. We don't get to eat many."

How Norma did love the fluffy little chicks. Katie picked one up for her to hold. It felt so soft against her cheek! When the girls brought the eggs into the kitchen, Erma was sleeping on the daybed in the corner of the room.

"Let's go swing," Katie suggested.

Aunt Sarah spoke up. "That's okay, but don't go too far from the house. I think when Erma wakes up from her nap, it will be better if Norma is nearby."

Soon Katie was pushing Norma on the swing, up, up into the maple tree. How good the cool wind felt on her hot cheeks. Her black curls blew around her face as the swing came rushing down again.

Katie was showing Norma how to pump the swing without being pushed when Aunt Sarah came to the door. "Come, Norma. Erma just woke up, and she needs to see a familiar face."

Erma was crying for Mom when Norma came into the kitchen. Seeing Norma, she ran and threw her arms around her. "Where's Mom? I want Mom!" she cried.

Norma hugged her close while her own tears fell on Erma's head. Then dashing her tears away, she took Erma's hand. "Would you like to see some little chickens? Katie showed them to me. Let's go find them."

"Let's take a cup along," Katie said. "Dad's doing the milking. We can get a drink of fresh, warm milk."

Erma liked watching the little chicks, but she soon had a kitten draped over her arm while Katie took them on a tour of the barn. The horses looked so big, and Norma and Erma both jumped when one of them blew air through his nose. Raymond was squatting by Uncle Peter as he sat milking a cow. Uncle Peter was patiently showing Raymond how to try his hand at milking.

He smiled at the girls. "Now I wonder why you brought a cup to the barn," he said teasingly. "Here, Raymond, can you make the milk come into the cup? Then you can have a drink....There, good. Now taste it."

Raymond smacked his lips. "That's the best milk I ever tasted! Norma, I did it myself!"

"Now let me finish," Uncle Peter said. He filled the cup again and again until each of the little girls had a drink. Erma giggled as Uncle Peter squirted milk into the cat's open mouth.

When Aunt Sarah called them for supper, Raymond came into the kitchen and stopped short, his blue eyes wide. On the table were plates of fluffy biscuits and chicken gravy. There were fresh sugar peas and lettuce salad from the garden.

"How many times a day do you eat?" he asked incredulously. Norma knew he was remembering wilted lettuce, brown bananas, and spotted produce from the grocery store.

Uncle Peter laughed. "Your Aunt Sarah is quite a little farmer, Raymond. As long as she has her garden and her flock of chickens, she won't let us go hungry."

After supper, the children ran out to play. They soon had a lively game of hide and seek going. When Aunt Sarah called them in, Uncle Peter was sitting at the table, reading a big, black book. A kerosene lamp was burning on the table.

"It's kind of dark in here," Raymond piped up. "Why doesn't someone turn the lights on?"

"The lights are on," Aunt Sarah answered. "We don't use electricity. We use kerosene lights, and they are not as bright."

Sure enough. Norma looked around for light switches, and there were none. But she rather liked the gentle hiss and cozy glow of the lamps.

Raymond went off to bed readily. All the active play had worn him out. Norma followed the girls upstairs. Snuggled up to Erma in the big bed, she suddenly realized that her doll Lillian was missing. Where was Lillian? She must be back home in the tarpaper shack. Of course, when Dad had gotten their clothes, he had not gotten Lillian. What would happen to her? Where was Mom? When would Dad come back for them?

"Norma, where's Mom?" Erma whispered anxiously. "Where is she? I want her!" And Erma began to cry. Norma couldn't hold back her own tears anymore. The little girls lay sobbing in each other's arms. Norma didn't try to stop her tears now. After it seemed like she had cried buckets of tears, she felt a gentle hand brush her hair back. It was Aunt Sarah. She sat on the edge of the bed. One of her arms was around Erma, and the other gently rubbed Norma's back. Gradually the sobbing stopped, and the little girls slept.

A rooster was crowing noisily when Norma woke up. "Come, Norma and Erma," Katie said. "Get dressed because Dad will soon be done milking, and breakfast is ready."

When the girls came into the kitchen, Aunt Sarah had her arm around Raymond. He was crying. "Norma!" Raymond exclaimed through his tears, "I didn't know where you were! I didn't know where anybody was." He dried his tears on his shirtsleeve as he came to stand beside Norma and Erma.

Soon breakfast was ready, and everyone sat up to the table. There was fried cornmeal mush with maple syrup and tall glasses of milk. Suddenly Norma remembered that their last breakfast had been cold biscuits. Was that really only yesterday morning? So much had happened since then.

Uncle Peter and Aunt Sarah

After breakfast, Mandy washed Erma's face and then combed her hair, braiding it into pigtails like Katie's.

"Here, Norma," Aunt Sarah said. "Shall I fix your hair too? I think your hair won't tangle so much that way, and it will be cooler." Norma nodded agreement, but it did feel rather strange to have her hair pulled back into pigtails.

Aunt Sarah was nearly finished when Norma heard Raymond give a shout of happiness. Then she heard a familiar voice. It was Walter! She could hardly wait until Aunt Sarah was finished.

"Hi, Sis!" Walter greeted her as Norma came into the yard. "Grandpa said I could come over to see you since we heard that you were here. Arthur's coming too. There he is now!"

Arthur left Barney tied to the hitching rack by the lane and came to the other children. Aunt Sarah called her own children to work in the garden and left the five little Brennemans to themselves. "Now we are all together," Raymond said happily. "I missed you boys."

"But Dad and Mom aren't here," Arthur said. "Where are they, anyway? What happened? Why are you all here?"

Soberly the children sat in the grass under the maple tree while Norma told the boys about the trip home from Brutus and the return the next day. "We don't understand it either," she said sadly. "We don't know where Mom is or when Dad will come back." Both older boys looked very sober. Raymond was wiping tears, and Erma was sucking her thumb with her head buried on Norma's lap.

"Well," Walter concluded with an adult air, "whatever is going on, we have to give Dad credit for bringing you to a safe and happy home. Uncle Peter and Aunt Sarah are very special people. You aren't the first children that they have taken care of when they needed a place.

"Look, Raymond! Do you see that high barn way over there? That's Grandpa Brenneman's, and that's where I live now. Sometimes I come over here to help Uncle Peter work. Art and I are allowed to stay and eat lunch with you. But let's have a good old game of tag first. You are 'it', Art!"

Dashing tears away, the children scattered. Soon they were laughing and shouting. Aunt Sarah smiled as she watched from the garden.

chapter seven

Inside Upside Down

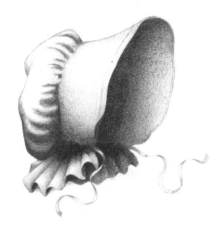

Brutus, Michigan: 1930

W hen Norma, Erma, and Katie came downstairs for breakfast the next morning, Joshua and Raymond were carrying wood for the cookstove.

"Katie, you set the table," Aunt Sarah instructed her. "Dad's not done milking yet. Norma, you and Erma come with me," she said, leading them into the downstairs bedroom next to the kitchen. There lay clothing scattered across the big bed.

"Norma, I thought it would be nice if you could wear long dresses like Katie does, since you are here at our house. I have dresses here that the other girls outgrew. Would you like to try several on to see if they fit?"

"If you want me to," Norma answered.

"I think we can find two for you to play in. Then we should find one that's nice for you to wear to church."

Church! Suddenly Norma remembered watching other people going to church. "I don't think I ever went to church," she answered.

"Well, tomorrow is Sunday, and we will take you with us to church. Here, let's try this dress. Katie just outgrew it.

"That looks fine. I thought so. You're just a little bit smaller than Katie. That means these others should fit you too."

The dress had tiny flowers on it. It buttoned in the back. It felt quite a bit longer than the dresses Norma was used to, but she rather liked the feel of it. It would be fun to look like Katie.

While Aunt Sarah was fitting a dress on Erma, Norma glanced around the room. There on the bureau was one of Aunt Sarah's white caps. She gasped, but Aunt Sarah was too busy to notice. The white cap was—why, it was just like that white cloth that she had found in the chest. The one she had asked Mom if she could have to make something for Lillian. The one that Mom had quickly thrown into the cookstove. She had not thought about it when Aunt Sarah had it on.

She had never seen her mom wear a cap like that. Why was it in the chest? Why had it made her angry to see it?

"Dad's in from the barn. We can eat now," Mandy called from the kitchen.

Norma found out that Saturday was a busy day at Uncle Peter's house. Mandy and Lydia were busy carrying water from the windmill to fill the water tank in the kitchen. Then they cleaned windows and floors. They scrubbed the porch and swept the sidewalk. Katie and Norma washed dishes. Then Aunt Sarah had them pick strawberries from the strawberry patch for the pies that she was making. After that, Norma and Katie took turns cranking the cream separator. Aunt Sarah was going to make fresh butter. She also promised whipped cream for the strawberry pies.

"See, Norma," Katie said. "Put your finger in here, and you can get foam on your finger and lick it off. Try it! It's good." Norma caught foam on her finger and tasted it. Mmmm! It was good.

Finally all the milk was separated. Aunt Sarah had said that after they collected the eggs and washed them, they could play for a while. Erma tagged along to the barn. Shouts of fun were coming from inside the barn. Raymond and Joshua must have gotten their work done. Quickly the girls gathered the eggs and cleaned them.

"Let's go see where the boys are," Katie suggested.

Raymond and Joshua were still in the barn. Just as the girls came to the haymow, Norma was surprised to see Joshua come flying through the air and land with a shout in the big, big pile of loose hay. Quickly he scrambled up the inside of the barn wall. The barn was made of huge logs. A ladder went up the end wall of the barn. A long rope with a knot hung from the rafters. Joshua grabbed the rope and jumped. Out he swung again, to drop down into the soft hay.

Raymond looked on, laughing, but such a wild ride didn't appeal to him. Katie scrambled up the ladder, and Norma followed. Out over the hay Katie flew and dropped squealing into the soft hay. She scrambled out of the way as Norma came flying after her. Then it was Joshua's turn, then Katie's, and then Norma's. Raymond and Erma cheered them on.

"Don't let your dress get caught on those big pegs," Katie said, pointing to the barn wall. "One time that happened to Betsy when she was younger. She couldn't get up or down. She had to hang there till Dad came and took her down." Katie laughed.

"She looked so funny, but she was scared," Joshua added. "If her dress had torn, she would have fallen way down."

"That's why I don't want to climb up there," Raymond said. "It's too high."

"But you won't catch your dress," Joshua teased.

When the children came in for supper, fresh pies sat on the cupboard, and the kitchen smelled wonderful. After supper, Aunt Sarah hung a curtain across one corner of the kitchen. They all took turns having baths in the big tin tub behind the curtain.

Norma's feelings were all mixed up as she snuggled into bed that night. She felt clean and warm and cozy. What fun they had had today! Uncle Peter and Aunt Sarah had a happy home, but suddenly her heart ached for Mom. Did Mom miss them? Had she stayed at Kingsley, or had she gone back to the tarpaper shack and found that they were gone? Would Mom come and get them? Norma wasn't sure how to feel. Did she really want to leave this happy home? But she did want Mom! Two big tears rolled down on her pillow.

When Norma woke up the next morning, Mandy and Lydia were singing in the kitchen. Aunt Sarah had laid out the dresses that she had washed carefully by hand yesterday and hung on the line to dry. Beside the dress was an apron to go over the dress. That's right, today was church! Quickly she put on the long dress and slipped the apron over the top. Katie helped her button the back of the dress. The apron had one button in the back, at the top. Then Norma helped Erma get dressed.

"Now you look like my sisters," Katie said happily.

Norma smiled, but her mixed-up feelings from last night had not gone completely away. What would Mom say if she saw her now? Would Dad get upset?

What would church be like? Katie had told her that at church they sang and spoke German. But Katie had added, "I don't understand it either. It's different from the Pennsylvania Dutch we speak at home."

The girls hurried to the kitchen. Aunt Sarah expected them to help set the table. When Raymond saw Norma and Erma, he looked surprised. "Norma, I thought you were Katie. You look different, but it looks nice."

When Mandy was combing Norma's hair after breakfast, she explained to her that this Sunday they would walk to church. It would be held in the schoolhouse. Next Sunday, they would ride in the horse and wagon to the church house.

The breakfast dishes were done quickly. Aunt Sarah came out of the bedroom wearing a black shawl. She had a black bonnet over her white cap. In her hand she carried two starched sunbonnets. "Here, Norma, you and Erma can wear these to walk to church. Katie wears one like it."

Raymond grinned at Norma as the family walked out the lane. He wore Sunday pants and a Sunday shirt that used to be Joshua's. On his head, he wore a small black hat like Joshua's. "We look just like part of the family," Norma thought.

When the family reached the end of the lane, they turned right, toward the Woodland School. Wilson Reeds were coming out their lane just across the road. As they neared the crossroad by the school, Norma could see families coming from all directions toward the school. There was Walter, walking with Grandpa Brennemans.

As they entered the schoolyard, one of the ladies came hurrying toward them. She shook hands with Aunt Sarah and then turned to Norma. "Hello, Norma," she said. "Do you remember me? My name is Elsie Gregory. Long ago, I lived close to you."

A faint memory stirred in Norma's mind—a memory of maple sugar candy. It was Elsie who had brought it when baby Elenora died. "I remember the maple sugar candy," Norma answered.

Elsie laughed and squeezed her hand again. "I forgot that, but I remember you. You are getting to be a big girl now. And this must be Raymond and Erma."

Everyone moved toward the school building. Norma felt excited. Now she would get to see what church was like. Hats and bonnets were piled on the shelf where students usually put their lunch pails. Norma followed Aunt Sarah. All the ladies and girls sat on one side of the schoolroom in students' desks or on benches. Norma thought they all looked alike. The men and boys sat on the other side. Everyone sat quietly.

Then someone near the front of the room on the men's side started a song. Everyone joined in. The song was in German and was sung very slowly. Norma couldn't help sing, nor could she understand, but she looked around at the singing people. There were fathers and mothers with babies on their laps. There were children and young people and gray-haired grandparents. These people looked peaceful and happy. As the singing swelled around her, deep down in Norma's heart a desire began to grow. She wanted to belong to these people. She just wished that she could understand the words of the songs.

After another song, one of the men stood up behind the schoolteacher's desk and began to talk. It was her Grandpa Brenneman! Dad hadn't told her that Grandpa was a preacher. While Grandpa's voice rose and fell, Norma studied his kindly face. Whatever he was saying, he certainly seemed to believe it. "I wish I could understand," Norma thought.

When Grandpa stopped speaking, Norma suddenly realized that everyone was turning around and kneeling at their seats for prayer. Quickly Norma copied the others. After prayer, several other men got up to speak. One speaker talked a long time. Norma fidgeted in her seat. Erma was sleeping with her head on Aunt Sarah's lap. A young mother took her crying baby out. A little boy lost his balance and tumbled off his seat. Quickly his father scooped him up and quieted his crying. Norma was wondering if they would have the strawberry pies for dinner when suddenly everyone was kneeling again. Quickly she knelt. Another song followed, and soon church was over. Everyone was filing out of the building.

The people stood outside visiting in the schoolyard. Norma and Katie joined a group of girls that looked about their size. One girl came up to Norma. "I'm Magdalena Reed. We live across the road from you." She smiled in a friendly way, and Norma smiled back. There were other girls named Catherine, Fannie, Esther, and Leona, but Norma couldn't remember them all.

After a while, Uncle Peter and Aunt Sarah gathered their family together, and they all walked home. Uncle Joe and Aunt Salome came for dinner. That meant Arthur was there too. The children were sent to change into older clothes as soon as they came home. Sunday clothes were carefully hung away. They were made of wool. Once a year, Aunt Sarah washed them carefully by hand and hung them dripping wet on the line to dry. "Wool wears clean," she said.

Aunt Sarah's delicious dinner ended with strawberry pie. After a moment of silent prayer around the table, the children ran out to play. "Let's play 'Kick the Can,'" Katie suggested. Everyone agreed.

When Joshua went to find an old can, Arthur turned to Raymond. "How do you like Brutus by now?"

"Well," Raymond answered slowly, "it's fun here, but—" His eyes filled with tears. "I miss Mom and Dad. I just feel so inside upside down. I want to stay, but I wish we would all be together again."

Joshua came running with an old tin can. "You be 'it', Art!" As Arthur closed his eyes, the children scattered to hide behind bushes and around the buildings. Norma ran to hide behind the elderberry bush by the garden. She smiled to herself, thinking about what Raymond had said—"inside upside down!"

Then she sobered quickly. "That's just how I feel," she thought. Why would she want to leave this happy home and go back to the tarpaper shack where they barely had enough to eat and Mom and Dad argued? But Mom was her mom. Aunt Sarah was so nice, but she was Katie's mom. Home was home—her home—arguing and all. Why couldn't she have been born into *this* happy home? But oh, how she missed the familiar presence of Mom.

"I see you, Norma!" Art cried, running back to the tin can to put his foot on it and call out her name. Norma jumped up to go join the others who were standing close to the tin can because they had been caught. Just then Joshua came running from behind the outhouse. With a mighty kick, he sent the tin can sailing.

"Aw—I didn't see you!" Arthur said, running to retrieve the can while all the children scattered to hide again. This time Norma hid behind the big maple tree.

Chore time came too soon. Arthur left with Uncle Joe and Aunt Salome. Uncle Peter sent Joshua and Raymond to get the cows in for milking.

After supper, the smell of popcorn lingered in the air as the family settled down to quiet evening activities. Raindrops pattered on the roof. Katie, Norma, and Erma sat playing with dolls on the daybed in the corner of the kitchen. The dolls were rather old and looked as if they had been played with many times. Norma thought of her doll, Lillian, but she pushed the thought aside. She looked around the kitchen. Aunt Sarah sat in the rocking chair reading a letter. Uncle Peter and Silas were each reading a book at the table. Joshua and Raymond played a marble game on the floor. Betsy, who had come for the weekend, sat on the porch steps with Mandy and Lydia. They were singing, "What a Friend We Have in Jesus." Norma studied Aunt Sarah's serene face. Hugging the old doll to herself, she thought, "Right now I think I want to stay here always."

chapter eight

Sunshine and Shadows

Brutus, Michigan: 1930

Norma took a cup from the dish rack and dried it carefully. Next she reached for a plate. Now the rack was empty. Katie was swishing her hand slowly around in the dishpan. She filled a cup full of soapsuds. Then she filled it with water and watched the soapsuds rise to the top. She took a big handful of soapsuds and stuck them on her chin. "See, I have a beard now. Here, let me make a beard for you too, Norma." Their faces full of soapsuds, the girls stood giggling at each other.

"Katie, *schik dich!*" Aunt Sarah said sharply. Both bearded girls looked up quickly. Aunt Sarah said something else to Katie in Dutch. Norma was learning some Dutch words, but even if she didn't know exactly what Aunt Sarah said, she knew what she meant. Quickly the beards came off, and Katie started washing dishes. Soberly, Norma began drying dishes.

Aunt Sarah didn't seem to be angry. She was stirring the white wash in the washing machine now. There was a big lever on the side of the washer. It had a handle. Lydia pushed the lever back and forth. *Swish, swish* went the washer. After a while, Aunt Sarah told her to stop. Then Aunt Sarah took a stick and fished the wash out piece by piece and fed it into a roller on the wringer. Lydia turned the other crank to make the rollers go that squeezed the water out. Norma liked to watch the flattened clothes fall out into the rinse tub. Then Aunt Sarah rinsed the clothes by hand and fed them into the rollers again.

Snap, snap, snap. Lydia took out the rinsed clothing, shook out each piece, and put it into the wash basket. Then she snatched up the clothes and took them to the clothesline. Soon they were flapping in the breeze.

"Katie and Norma, you take turns turning the cream separator. You girls will have to help. Mandy's gone to work for Grandma Brenneman." Putting another load of wash into the washer, Aunt Sarah instructed, "When you are finished separating the cream, I want you to pull weeds in the garden before it gets too hot. I think it's dried off now from last night's showers."

Norma didn't mind working. It was actually fun. She had never helped to garden before. Carefully, she pulled the little weeds around the onions. They were easy to weed, but when she got to the next row, Norma wasn't so sure of herself. Katie was at the other end of the row, and the girls were working toward each other. What *was* growing in this row? She thought of asking Katie, but she was too embarrassed to do that. It seemed like Katie knew so many things about animals and plants and birds that Norma had never learned. She would just do her best.

Suddenly she heard Aunt Sarah's voice behind her. "That's not grass. You pulled up the carrots."

Norma's heart sank. She looked up in dismay. Would Aunt Sarah get angry at her?

No. Aunt Sarah continued kindly, "We'll just get some seed and plant some more." Norma looked at her gratefully. Aunt Sarah was so kind!

The sun became hot on the girls' backs as they bent over the plants in the garden. A gentle breeze made Norma look up to watch the windmill turn slowly. Erma was playing at the swing. Her bare feet hung from one side of the swing, and her head hung down on the other. She pushed herself back and forth with her feet. Erma didn't cry for Mom so much anymore. It was mostly just at bedtime.

"Where is Mom now?" Norma wondered. Did she miss them? She didn't have a car to come. Did Dad think about them sometimes? He couldn't phone because Uncle Peter's didn't have a phone. Mom and Dad seemed so far away.

Lydia called for lunch. Happily the girls left the hot garden and ran to the pump at the windmill. The cool water felt good as they splashed it on their faces and washed their hands. Cupping their hands, they drank thirstily. Then they hurried to the house.

Joshua and Raymond came into the kitchen with the men. Their hair was wet and plastered down on their heads. Droplets of water clung to it. Their faces were red and slightly smudged with dirt.

"We were hoeing corn, Norma," Raymond announced. "It takes a long time, and it's hot out there. And I rode a horse like Arthur does," he continued excitedly. "Uncle Peter helped me ride Molly." Norma smiled at Raymond's happy face.

The week passed quickly. Norma had her turn at weeding corn too. The sandy soil made the weeds come out easily. It was fun when they all worked together. Uncle Peter, Silas, Joshua, Raymond, Katie, and Norma worked spread out across the cornfield.

Nearly all the weeds looked the same. "These weeds are called milkweed," Uncle Peter explained.

"Do you get milk from them?" Raymond asked in surprise. Katie and Joshua giggled.

"No," Uncle Peter explained patiently. "But see how the stem is milky when you break it? If we don't get them all pulled, they will get pods on them that will burst open and spread seeds all over the field. Then our corn will get crowded out and won't grow right. But with all these helpers, the weeds don't stand a chance." He smiled at Norma.

"I like corn!" Raymond said emphatically. "I don't think I'd like milkweed."

"Actually," Uncle Peter said, "this corn is called field corn, and it's for the pigs, chickens, and horses. The corn we eat is better than that. It's sweet corn, and it grows in Aunt Sarah's garden."

There were so many things to learn on the farm. Norma's heart warmed toward Uncle Peter for the kindness and patience that he showed to Raymond. Raymond didn't learn things quite as easily as some other boys his age. Norma felt relieved to let Uncle Peter carry some of the responsibility that she had always carried for her little brother.

What fun haymaking day was! Bertie and Flora, the big farm horses, were hitched to the big, flat wagon. Raymond and Norma watched curiously as Uncle Peter and Silas carried two large slings made of ropes and wooden slats to the wagon. Carefully they hung the slings on the ladder that stuck up in the front part of the wagon. Next Uncle Peter hooked something that he called the loader to the back part of the wagon. Old Jerry, the other farm horse, was harnessed and tied near the barn.

"Dad, Dad, can we ride along to the field?" Katie begged.

"All right, this first trip," Uncle Peter said, "but you must sit down near the front of the wagon. I don't want anyone falling off."

Quickly the children scrambled onto the waiting wagon. "Giddy-ap!" Uncle Peter called to the horses. Norma held Erma tightly on her lap as the steel-wheeled wagon rattled out to the field.

Raymond grinned at Joshua. "We're real farmers, aren't we?"

"Hey, look!" Joshua exclaimed. "Daniel Brubachers are making hay today too!"

The sweet-smelling sun-dried hay lay in neat rows in the hayfield. Stopping at the edge of the hayfield, Uncle Peter said, "Now you must get off. You may watch, but you must stay at the edge of the field."

Carefully Silas drove the wagon onto the field so that the wagon wheels straddled the windrows of hay. Then Uncle Peter took one of the big slings off the ladder where he had hung it. He spread it out across the wagon bed. When all was ready, Silas called, "Giddyap," and the horses began pulling the wagon.

Norma watched with fascination as the big teeth on the loader scooped up the loose hay into a web-like pocket that carried it up and dumped it on the sling-covered wagon. Down the field the horses and wagon moved. The contraption ate up the hay as it went. The barefoot children ran along the edge of the field, watching.

After a bit, the wagon stopped. Uncle Peter pulled the ropes to close the big sling full of hay. Then he spread the second sling on top. Next he adjusted the loader so the web could dump the hay higher for the top sling. Soon the wagon moved again, gathering up more of the hay to fill the second sling.

"Let's hurry back to the barn so we are there in time to unload," Joshua suggested. "Anyway, I'm thirsty."

"Me too," Raymond echoed. Off the children ran to flop on the grass by the windmill until the loaded wagon returned.

"Dad says I can lead Jerry on the barn hill," Joshua said happily. Soon the horses could be seen plodding slowly toward the barn with their load. Up the barn hill and into the cool, quiet barn they went.

"Come on, Norma," Katie said. "You don't want to miss this!" Now Silas led Jerry to the barn hill. Norma stood watching with the other children as Jerry's harness was connected to ropes from high up in the haymow. Uncle Peter was also fastening big, thick ropes to the top sling on the hay wagon.

"Now, Joshua, you lead Jerry down the barn hill," Uncle Peter said. "Don't go fast, and listen when I say stop."

"Norma, look at that!" Raymond shouted as Joshua led Jerry down the hill. The ropes and pulleys that were connected to Jerry slowly lifted the big sling of hay off the wagon. Uncle Peter tended the ropes as the big sling was swinging back over the haymow. Suddenly the sling opened, and out dumped the hay.

"Come on!" Katie yelled. Quickly the children jumped into the loose hay and spread it to the far corners of the haymow before another load came. The children jumped back as the sling emptied another load of hay for them to scatter. Now the wagon was empty. The men went for another load, and the children raced to the water pump.

"I'm thirsty!" "I'm hot!" "That hay is prickly!" "Joshua, you have hay sticking out of your hair." "You have it sticking out of your ears!" "I do not!"

Soon the children had a full-fledged water battle going. "Joshua, I'll get you back," Katie gasped as a handful of cold water hit her squarely in the face. The creak of the wagon sent them all scrambling to the barn to smooth out the next load of hay.

Norma fell asleep that night as soon as her head hit the pillow. When Aunt Sarah came into the bedroom later to check on the little girls, she smiled to see no damp pillows or tear-stained cheeks.

One day Aunt Sarah sent the children wild strawberry picking. Then they sat under the maple tree and took the caps off the tiny but very sweet little berries. The job seemed endless, but the kitchen cupboard was lined with jars of canned berries and jelly by the end of that day. Uncle Peter had taken the scythe and cut the grass along the lane and around the house. The children's bare feet turned green with grass stains from running around in the freshly cut grass.

That evening, Katie and Norma sat on the porch making chains with dandelion stems. "Look, Katie," Norma said with a laugh. "Our feet are green, and our hands are red from strawberries."

"Let's make our faces yellow!" Katie said. Taking a dandelion flower, she rubbed it on her nose and cheeks. Laughing, Norma did the same. Coming out of the house, Aunt Sarah smiled at the colorful girls and sent them off to the pump to wash up for bedtime.

The next day, Aunt Sarah and Mandy were out in the garden early, picking baskets and baskets of peas. By the time the sun was hot, the peas were all picked. The girls sat in the shade of the maple tree and shelled peas. Norma quickly learned how to pop the pea pods open and strip out the tender green peas. Erma wanted to help too. The girls took turns helping her open the pods so she could strip them out herself. As the bowls of shelled peas piled up, Aunt Sarah came and emptied them. She took the peas into the house to can for winter use.

Mandy was a good storyteller. She kept them entertained while their fingers flew. "Long, long ago, when Dad was a young boy, all our farm was full of trees," she began. "There were only Indians living here. No houses or barns, and no roads—just Indian trails and wild animals."

Norma's hands were still. She gazed around, trying to imagine this. A little shiver of fear went through her. Coming from Grand Rapids, she thought it seemed wild enough now to suit her without more trees and Indians and wild animals. She shivered again.

"Then some men came in and cut down lots of trees and hauled them away to saw them up for boards," Mandy continued. "When Dad bought land and came here, there were lots of stumps from trees that he needed to clear away before he could plant fields."

"Tell about the hole in the roof," Katie interrupted.

"Sometimes they covered the house windows so they wouldn't break, and then they used dynamite to blast the stumps out," Mandy continued. "It made a big noise, and roots would go sailing into the air. One time, Dad put fifty sticks of dynamite under a big, big stump! Then he lit the dynamite and ran away from it. With a big blast, the pieces of the stump flew way up in the air. The old, stubborn stump was out! But then Dad saw a big piece of wood three feet long on the house roof. It had poked a hole into the roof!"

"I'm sort of sorry that most of the stumps are gone," Katie said, "because I'd like to see a big blast sometime."

"Well, I'm not sorry," Aunt Sarah said, coming from the kitchen for more shelled peas.

The horse and wagon were coming in the lane. When it stopped, Raymond and Joshua jumped off and came running to the girls. Raymond announced, "We went with Uncle Peter to peddle butter and eggs in Brutus. Then we got flour and sugar and salt and some more things. It was fun to take such a long ride!"

That night Norma lay in bed listening to the frogs singing their evening songs. Nearby a whippoorwill sang. At first she had been afraid of the nighttime sounds until Katie told her what they were. As she listened to the frogs, she thought about Raymond's questions that evening. "Norma, do you think Mom and Dad forgot about us?" His lower lip had trembled. "Maybe they just don't want us anymore."

This time, her own tears did not come. Instead, down inside, a little feeling of resentment stirred. Didn't Dad know how much he was hurting them? Did he even care? Why couldn't he just be like other dads and take care of his own children? Why wasn't he like Uncle Peter and Aunt Sarah?

chapter nine

I Never Knew That!

Brutus, Michigan: 1930

Norma tied her sunbonnet under her chin and then stooped to tie Erma's. It was Sunday morning. Aunt Sarah bustled about, making sure that the children had clean faces and were all ready to go. Betsy, home for the weekend, was smoothing the skirt of her dress and carefully tucking a stray curl under her white cap.

Mandy looked at her mischievously. "Do you think Christian Kilmer will actually notice if your hair's not just right?"

Betsy blushed and made a quick slap at her sister. "Go on, you!"

The rattle of the horse and wagon sent everyone to the door and out the sidewalk. Silas stood holding the horse while they all climbed into the wagon. Uncle Peter lifted Erma up to sit with Aunt Sarah. The other children sat on low benches on the back of the wagon. Today was church in the church house instead of at the schoolhouse.

"Now be careful," Mandy said as the children found their places. "Don't step on Betsy's skirt or Christian Kilmer might—"

"That's enough, Mandy," Aunt Sarah said firmly from the front of the wagon. Mandy stopped, but she gathered her own skirts around herself and sat down daintily, making a face at Betsy. Silas, Joshua, and Raymond rode with their feet dangling out the back of the wagon.

Norma rode along enjoying the crisp morning air and the twitter of the birds along with the *clip clop* of the horses' feet. More than that, she felt the cozy feeling of belonging.

Looking back, she could see a wagon coming behind them. "Here come Isaac Kilmers," Joshua said. "Daniel Brubachers and Wilson Reeds are ahead of us." When they got to the stop sign, they could see two wagons coming down Gregory Road. One of them was Grandpa Brennemans. Walter waved at them from the back. Into Brutus the wagons went. Turning right near the Purple Inn, the horses slowed as they came to the steep hill before the church. Uncle Peter stopped, and

The old Brutus Mennonite Church

Silas, Betsy, and Mandy got out of the wagon and walked so the horses would not have so heavy a load. At the top of the hill, they climbed back in again.

Uncle Peter stopped by the front of the church so Aunt Sarah and the girls could get out. Then he and the boys went to the hitching rack to tie the horse and wagon. Norma took Erma's hand and followed Aunt Sarah in the door on the left side of the church. The men and boys were going in the door on the right side.

"This is the first time that I've ever been in a real church building," Norma thought, looking around curiously. Everyone found their places on the three sections of benches. Erma sat with Aunt Sarah in the left section, where the women sat. Norma joined the girls in the center section of the church where the children sat—girls on one side and boys on the other. A wooden rail ran through the center section, dividing the girls from the boys. The youngest schoolchildren sat in front, and the youth sat in the back. The men sat on the right section of benches.

Sunshine streamed in the windows on the long, desk-like pulpit at the front of the room. Behind the pulpit on a long bench sat Grandpa Brenneman with the other preachers. She studied his kindly face as he rose to speak. There was a quiet peace and confidence that drew her heart to him. As Grandpa talked, some of his expressions suddenly reminded her of Dad. Then it struck her that Dad must have come here to church when he was a boy. She tried to imagine Dad sitting here in church, helping to sing the slow German songs. What was it that Grandpa and these people had that Dad didn't have? If she could understand German and know what they were saying, would she get an answer to her question?

After church, Norma stood with a group of girls her age outside the church. She noticed several people walking down the gentle slope behind the church to the cemetery. "They're going to look at their baby's grave," Magdalena said. "Their baby died not long ago."

"We have three babies there too," Katie said soberly.

Norma looked at her in surprise. "I didn't know that! How old were they when they died?"

"Henry and Jacob were just tiny babies." Katie answered. "We don't remember them. But Mandy remembers Gideon. He already had his first birthday. He died from the flu."

"Poor Aunt Sarah," Norma thought. She was remembering baby Elenora and how sad it was for one baby to die. "I had a little sister that died," she volunteered. "Her name was Elenora."

"Norma, I think your little sister is buried here too," Aunt Sarah said.

Norma turned in surprise. She had not known that Aunt Sarah had walked up behind her. Her eyes widened—her little sister! Baby Elenora! Vividly she remembered the box with baby Elenora being lifted out the window—and the sad and empty feeling that remained.

"Would you like to go and see her grave?" Aunt Sarah asked kindly.

Norma nodded wordlessly. Taking Erma's hand, Aunt Sarah led the way. She stopped by a simple marker that said, "Elenora." Norma stood looking quietly at the little grave. "I never knew where they took her," she said softly. "Dad handed her out the window to someone. Then he shut the window—and she was gone."

"When she was buried here, your grandpa was here too. He read a Scripture and prayed a prayer."

Norma looked up, her eyes shining with unshed tears. "I didn't know."

"You know, Norma," Aunt Sarah continued, "it's only Elenora's body that is buried here. When babies die, they go to heaven to be with God, where there's no more sickness—just happiness."

"I didn't know that either," Norma whispered.

"Shall we go now?" Aunt Sarah asked, putting her hand gently on Norma's shoulder. "I think Uncle Peter is ready."

Norma was quiet on the way home. Now she knew where baby Elenora had gone. And Grandpa had been there at Elenora's grave. Aunt Sarah said Elenora was happy now in heaven. Where was heaven?

What was heaven like? Was Elenora lonely in heaven? Who takes care of babies in heaven? It seemed like there would be a lot of babies there. Aunt Sarah had lost three babies. Maybe Elenora was there with Aunt Sarah's babies. Then she wouldn't be lonely. And God was there. Did He take care of the babies? Looking at Erma perched happily between Aunt Sarah and Uncle Peter on the wagon seat, she thought, "I'm glad I have one sister that's not in heaven."

One Monday morning, Norma was coming from the barn, carefully carrying a basket of eggs. She had learned to gather eggs by herself now.

Lydia was leaning into the well by the windmill. Then she straightened up and lifted a hoe out of the well. What was she doing? Hoes were for the garden! Curiously, Norma stopped by the well. "What are you doing, Lydia? There are no weeds in the well, are there?"

Lydia laughed. "No, I was just putting the milk in the well."

Norma looked at her closely to see if she was joking. Seeing her puzzled look, Lydia said, "Come see."

Norma had never really looked down into the well before. She set the basket of eggs in the grass and leaned over the well. What she saw surprised her. Inside, the well had wooden sides and a sand floor about six feet down. In the middle there were pipes that went down farther to where the water was. Along the cool edges of the sand floor in the well were covered pails.

"We put our milk in here to keep it cool because we don't have an icebox like some people do," Lydia explained. "Sometimes we put cream and butter in here too."

"But what did you do with the hoe?" Norma wondered.

"Oh, we use that to hook onto the pail handles to lower a pail into the well or to get it out again," Lydia said, carefully replacing the wooden board over the pump bed.

Just then Raymond and Joshua came running around the corner of the house. A little brown puppy scampered at their feet. "Norma, Lydia, guess what?" Joshua announced. "Manasseh Kulp's dog had puppies, and he brought us one. Dad says we can keep her, and we're going to call her Nellie."

Raymond squatted down beside the puppy, his eyes shining. The puppy jumped on him, licking his face and barking happily. Raymond reached for the puppy, and she wiggled away. Soon both of the boys and the dog were tumbling around in the grass. Norma smiled at them. Raymond had always wished for a puppy.

One happy summer day blended into the next. Norma and Erma had their shared birthday. While Uncle Peter's family acknowledged birthdays, there was no special celebration. Norma wondered, "Does Mom remember our birthdays?" No word came from Mom or Dad.

One day when Norma and Katie walked to the mailbox at the cross-road, she dreamed of what it would be like to get a letter from Mom. Suddenly she thought, "What if something bad happened to Mom? Would we even find it out?" Pushing these thoughts aside, Norma hurried to catch up with Katie. Hearing the *clip clop* of a horse, the girls looked up to see Arthur on Barney trotting toward them from the other side of the crossroad.

"Hey, Norma, wait!" Arthur called, urging the unwilling Barney to go a bit faster. Pulling the mule to a stop by the mailbox, Arthur slid to the ground, still holding Barney's reins. "I came for the mail too. I was afraid you'd leave before I got here." Then sobering, he added, "I really miss you, Norma! How are you and Raymond and Erma doing?"

"We are doing pretty good," Norma responded. "Raymond is so happy that we got a puppy. He plays with it all the time. Erma hardly ever cries for Mom. We have a nice place to be. What about you?"

"I'm okay," Arthur replied. "I really like Uncle Joe, and Aunt Salome makes good food. But I do miss all of you. Barney helps, though. He's a good friend—when he behaves!" Arthur laughed, giving the mule a friendly pat on the neck.

"Guess what, Norma? I overheard Uncle Joe and Aaron talking. They said that long ago, Aaron's brother Owen and Dad left Brutus and went far away to a place called Alberta to find good farmland.

Some people didn't make out very well and came back, but Dad and Owen traveled still farther away. They took a couple cows along. They milked the cows and just ate biscuits and milk. They slept in a wagon. It sounds like fun. I wish I could have been along! They even got caught in a big snowstorm. Dad found Mom at a town called Mayton. Hey, Norma, do you think we have another grandpa and grandma far away?"

"I don't know," Norma answered, "but one time long ago, I think Mom told me that she had brothers and sisters. I can't really remember what all she said."

"I wonder why Mom and Dad never told us all that stuff. And you know what else?" Arthur continued. "He said Mom and Dad moved back to Brutus when you were a baby. Aaron said we lived in a little shack by Bert Lake in the summer, and then we lived with him and Lovina when it got cold."

"Lovina! Our Lovina?" Norma wondered.

"Yes, that's Owen's wife. No wonder Lovina was Mom's friend. And he said Raymond was born at Lovina's house. I wish Dad would have told us about that. I'd like to hear about the snowstorm."

"Mom's going to wonder where we are. We better get going," Katie suggested.

"Oh, Arthur, I'm glad to know that you are happy. Ask Uncle Joe if you can come to visit us sometime," Norma said. "We better go on now."

"See you later, Sis!" Arthur jumped onto Barney and trotted away, turning backwards and waving as he went.

The smell of freshly baked bread greeted the girls as they came into the kitchen with the mail. Norma breathed deeply. Crusty loaves of bread lay on a cloth on the table. Aunt Sarah was busy washing out the crock that she had set her yeast in to rise the night before. A long, wooden box with a tight-fitting lid sat in the middle of the kitchen. Norma had watched Aunt Sarah mix her bread in the box.

"Girls," Aunt Sarah said, "I think you can carry the bread tray out on the back porch for me if you are careful." The girls both grabbed an end of the three-foot-long box. Backing toward the porch, Katie missed the doorway and thumped into the wall. She looked so surprised that Norma burst into giggles. Overcome with giggles, the girls set the dough tray down in the doorway.

"Now girls, be careful," Aunt Sarah chided as the girls picked up the box to try again. "Katie, I want you to go gather the eggs this time. Norma can help me."

After Katie left with the egg basket, Aunt Sarah placed a cutting board and knife on the table. "Here, Norma, you can cut up these potatoes for supper. Cut them in pieces like this," she instructed.

"I wanted to tell you something, Norma," Aunt Sarah continued, carefully peeling the brown skins off the potatoes. "I got a letter from your dad." Norma's hands stopped, and she looked at Aunt Sarah. "Your dad said that he is stopping in here. He will not stay long— maybe for supper. I thought you should know ahead of time. He wants to bring us some money to help pay for your food and clothing."

Norma looked soberly at Aunt Sarah. "Will Mom come? Will he take us home?"

Aunt Sarah put her arm around Norma's shoulders. "No, your mom won't be along. Do you want him to take you?"

Norma looked troubled. "I don't want to go away. I like it here, but—I do want to see Mom. I wish Mom could come here." Norma's eyes filled with tears. Quickly she brushed them away.

"Your dad is planning that you stay here, Norma. I'm sure you do miss your mom. That is how it should be. I will try to be like a mother to you for now." Aunt Sarah squeezed Norma's shoulders. With a sigh, Norma leaned against her and quickly dashed away another tear.

Just then the screen door slammed, and Raymond came running into the kitchen. His blue eyes were big. "Dad's here!" he exclaimed. Then he burst into tears. Aunt Sarah gathered him into her arms and wiped his tears with her apron. With her arm around him, they went out to meet Dad.

Dad was just getting out of the Model T. "Hello, John," Aunt Sarah called. "Just come on in!" The children stood shyly beside Aunt Sarah. Part of Norma wanted to run and throw her arms around Dad. The other part of her wished he would go away and leave them alone. Would he care that she was dressed like Katie now?

"Hi, Norma and Raymond," Dad greeted them. "You look like you've been playing in the sun."

"Where's Mom?" Raymond wondered.

Erma sat on the grass with her arm around Nellie, the puppy. "I want Mom!" she piped up suddenly.

"Mom didn't come with me," Dad said. "But look what I brought

Dad

you." He held a piece of candy out to Erma. Raymond stepped closer, his eye on the candy. Dad laughed. "Here, Raymond. Here's one for you too." When he handed Norma a piece, she thanked him quietly.

"Are you going to take us away, Dad?" Raymond wondered somewhat anxiously. "When will we get to see Mom?"

"Raymond," Aunt Sarah interrupted, "why don't you show your dad the barn and tell Uncle Peter that supper will be ready in about fifteen minutes. Do you want to go with them, Norma?"

"I'll help you," Norma replied. Dad and Raymond headed for the barn. Raymond was chattering happily now, telling Dad about life on the farm.

Erma followed Aunt Sarah and Norma into the house. "I want Mom!" Erma said plaintively. "Where is Mom, Norma?"

"I don't know," Norma answered. "But look, Erma, here are the spoons. Can you put one at each plate?"

The children were quiet during supper while Dad and Uncle Peter talked about crops and weather and suchlike. Soon Dad was ready to leave again.

Raymond wiped away tears as Dad drove out the lane. When Nellie came and jumped on him, he hugged her so tight that she whined in protest.

"I want Mom," Erma repeated. Norma felt sad and glad and angry all at once. Pleasant memories from the tarpaper shack came rushing back. Wouldn't it be nice to be all together again with Mom and Dad and Walter and Arthur?

Suddenly she remembered Lillian, her doll. Whatever had happened to her? With that came memories of Dad's anger, fighting, and unhappiness. Looking at Aunt Sarah's kind, peaceful face, she was glad that Dad had not taken them away.

Anger chased the gladness away. Why couldn't they be a normal family? Why had Dad left Mom at Kingsley? Why had he done this to them? Why couldn't he be like Grandpa or Uncle Peter?

Erma cried herself to sleep that night. Norma held her close and wiped fiercely at her own tears.

chapter ten

I Wish I Really Belonged

Brutus, Michigan: Summer 1930

The dewy grass felt cool to Norma's bare feet. Joshua and Raymond waited impatiently by the lane.

"Come on, girls, let's go," Joshua called, swinging his molasses pail round and round like the paddles on the windmill.

"Now stay together and get off the road if a car comes," Aunt Sarah instructed them. "Here is another pail, Mandy. Don't eat yourself sick."

Finally they were all ready. There was a dash for the end of the lane, the girls' pigtails bouncing and bare feet flying.

Norma raced with the rest, but soon she heard Joshua shouting from up ahead, "I beat! Lydia is always the cow's tail!"

"I guess we'll see who has the most huckleberries by the end of the day before we talk too big," Mandy chided.

Down the hill the children hurried, around the corner and over the little bridge crossing the Maple River. Their bare feet slowed as they climbed the hill and turned left past Amos Gregory's.

"How far do we have to go yet?" Raymond wondered. "I can't wait to taste huckleberries!"

"See, right up there is Maple River Road," Lydia answered. "Then soon we'll be at the huckleberry marsh. I wish Betsy were along to help us. She's a fast picker!"

"Now you children stay close enough that you can see Lydia or me," Mandy said. "We don't want to lose you in the marsh."

Raymond sat right down by the berries and started stuffing his mouth. "Don't forget to put some in your pail!" Katie laughed, looking at Raymond's purple face.

Norma picked berries close to Lydia. She could hear someone talking from somewhere across the marsh. "There must be other pickers out here too," she thought. Her pail was starting to get heavy when she heard Mandy scream. There was a loud, familiar-sounding laugh.

Then she heard Mandy's voice. "Walter Brenneman, you are going to pay for that! You scared the wits out of me!"

She heard a quiet chuckle. Jumping up quickly, Norma peered around the bushes. There were Walter and Grandpa Brenneman! Walter was laughing. Norma thought she saw a hint of a smile on Grandpa's face.

"Well, well," Grandpa said. "It just looks like Sarah has some good pickers out here this morning. How about if we get all these pails full and I give you a ride home on the wagon. Old Ned is tied down the road apiece."

The children smiled their delight. Tired pickers put on a burst of speed. Norma moved over to pick berries close to Grandpa.

"You have quite a pail full of berries there, Norma," Grandpa said with a smile. "You must have been busy this morning."

Norma smiled shyly back at him. It felt so safe to be close to Grandpa. She forgot her worry about snakes or wild animals and quickly worked to fill her pail. It would be fun to ride home with Grandpa! She moved a little closer to him.

Suddenly she remembered picking in a different berry patch long ago. A cold, tight feeling chilled her heart, and her smile froze on her face. Desperately she tried to put the memory aside, but Dad's leering face would not go away. Her hands stopped picking at the memory of the strange fear that gripped her as she ran fast to avoid Dad's evil intentions. She almost dropped her pail now and ran, but Raymond's shout, "My pail is full!" brought her focus back to Grandpa's kind face. Stepping a little closer to the security he offered, she started filling her pail again.

Later, sitting among the full berry pails with her feet dangling over the side of Grandpa's wagon, Norma took a deep breath of the fresh, clean air. Tossing a curly pigtail over her shoulder, she gave a contented sigh and swung her bare feet a little harder. She looked at all the pails of berries. Almost she could smell Aunt Sarah's huckleberry pies and see the shining jars of huckleberry jam that would line the kitchen cupboard. She listened to old Ned's feet clip-clopping on the gravel road, and she watched Grandpa's big, gentle hands as they held the reins. He wasn't just her cousin Katie's grandpa like Aunt Sarah was Katie's mom. He was her very own grandpa, and she loved him.

One day in late summer, Norma came from the barn carrying a basket of eggs. When she reached the back porch, she heard Aunt Sarah and Mandy talking in the kitchen. "Mom, will Norma and Raymond go to school here at Woodland? How long will they live with us?"

Norma stopped in her tracks. She listened breathlessly. "Yes," Aunt Sarah replied. "Your Uncle John doesn't have any plans to take them away any time soon. He agreed that they attend school here. I expect they will at least be here for this whole school year."

"Oh, good," Mandy answered. "I hope he never takes them away. I like having them here."

Norma didn't listen to any more. She set the egg basket on the back porch and hurried out to get a drink from the pump. Conflicting emotions filled her heart. Dad could come and get them any time he chose. He could take them away from Aunt Sarah, the farm, and Grandpa, back to the paper shack. But she didn't want to go! Then relief washed over her. Aunt Sarah had said they would at least be here for school time. Her heart warmed at Mandy's words. Norma knew Aunt Sarah wanted her to be here, but it was reassuring to her that Mandy did too. Then her eyes filled with tears. When would they see Mom?

Aunt Sarah sat by the kerosene light in the evenings and stitched and mended to make sure everyone had clothing for school. Each girl had two dresses and two reversible aprons to wear over the dresses. The dresses were made from printed flour sacks. When the aprons got dirty, you turned them inside out for a fresh, clean look. Aunt Sarah's girls always wore aprons. It saved a lot of wear on the dresses.

Raymond was excited about the new overalls Aunt Sarah made for him and a molasses pail of his own to carry lunch in. He would be in the first grade.

But first there were carrots and potatoes to get out of the garden. Cabbages were brought in and shredded and packed into crocks for sauerkraut. These were put in the basement alongside the bins of potatoes and carrots.

Aunt Sarah sent the children berry picking again. This time it was blackberries growing along the roadside.

"I'd much rather pick huckleberries or strawberries," Norma stated, looking at her scratched hands and arms.

"Me too!" Mandy agreed. "But now the berry picking is done for the summer. Listen! I hear the cowbell. Mom said we could quit when the boys bring the cows in. Let's go! The boys caught some trout this afternoon. We're having fried trout and fresh blackberries for supper. Yum!"

The girls hurried toward the house.

"Did you know that some of the neighbors are getting together to help Wilson Reeds pick up potatoes tomorrow?" Lydia asked, hurrying along with the rest. "They usually get the Indians to help them, but they need a little extra help right now. They raised so many potatoes because they sell them."

"Oh, good!" Katie responded. "Norma gets to help too. It's fun when the neighbors work together."

The next morning, Uncle Peter and the children joined the group in the Reeds' potato fields. Grandpa and Walter were there. So were the Kilmers and the Gregorys and others that Norma didn't know. Friendly banter and laughter filled the air as everyone bent their backs to search for potatoes in the sandy soil. Magdalena ran over and joined the girls. Norma felt rather shy around the big Reed boys, as George and Martin came to take the full sacks to the wagon.

She glanced over at Grandpa and Uncle Peter. Grandpa didn't look like a preacher now. He was dusty and dirty like the rest of them. Grandpa and Uncle Peter visited quietly as they moved swiftly across the field. Norma worked quickly, trying to keep up with Mandy, but Mandy was fast. Her heart warmed as she realized that she belonged to this group too. Friendly neighbors all worked together. When Magdalena's mother Susannah and her sister Emma came out with jugs of cool mint tea for everyone, Norma accepted the tea gratefully. Susannah smiled kindly at her. Norma decided that Magdalena had a nice mother.

The grain fields were harvested one after the other. Norma watched in fascination as Uncle Peter operated his horse-powered threshing machine. Uncle Peter stood on the platform in the center where he guided the horses. Four beams ran out like spokes on a wheel. A team of horses was hitched to the end of each beam. With every round, the horses had to step over the tumble rod running to the threshing machine.

Mandy called the children away from watching. "Mom says to come and bring your straw ticks down from your beds."

Eagerly Katie jumped up. "Come on, Norma, this is fun!" Lydia and Mandy helped the younger children with their clumsy mattresses.

"Let's carry them to the other side of the lane," Lydia instructed. Carefully the straw ticks were laid in the soft grass by the field.

"Now," said Katie, "we open the snaps at the end like this and shake! Shake! Shake! Whee! There goes all my old straw."

Soon the children were all laughing and shaking their ticking.

"Goodbye, old straw," Joshua shouted as he gave a mound of humpy straw a mighty kick, sending the old straw flying.

"Now my bed will be hard tonight," Raymond said worriedly.

"Oh, no!" Mandy answered. "Your bed will be very soft because we will put fresh straw in." Mandy shook the last clumps of straw out of Raymond's ticking. "Let's get these things washed so they can dry and we can fill them up tonight."

Peals of laughter and bumping noises came from the upstairs when the children were sent to bed that night. What fun it was, jumping into the big, puffy, sweet-smelling mattresses! Again and again they jumped and tumbled until finally Uncle Peter called up from the stairway for them to settle down.

Norma snuggled into the soft mattress beside Erma. She thought of all the busy and interesting fall days; she thought of dear Grandpa— her grandpa—and kind Aunt Sarah. "I wish I really belonged here," she thought, "but at least Aunt Sarah said we will stay till next spring. Spring is far away." She snuggled down into the soft ticking and fell asleep.

chapter eleven

Woodland School Days

Brutus, Michigan: Fall, Winter 1930

The Brubacher kitchen buzzed with excitement. Five molasses pails waited by the door. The first day of school had finally arrived. Joshua and Raymond fidgeted impatiently while Aunt Sarah made sure their faces were clean and their hair was combed.

Norma was helping Lydia and Katie finish the breakfast dishes. Quickly the girls hung up the damp tea towels and, grabbing their books and molasses pails, joined the boys.

"Let's hurry so we can walk with the Reeds. They are coming out their lane right now." Wilson Reed's lane was directly across the road from Uncle Peter's. They reached the road about the same time that Daniel, Magdalena, and Anna did. Anna skipped happily out the lane.

She would be in first grade. Five-year-old Aaron stood halfway out the lane waving rather sadly as he watched his playmate go off to school.

Norma thought of Erma. It felt strange to go away and leave her. Mandy was working at Manasseh Kulp's, so Erma would only have Aunt Sarah. Aunt Sarah would take good care of her, but Norma hoped she wouldn't cry. It helped to know that she had Nellie and the kittens to play with.

The half-mile walk down the gravel road didn't seem long. Norma was used to walking much farther to school. What would this teacher be like? She was glad that she had learned to know some of the girls at church, and of course she had Katie. As they neared the crossroad by the school, they saw children walking from all directions. The sound

Woodland School

of hooves made them all move instinctively to the side of the road. It was Art on Barney. Art had farther to come than most of them. "Hi, everybody," he called as he passed.

The boys ran shouting around the schoolyard in a quick game of tag before the school bell called them in. The girls stood in little groups talking. Norma noticed there were two girls who didn't wear pigtails and long dresses like the girls at church. She found out that the blond girl who was about her age was Mary Evelyn. The other was her sister Naomi.

There were two doors to the schoolroom. When the school bell rang, Norma followed Katie and the line of girls going in the door on the left while the boys filed in the door on the right. Molasses pails were lined up on a shelf in the entry room. Aunt Sarah had marked each pail with a different color of yarn tied to the handle. Norma looked at the

Woodland School—spring 1930, younger students (School year before Norma arrived. Characters in story underlined.)

Back row: Lizzie Sauder, Katie Brubacher, Mary Evelyn Martin, Leona Brubacher

Middle row: Unknown, Cathrine Sauder, Fannie Gregory, Harvey Kilmer, David Kilmer, Ammon Gregory (in front)

Front row: John Gregory, Benny Eby, Emanuel Brubacher, Magdalena Reed, Naomi Martin, Hattie Gregory, Esther Sauder, Joshua Brubacher

cheerful classroom. It looked quite different than when it was set up for church services.

Everyone was being assigned a desk. Some were single desks and some double. Norma wished she could share a desk with Katie, but the teacher showed her to a single desk. Sitting down on the wooden seat, Norma noticed that Katie and Mary Evelyn were close by. Mary Evelyn smiled at her. Norma smiled back. "I think we will be good friends," Norma thought.

Norma wasn't disappointed with school. The schoolchildren accepted the Brenneman children and treated them as equals. Norma enjoyed having Art nearby. She worried about him a little when he got into mischief and the teacher sent him to the entrance room to work alone awhile. He soon learned that Miss Kuebler kept order.

What fun it was to run outside and skip rope and play hopscotch at recess. The busy fall schedule hadn't left a lot of time for play. Best of all, Norma liked the cozy feeling when books were laid aside and the teacher read them stories.

One day when the children came home from school, Aunt Sarah drew Norma aside. "Norma, I wanted to let you know that your dad is coming to visit again. He is planning to stay for the weekend. He will sleep here on the daybed in the kitchen."

Norma nodded silently. When she reached for the pail to help carry water to fill the water trough, Aunt Sarah added, "Your dad said he'd rather take you children to the English church than to go along with us to our church. You will come back here for lunch." Norma nodded again, looking at the floor. Aunt Sarah put her arm around Norma's shoulder and gave her a quick hug. "You may go now."

Norma grabbed the pump handle and pumped viciously. Why? Why did Dad have to come and spoil their peaceful life? Why didn't he just send some money to Aunt Sarah and stay away? Whenever he came, memories flooded back to Norma. Good memories and bad memories. Memories of Mom and the family all together. Memories of happy times, but mostly memories of poverty and fighting, uncertainties, insecurities, and fears. Erma would get upset and cry for Mom. Raymond would have some tears too, but he would probably be mostly happy to see his dad. Every boy naturally is drawn to his dad.

Why couldn't Mom be the one to come? It would sure be nice to see Mom again. Then Norma remembered when Mom had visitors in the evening while Dad was working and the children were sent to bed. She remembered the sharp words when Dad was home. What was Mom doing now? Did she even miss them? Norma gave the pump several more vicious pumps until the water sloshed over the pail onto the ground. Recklessly, she grabbed the full pail and headed for the house. Water slopped out, wetting her skirt. Her heart was filled with dread at the thought of Dad coming. She certainly didn't feel like going away with Dad to the English church.

But Dad came anyway. He gained the children's favor with pieces of candy. He even brought candy for Katie and Joshua. As Dad and Uncle Peter sat visiting, Erma went and leaned against Uncle Peter's lap, but Raymond hung close to his dad.

Norma was polite, but her heart was in a turmoil. She had never really felt close to Dad, but she looked at him and wondered how it would be if he were a real dad and gave them the love and understanding that she felt from Grandpa and Aunt Sarah. How could he be so different from the rest of his family?

Sunday morning came. Raymond was excited about a ride in the Model T. He sat up front with Dad, his blue eyes sparkling. Norma and Erma sat in the back. "Where's Aunt Sarah?" Erma wondered.

"They are going to walk to the school for church," Norma answered. "We are going to the church building, but we will come home to eat."

"It sure doesn't take as long to get to church with a car!" Raymond remarked as the Model T chugged up the steep hill before the church. Dad smiled at his enthusiasm.

Norma took Erma's hand and followed Dad to the church. She swallowed a lump in her throat and went in the door on the women's side. Most people were already seated in church. She and Erma slipped into one of the back benches on the women's side.

Soon the singing started. It was English words and was sung faster than at Uncle Peter's church. "What a Friend We Have in Jesus." That was one of the songs that Betsy and Mandy sang! From then on, Norma was all ears. For the moment she forgot Dad across the aisle with Raymond.

When the preacher got up to speak, she could understand! The preacher was telling a story about a man who took care of sheep. He had a hundred sheep, but one got lost. Norma listened breathlessly as the preacher told the story of the shepherd hunting through the cold, dark mountains to find his lost sheep. She felt happy when he found it and carried it back home. The preacher said the shepherd was like Jesus. Jesus loves us like the shepherd loved his sheep. Jesus was the one they sang about in the English songs. She glanced at Dad. He had his arms folded and was looking at the floor.

The preacher seemed to know a lot of stories. Now he was telling about a boy who ran away from home. He wasted all his money and ended up taking care of pigs and wishing that he could eat the pigs' feed. Norma thought of the slop that the boys fed to Uncle Peter's pig and decided he must have been terribly hungry! She was starting to feel a little hungry herself, but not *that* hungry! Then the boy went home, and his father was so glad to see him that he made a big meal. (Suddenly she could almost smell Aunt Sarah's fried chicken. Katie said that was what they were having for lunch.) The preacher was talking about Jesus again—about how Jesus wants us to come to Him. Norma couldn't follow it all, but she observed that this preacher spoke kindly and like he meant it, just as Grandpa did.

Then they were singing again. Norma liked the English songs and tried to help along the best she could. "What can wash away my sin? Nothing but the blood of Jesus."

When church was over, Norma stood shyly, holding Erma's hand. She felt rather lost since she didn't know these people. Several children stood nearby, staring at the strangers. Dad looked like he was headed for the door, but just then Norma overheard two ladies talking. "Yes, that's Henry Brenneman's son John. You know he left his children at Peter Brubacher's because he and his wife separated."

Norma felt her heart drop. She gave Erma's hand a tug and headed for the door. Before she could get out of church, she was stopped by a warm, friendly voice. "Well, hello, girls! I'm Rosie. How are you girls this morning? We are glad you came." Norma looked up into Rosie's friendly face. Her heart lifted a little. She shook the hand Rosie held out to her. "I'm sure you girls have names. Can you tell me what they are?"

"I'm Norma and this is Erma," Norma answered quietly.

"Well, I see that you are taking good care of your sister," Rosie said with a smile. "But I don't want to keep you. I believe your dad is ready to go."

Norma smiled at her again and hurried to the Model T.

"Dad, when are you going to come and take us away from here?" Raymond wondered on the way back to Uncle Peter's. "Are you going to take us home? When will we get to see Mom again?"

Dad didn't answer right away. "This is the best place for you now," he answered shortly. "You're going to school here and you have enough to eat. Right?"

"Y-e-s," Raymond answered, "But—"

"That's good for now then," Dad interrupted. Dad left soon after lunch, and life returned to normal.

Betsy and Mandy were both working away. Norma missed Mandy. Sometimes the girls came home on weekends, but not always. At twelve or thirteen years old, children were expected to help earn their keep, and they were sent out to work for others.

The weather turned cooler. Aunt Sarah and Lydia were busy knitting mittens and scarves. Aunt Sarah patched and stitched so each child had heavy woolen outerwear.

Years earlier, Uncle Peter had bought a knitting machine to make and sell tube socks to the Gehrhart Knitting Company. It had been a good winter project for the family, but that had come to an end. Now the big, hand-cranked machine was put to use to keep the family in warm socks for the winter. Uncle Peter came home from town with boots for Norma and Raymond. Raymond soon put his on and ran outside to "see how they worked." Norma smiled gratefully at Uncle Peter as she slid her feet into the new boots. They fit fine with a little room to grow. Boots of her own! She remembered walking to school with holes in her shoes. Now she had shoes and boots!

Several mornings later when Norma woke up, she heard shouting coming from the boys' room. "Look out the window! Look out the window!"

Quickly she and Katie slid out of bed and ran across the chilly room to the window. The scenery had changed overnight. Everything was white. Big, fluffy snowflakes floated to the ground. "Erma, come and see!" Norma urged. Rubbing sleep from her eyes, Erma came to join the girls. Suddenly her eyes opened wide. Snow!

"Oh, look, Norma," she giggled. "Look at Nellie." Nellie was running in circles in the fluffy snow.

Quickly the girls dressed and hurried to the warm kitchen. Raymond and Joshua had beat them there. They were getting ready to go out to the barn. "Hey, Norma!" Raymond rejoiced. "We get to wear our new boots, and I can't wait to slide down the barn hill. It's really snowing! I wonder how deep it is."

Aunt Sarah's warm wheat mush with thick cream tasted so good. Then everyone was bundled up in warm clothes for the walk to school. No one was more grateful than Norma as she slipped her hands into the new, warm mittens. How well she remembered the two-mile walk to school last year without mittens or warm scarves or boots. She remembered how some of the older girls would take her close to the woodstove and rub their hands and feet to warm them up before school started. Happily, she followed the other children out the door.

Uncle Peter was going out the lane to deliver butter and eggs in town. "Look at the wagon. It looks funny without the wheels," Raymond said with a chuckle.

"That's 'cause Dad put the sleigh runners on now so it will go better in the snow," Joshua explained.

Laughing and sliding, the children ran out the lane, where they met the Reed children. The Reed children were all warmly dressed too.

"Look, Norma," little Anna said shyly. "Mother made new mittens for me." Norma smiled at her. There was something special about Anna.

"I hope we get two feet of snow," Daniel stated.

"Me too," Joshua agreed.

"We'll get more than that before the winter's over," Lydia said, tipping her head back and catching fluffy snowflakes in her mouth.

All day the snow fell. Recess activities changed to games of "Fox and Geese" on trails in the snow. The younger children built snowmen.

When Norma came into the schoolroom from recess, she carefully hung her mittens on the rack where the warm air came up from the wood furnace in the basement. By the next recess, they were warm and dry again.

On the way home, the girls hung back and let Daniel break the deep snow. Joshua and Raymond followed after him, stopping occasionally to see how high they could kick snow in the air or throw a snowball at each other.

Magdalena stopped beside the beaten track. Turning her back to the soft snow, she put her hands at her sides and let herself fall back into the snow. With her arms straight out, she raised them to her head. Up and down, up and down went her arms. "Lydia, help me get up so I don't ruin my snow angel," she called. Lydia reached out a hand and helped Magdalena to her feet. There in the snow was the outline of an angel.

"Magdalena, help me make one too," Anna begged.

"Here," Lydia said, "I'll help you. Like this. Turn around and give me your hands. I'll help you lie down. Now move your arms up and down." Laughing, Norma and Katie dropped backwards into the snow.

Soon a row of four little angels guarded the path to school.

"We'd better go, or Mom's going to wonder what took so long," Lydia said, brushing snow from Anna's back.

When the rosy-cheeked girls came into the kitchen, Erma was napping on the daybed. The kitchen was warm and cozy and smelled like fresh bread. When the door slammed, Erma woke up. Seeing the girls, she ran to Norma. "Norma, I played in the snow with Nellie. Aunt Sarah helped me make an angel in the snow. Nellie was a bad dog. She spoiled the angel."

Now that the weather was cold, there was butchering to do. Uncle Joe and Grandpa came to help when the children were at school. Several pigs were killed and hung in the barn to cool the meat. Salome and Grandpa came to help several days later. Mandy and Betsy were home too. Uncle Peter put some of the fresh meat in the snow. Then he covered it with a metal tub. Silas brought a big chunk of wood to set on top of the tub. The meat would keep for quite a while. There were sausages to make and meat to can. Everyone was busy. Norma helped to keep Erma out of the way. Nellie ran eagerly around, hoping someone would throw her a scrap.

Aunt Sarah cooked the bones to remove the last of the meat. She ground up the scrap meat to make "puddins." Mandy had brought several crocks up from the basement and scrubbed them clean. Aunt Sarah seasoned the meat scraps and put them, along with the broth, into the crocks. Then she covered it with a layer of lard. When it hardened, she turned it upside down and put it in the cool enclosed porch. That meat didn't need canning. Then she rendered the fat and put the lard into crocks to cool.

The schoolchildren crowded around the warm cracklings taken from the lard press that was used to stuff the sausages. Norma tasted the warm cracklings and looked at all the sausages and canned meat. She remembered the time Dad brought meat home for supper and Mom trimmed the bad part off and cooked it. What a treat it had been! Now looking at all the fresh meat, she gave a sigh of contentment. It was good to live on a farm!

The snow had come to stay. Snowstorms came and went, and the snow continued to pile up. Uncle Peter kept a path shoveled to the barn. When the wind whipped the snow into big drifts, Aunt Sarah hung a thick blanket over the west kitchen door to keep out the cold air that came in through the cracks. Blocking that door didn't matter because everyone used the door to the back porch anyway.

On Sunday morning, Aunt Sarah warmed bricks at the woodstove. When Uncle Peter brought the horse and sleigh to the walk, she put the warm bricks into the straw on the back of the wagon. Bundled up in a warm woolen cloak Aunt Sarah had made, Norma snuggled down with the rest of the children on the sleigh. A heavy woolen blanket covered the straw. Norma put her feet close to the warm bricks. It felt so good. She looked at the snow-laden trees and the white, sparkling snowbanks. She felt warm and secure. Aunt Sarah took such good care of them!

As the sleigh glided quietly and quickly over the snowy road, Norma reached under the blanket and took Erma's mittened hand in her own. "I want to grow up to be like Aunt Sarah," she decided. "If I ever have children, I'll take good care of them too."

chapter twelve

The Big Black Word

Brutus, Michigan: 1930 to Spring 1931

"Joshua Brubacher, watch where you are going!" Katie scolded, picking herself up out of the snowy bank by the side of the road.

"I slid the farthest. I slid farther than you, Daniel!" Joshua shouted.

"Maybe you did," Katie fumed, "but at least he didn't knock anyone off their feet. Where *is* my lunch pail?"

"Here," Norma answered, pulling the molasses pail out of the snow. Quickly she jumped aside as Magdalena slid past her.

The children were on their way home from school. Running and sliding in their boots on the hard-packed snowy road was great fun.

"When I get bigger," Daniel stated, "I'm going to get ice skates like

George and Martin have. Then I can skate fast at the dam. You should see how fast they go."

"You know what?" Raymond piped up. "We can't even see the fences anymore. The snow is deep! I never thought I'd walk right over a fence!"

"I can't wait till Christmas," Magdalena said, giving a hop and a skip. "Mother and Emma are making some cookies today."

"Maybe we can have a taste when we get home," Anna suggested.

"Maybe a tiny one," Magdalena agreed, "but mostly we'll just have to wait for Christmas."

Norma knew Aunt Sarah too had put a few cracked eggs aside to make cookies. They had never really done anything special at Christmas with Mom and Dad, except of course the one Christmas when Mom gave her Lillian. "I wonder what happened to Lillian," she thought sadly.

"Our mom's going to make cookies too," Katie said, "and I think we will get some maple sugar candy. I just can't wait."

Finally Christmas came. When the children came into the kitchen, their eyes got big. There was an *orange* at each place at the table. And what did they smell? Uncle Peter not only had bought oranges, but he must have gotten a little chocolate, because beside each place was a steaming mug of hot chocolate! It seemed like the silent breakfast prayer was long that morning. When she opened her eyes, Norma saw that Joshua had been leaning in as far as he could with his nose above his hot chocolate while he prayed. Uncle Peter didn't notice. Quickly the warm porridge disappeared, and the children started to peel their oranges. Norma couldn't remember when she had last tasted an orange. The children savored each juicy bite. They drained their mugs of hot chocolate to the last drop. What a special breakfast that was!

Grandpas, Uncle Joes, and Martin Kilmer and Mary, just married this month, were coming for lunch. It was so nice to spend the day with Walter and Arthur! Lunch was a special meal of ham and fluffy mashed potatoes, with pudding and cookies for dessert. Norma nibbled her cookie slowly. She wanted to enjoy every crumb. Aunt Sarah made good cookies!

Last of all, they handed around a little glass dish with pieces of maple candy. "I wish we had Christmas every day," Raymond said, reaching for a piece of candy.

The children spent the afternoon sliding down the barn hill on their homemade sleds. There weren't a lot of other hills to slide on. Then they made snowmen and played tag in the snow.

"How's school, Norma?" Walter wondered when they stood waiting for their turn on the wooden sled.

"I like it," Norma answered. "We have a nice teacher, and the children are nice to us."

"Good!" Walter responded. "Does Art behave himself?"

"Pretty good," Norma answered. "Sometimes he has to go study in the entry, but mostly he behaves. Raymond likes school too. The teacher is patient with him."

"Let's step over here, Norma," Walter said, giving a little tug at her coat sleeve. He drew her away from the others and closer to the barn. "There's something I think I should tell you. I don't want you to hear it somewhere else. I overheard Grandpa and Uncle Joe talking. They said our dad and mom are getting a divorce."

"A what? What does that mean?" Norma asked soberly.

"A divorce is a paper that says they are not married anymore and they're not going to live together again. I looked it up in Uncle Joe's dictionary. I'm sorry, sis," Walter said gently.

"But what about us?" Norma wondered. "Does that mean we get to stay here? What about Mom? What will she do?"

"I don't know," Walter replied. "I don't even know anyone else that has a divorce, so I don't know how it all works. I didn't want to spoil your happy day, but I just thought you should know."

"I guess—I guess if we can stay here always, that won't be so bad. But, Walter, that means we'll *never* be all together again! Oh, I'm all mixed up! Sometimes I just wish we would all be back home, and other times I hope we never have to leave here. What if Aunt Sarah can't keep us always? What will we do?"

"I don't know, Sis, but I guess we'll just have to look out for each other. Come, let's play. We can't change it anyway. Let me give you a big push on the sled. It's your turn."

Norma wanted to just get away from everyone for a little, but she climbed on the sled instead. Down the hill she flew.

That night, when Norma snuggled down under the warm covers, it seemed like she saw a big black word written across the ceiling: DIVORCE. When she rolled onto her side, she saw it on the wall: DIVORCE. Walter had said he found it in the dictionary. She decided right then that if there was any word in the dictionary that she hated, it was that word—DIVORCE.

Then she remembered the two ladies at the English church. Would they say, "Their parents are divorced"? Were there other children somewhere whose parents were divorced? She didn't know anyone. "Never together again." Always in the back of her mind, she had hoped that sometime, somehow, Dad and Mom would come for them and things would be different. Mom and Dad would be happy, and they could all live together again. Slowly, as she lay staring at the ceiling, that dream died.

What if Aunt Sarah couldn't keep them always? What had Walter said? "We'll look out for each other." She put her arm protectively around sleeping Erma and whispered almost fiercely to herself, "I will. I will look out for her—always."

The next day at school, Norma had a hard time concentrating. "Will I ever see Mom again? What if I never do? Walter said that we would look out for each other, but we are all pretty young yet. Where would we go if Uncle Peter and Aunt Sarah couldn't keep us?"

Suddenly Norma realized the other children were putting their books away for recess. She looked at her work in dismay. She had hardly done anything. She hurried out to join the others.

When the children ran out for recess, they saw a group of men and boys at the crossroad by the school, shoveling snow from the snowbank back onto the road. "What are they doing?" Norma asked Katie.

"They are putting snow on the road where the wind blew it bare. That's so the sleighs will slide better," Katie explained.

Norma saw Jesse Brubacher come over to talk to the teacher. "Come, children," the teacher called. "We are going to go over and pack the snow down for the men." Laughing and shoving, the children ran to the road. *Tramp, tramp, tramp!* Many feet worked together, packing the snow so the wind wouldn't blow it away. Now the sleighs could all slide smoothly across the road. No bare spots were left. The children ran back to their play. The men took their shovels and went home.

That evening, the wind whistled around the house. Everyone gathered in the warm kitchen after supper. Aunt Sarah popped popcorn and set it out for a snack. Lydia added a dish of sliced apples. Norma joined the happy circle around the table. She took the big black word DIVORCE and stuffed it way down under all her other feelings. Aunt Sarah would never send them away if they had no place to go. At that thought, she gave a sigh of relief and reached for popcorn for herself and Erma.

One snowy day followed another, but by late winter the coldest winds had stopped blowing. One morning after breakfast, Uncle Peter announced, "The way the weather is looking, I think Silas and I had better get set up for making maple syrup. When you children come home from school, we should be ready for you to hang up the buckets."

"Yum!" Joshua rejoiced.

"How do you make maple syrup?" Raymond wondered. Norma was glad he asked because she wondered too.

"We'll show you, Raymond," Uncle Peter said. "You'll be able to help too."

The children hurried home from school. There had been a lot of talk about maple syrup making at school. It seemed that almost all the families were getting ready to do the same thing. Uncle Peter and Silas were loading the sleigh with wooden buckets. The children took their lunch pails to the kitchen and then ran to the sleigh. Norma helped Erma get up on the sleigh with the other children. Aunt Sarah was coming along too. Away they went around the left side of the barn and back across the snowy fields to the trees.

"These trees are special trees," Uncle Peter explained to Raymond. "They are called sugar maples. When it starts to get warmer in the spring, there's sap down in the roots of the tree that goes up inside the tree and out to the branches to make the green leaves grow. We're going to get some of that sap and turn it into maple syrup."

"How will we get it out of the tree?" Raymond wondered.

"You'll see pretty soon," Uncle Peter said with a smile.

When the horses stopped close to the maple trees, Uncle Peter got his hand drill out of the sleigh. Silas carried a hammer and had his big coat pockets filled with little wooden pegs.

"Bring a bucket, Joshua," Uncle Peter instructed.

Everyone crowded around to watch. Carefully, Uncle Peter put his drill bit against the tree at a spot about as high as Norma's shoulder. Then he cranked it until he had drilled a hole in the tree about the length of his finger. Quickly Silas took one of the little pegs from his pocket and hammered it into the tree. The little peg was hollow, making a little spout. Joshua hung a bucket under the spout on the tree. Everyone's eyes were on the spout. Sure enough, *ploink...ploink,* sap dripped from the spout into the bucket.

Quick as a wink, Joshua's finger was right there waiting to catch the next drop. "I want to taste it too!" Katie said, sticking her finger out to catch the next drop.

"Me too!" Raymond added. After his taste, he said, "It doesn't quite taste like maple syrup."

"No," Uncle Peter answered. "We will gather the sap and cook it to make the syrup."

After they all had a taste, Uncle Peter said, "Now we have work to do. You children get the buckets off the sleigh and bring one to each tree." Then he set to work drilling holes. Silas pounded in the spouts. After a while, almost everywhere that Norma looked, she saw buckets hanging from the trees. They moved deeper into the woods, working as they went.

It was so much fun to work together as a family. After the job was done, everyone got onto the sleigh and rode back to the house for a supper of johnnycake with canned berries and milk.

For the next number of weeks, the children got up early enough to help empty the sap buckets. From tree to tree they went, carrying buckets to Uncle Peter to dump into the tank on the sleigh. When the tank was full, Uncle Peter drove the sleigh to the sugar shanty and emptied the sap into a big vat to cook it. Joshua and Raymond carried wood to the shanty to keep the fire going.

All day while the children were in school, Uncle Peter or Aunt Sarah tended the vat of sap. Occasionally, they took a wooden ladle and skimmed the top off the boiling sap. This part was thrown away. By the end of the day, what they had left was not sap anymore, but real maple syrup.

The next day, they started all over, emptying the buckets into the tank on the sleigh. When Aunt Sarah served pancakes and fresh maple syrup for breakfast, Norma thought it was the best breakfast she had ever had. "Now this tastes like the real syrup!" Raymond declared. "But where does the maple sugar candy come from?"

"Well," Uncle Peter answered, "tomorrow is Saturday, and there's no school. How about if we show you how we do it then?"

"Do we get to taste it then?" Raymond wondered.

Uncle Peter's eyes twinkled. "Don't you think all my sap gatherers should get a treat?"

Raymond gave a little bounce on his chair. "I helped to empty sap pails. I really did!"

"Yes, you did," Uncle Peter said. "And you'll get to have maple sugar candy."

Saturday was a busy day. Aunt Sarah put the girls to cleaning, baking, and getting ready for Sunday. Betsy and Mandy were home for the weekend. Aunt Sarah had invited Jesse Brubachers for Sunday dinner. Grandpa and Grandma were coming too. Everyone worked hard. When it was time to empty the sap pails, everyone climbed onto the sleigh to go along.

With Betsy and Mandy to help, the pails were soon empty. Betsy stirred the sap in the big vat. When the sap turned to syrup, it was loaded onto the sleigh, and they all rode back to the house. Aunt Sarah had a big kettle on the cookstove. Into the kettle went some of the syrup. Then she started cooking the maple syrup some more. Once in a while, she dropped a little syrup into a bowl of hot water. The children gathered around eagerly. Mandy handed each of the children a tin plate.

"Do we each get a whole plate full of candy?" Raymond asked, his eyes big.

"No," Katie said laughing. "We are going to get some clean snow on our plates. Then Mom will drizzle syrup on the snow, and the syrup will cool quickly into soft maple candy. We get to eat that right now. We'll make some hard candy to eat later."

When she dropped some syrup into the cold water and it turned into a little ball, Aunt Sarah said, "Now go get snow on your plates and come." The children ran outside for snow and then lined up eagerly for their candy. Norma held her plate close to the kettle. Carefully, Aunt Sarah drizzled syrup onto the snow on her plate. First she made an "N," and then she made curlicues around it. The syrup cooled quickly into a soft, chewy candy.

"Now take it over to the table before you eat it," Aunt Sarah instructed. "I don't want the clean floor all sticky for Sunday." The children sat around the table enjoying the soft candy. Erma's sticky face and hands showed her enjoyment.

"It dothn't work to puth too muth in your mouth at oncth," Raymond announced.

"Yeth, I know," Joshua agreed. The two boys' plates were empty long before Norma and Katie had finished theirs.

"Do we get more?" Raymond wondered.

"Not now," Aunt Sarah answered. She had been cooking the syrup a bit longer. "We will make the rest into hard maple sugar."

Raymond watched as she poured the syrup into a buttered pan to harden. "I guess I'm too full anyway," he admitted.

"Now," Aunt Sarah instructed, "you girls make sure the younger ones get cleaned up at the basin, and check the floor too." Norma licked the last sweet stickiness from her fingers and went to wash at the basin in the corner.

The next day, the Brubachers and their company sat around the lunch table. Uncle Joe, Aunt Salome, and Art were there too. It felt so good to have Walter and Arthur there even if there was other company. Norma smiled across the table at Arthur. Raymond sat happily between his two big brothers. The children had been taught to be seen but not heard at the table. They sat fairly quietly with the occasional whisper between them.

Jesse Brubacher was talking now. "Yes, Peter, I remember being here long ago—must have been soon after you moved here. If I remember right, you had the young folks here for a meal." Uncle Peter chuckled. He knew what was coming. It was a favorite story. "Anyways," Jesse continued, "the young fellows seemed to be very helpful that day. They offered to do the work and seated the girls at the table, smiling nicely at them. Sarah, did you know what they were up to?"

Aunt Sarah covered her smile with her hand but didn't answer.

"Well, anyways," Jesse continued, "the boys went around the table pouring coffee for the girls. When the coffee was all poured and the girls were drinking it, Abe Sauder opened the coffeepot and looked in. 'What's this?' he asked. Then he pulled a dishrag out of the coffeepot! How those girls did shriek! You knew about it all the time, didn't you, Sarah?"

Aunt Sarah and Jesse's wife were laughing and wiping tears from their eyes. Norma smiled. She had never seen that side of Aunt Sarah.

The kitchen quieted as everyone paused for the silent prayer that followed the meal.

Grandpa sat close to the door. As the children passed him on their way out to play, each one stopped a bit. Grandpa had pulled a familiar little tin container out of his pocket. He had opened it and was giving each of the children a pink peppermint candy. "Thank you," Norma said quietly when she took her mint.

"This one remembered her manners," Grandpa complimented her. Norma smiled shyly at him—her own dear grandpa.

chapter thirteen

Spring Fever

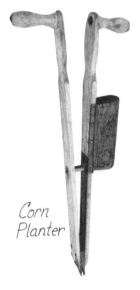

Corn
Planter

Brutus, Michigan: Spring 1931

The sap quit running. The wooden buckets were washed and put away for another season. The snowbanks shrank smaller and smaller, and little buds pushed out on the trees and bushes. The children in school were restless. More than one boy had to spend time working in the entry room because of misbehavior.

One morning when school started, Arthur hadn't shown up at all. Norma worried about him until she heard the clip-clop of Barney's hooves in the schoolyard. Classes had already begun. When Arthur arrived at the classroom door with tousled hair and red face, the teacher scolded, "Arthur, you are late!"

"Well," Arthur stammered, "it—it wasn't me. It was—it was Barney."

"And just how do you blame your lateness on a mule?" the teacher questioned.

"Well, you see, when I got to the mailboxes down by the crossroad, there was this big, deep puddle. Barney walked into the middle of the puddle and took a drink. Then he wouldn't go. I tried. I yelled and kicked him, and I heard the school bell ringing, but I couldn't come."

The schoolchildren were beginning to snicker. "Then," Arthur continued, "I jumped down into the water and went and got a big stick, and *whack!* He started to move. I quick jumped on and came as fast as I could. I think Barney doesn't like to go to school in the spring, just like—"

"That's enough, Arthur, take your seat," the teacher interrupted.

At home, Aunt Sarah was kept busy scrubbing mud out of skirts and trousers. She carefully washed and took apart the printed cloth sacks that flour came in. Then she ironed them and cut out new dresses for the growing girls.

Aunt Sarah patiently showed Norma and Katie how to hand-stitch new dresses for their dolls while the older girls stitched dresses and shirts. Erma played at stringing buttons on a piece of yarn. The sewing needed to be done before spring housecleaning and canning began.

"Mom!" Joshua said as he stuck his head in the back door one afternoon. "Buttercup had twin calves."

"Twins! Oh, Mom, please!" The girls stopped their sewing. "May we go see?"

Aunt Sarah looked at their eager faces. "Yes, let's all go," she agreed, laying her own sewing on the table.

Everyone hurried to the barn. How cute the little calves looked, trying to balance on their wobbly legs. "Look," Erma said, "Buttercup is tasting the calves."

"That's the way mother cows wash their babies," Aunt Sarah explained, smiling.

Soon the little calves were busy nuzzling their mother for milk, and the girls reluctantly returned to their sewing. It would soon be time to make supper.

"What is that noise?" Norma wondered on the way back to the house. "I heard it awhile already, but it seems louder than it used to be."

"Oh, I think you mean the spring peepers," Aunt Sarah answered. "It's little frogs—a whole lot of them. The bigger they grow, the louder the noise is."

"It must be a lot of frogs," Norma thought. "It would be fun to go find them."

With spring came Easter. Each child was given one hard-boiled egg. What a treat it was! Hardly ever did they get an egg, since they were sold for groceries.

The snow melted, and when the first warm rain came, Aunt Sarah and the girls went mushroom picking. In the woods among the rotted logs and stumps they found a gold mine of morels. Carefully they gathered them to be taken home and fried in fresh butter.

The fields were drying out, and Uncle Peter was getting ready to plant corn. Back and forth the horses plodded over the fields, turning up the soil with the plow. Lilacs bloomed by the side of the house. Norma loved their sweet fragrance and their dainty flowers. One day she stood burying her face in the sweetness and taking deep breaths— but her heart was heavy. The roads were better now, and Dad was coming for a visit. Aunt Sarah said that he would take them to the English church again. If only they could at least go to church where she knew the people. Then Norma remembered the stories the preacher told and the songs that she could help sing. She found herself looking forward to that.

When Sunday came, she took Erma's hand and slipped into the back of the church again. The other children sat up front, but Dad seemed to prefer coming in just before the service started. Someone came in and sat next to her and Erma. She looked up into the smiling face of Rosie—the woman who had spoken so kindly to her the other time they came. Norma smiled back. It didn't seem quite as lonely having

Rosie next to them.

The first song was a cheerful one that Norma had never heard Betsy and Mandy sing, but she liked it immediately. "I am so glad that Jesus loves me, Jesus loves me, Jesus loves me...."

Soon Norma was lost in the story the preacher was telling. This Jesus that they sang about came down from heaven as a baby. He did many wonderful things, but wicked men killed Him by hanging Him on a wooden cross. It was such a sad story. The preacher said Jesus died so we can go to heaven.

What was he saying now? Jesus came out of the grave—He was alive again! Then He went up to heaven. We can go to heaven too someday if we love Him. Norma wondered if Katie and Joshua ever heard this story. She had never heard Uncle Peter and Aunt Sarah tell it to the children. This preacher spoke so clearly and plainly. His sermon didn't seem as long as the German ones that she couldn't understand.

Then they sang another song: "Alas, and did my Saviour bleed... He loves me, He loves me..." Did that mean that Jesus loved her, Norma Brenneman? The preacher said Jesus loved everyone. That sounded like Aunt Sarah. Maybe Jesus was like Aunt Sarah. She seemed to love everyone. How many times she had felt Aunt Sarah's arms around her when she felt sad. Maybe that's what Jesus was like.

Church was over. Norma and Erma headed for the back door. This time they were stopped by another friendly voice. "Hello, girls. You must be Norma and Erma. Rosie Weaver told me your names. My name is Rosetta Kauffman. My husband is the preacher. His name is Clyde. We're glad to have you girls here. Let's see, how old are you?"

"I'm ten," Norma answered. "Erma's four, but soon we'll both have a birthday."

"Well, isn't that nice," Rosetta said. "When are your birthdays?"

"We have the same birthday," Norma answered. "It is June 26."

"Well, well, I'm sure you were happy to have a little sister on your birthday. What a nice birthday gift!"

Norma nodded, smiling.

Dad was walking to the Model T. Norma and Erma hurried to catch up with him and Raymond.

As it warmed up more, Norma listened to the voices of the little spring peepers grow deeper. The snow was gone. Walking home from school, the children could see the horse and plow working up the fields at Daniel Brubacher's. The Reeds were planting potatoes. Daniel Reed grumbled about sitting in school on a nice, sunny day. Magdalena quickly reminded him that he'd be complaining about planting and hoeing potatoes soon enough.

One day when the children came home from school, Uncle Peter, Silas, and Mandy were walking slowly across the field carrying a long pole. Four chains were fastened to the pole at about three-foot intervals. The chains dragged in the dirt, making four straight rows. "Whatever are they doing?" Raymond wondered.

"They're getting ready to plant corn," Joshua said. "Let's get into our old clothes. Then we can watch."

When Norma went out to make sure the chickens had water, she had a surprise. Ten little fluffy chicks were running around in the henhouse. The hen that had been nesting in the corner of the henhouse was clucking proudly. Norma picked up a fluffy chick and held it to her cheek. She couldn't wait to tell Aunt Sarah.

On her way back to the house, she noticed that Uncle Peter, Silas, and Mandy were dragging the chains crosswise in the field. Now the chains made a pattern of blocks. Joshua and Raymond were coming out of the barn. Joshua carried a bucket full of corn kernels. Raymond had a wood-and-tin contraption that Norma didn't recognize.

"Look, Norma," Raymond said. "Joshua showed me how this thing works. It's a corn planter. Here is where you put the corn in. Then you poke this pointy end in the ground like this and squeeze these two levers together. That lets the corn drop out into the ground."

Uncle Peter had reached the edge of the field by now. "Why did you make blocks in the dirt like that?" Norma asked Mandy.

"That's so we know where to put the corn seed in. If we put seed everywhere the lines cross, then Dad can cultivate the field in both directions to keep the weeds out."

"Here, Norma," Uncle Peter offered. "Do you want to put the first seed in?" Uncle Peter filled the corn planter and handed it to Norma. "I'll help you. Here, put your hands here." Uncle Peter's work-worn hands closed over Norma's. "Now set the planter right here where the lines cross and squeeze the levers together like this." Sure enough, there in the dirt lay two kernels of corn. "Now try it yourself," Uncle Peter encouraged.

Down the row Norma went, leaving a row of little kernels behind her.

"I want a turn! I want a turn!" Raymond said, jumping up and down on one foot excitedly.

"You'll get your turn," Uncle Peter said smiling at him. "See, Norma, now we cover the corn like this." Uncle Peter used his foot to push a little dirt over the corn. "Now, let's give Raymond a turn, shall we? Maybe you should run and see if Aunt Sarah needs you now. You will get to help out here again."

Happily Raymond took his place at the corn planter. Suddenly Norma remembered the new chicks. Coming into the kitchen, she announced, "We have ten new little chicks."

"Good, good!" Aunt Sarah rejoiced. "Biddie did a good job hatching out her eggs. Sometimes I have to bring eggs in here in a box by the woodstove and tend them myself until they hatch, but this time Biddie did it."

"Oh, Mom!" Katie spoke up. "I'm so glad Dad put chicken wire over the top of the chicken yard. Now no hawks can come down and steal chicks like they did one time."

Norma looked at Katie in surprise. "That would be terrible! The little chicks are so cute."

"It was terrible," Katie said. "I just felt like crying."

"You girls can go help with the corn planting," Aunt Sarah instructed. "Silas is going to borrow Grandpa's planter too."

Up and down the fields Silas and Mandy went with the planter. Katie and Norma followed, covering the kernels with their bare feet.

Planting corn was more fun than Aunt Sarah's next project for them. It was time for spring housecleaning. Bedding was taken off the beds and hung out the window to air. The windows were closed on the ends of the blankets. Soon they were flapping in the breeze. The ceiling and walls were wiped down. Furniture was wiped off and the floors scrubbed. *Scrub, scrub, scrub.* Everything smelled like pine oil. The windows were shined and the beds remade. Then it was time to start on the downstairs.

Norma liked the good, clean feeling. She found herself looking forward to that when her arms were tired of scrubbing. When the downstairs was done and the windows all shined, Aunt Sarah put the girls to scrubbing the porches and the sidewalk.

At last cleaning was all done. The girls' hands were red and chapped, but the job was finished for another year. Norma couldn't imagine that any spider or mouse would want to live in Aunt Sarah's house.

Then it was time to plant garden. Norma knelt in the warm, sandy soil and carefully helped Katie plant peas, beans, red beets, and turnips. Aunt Sarah planted the tiny seeds such as carrots and lettuce. Raymond and Joshua planted potatoes and onions.

Every morning when she went to gather eggs, Norma checked the garden. One morning she saw little green onion shoots and tiny pea leaves poking through the ground. Just then she saw Aunt Sarah coming out to the well. "The garden's growing," Norma announced happily. Aunt Sarah set her pail down by the well and came to see. "I never planted a garden before," Norma said. "It will be fun to watch it grow."

"Yes, it will be so nice to have fresh vegetables again," Aunt Sarah agreed. "Soon we will have weeding to do, and after a while it will be canning. You and Katie will have to be my helpers now since the older girls are working away more." Aunt Sarah smiled at Norma.

"I like to work—especially outside in the garden," Norma said smiling back. "I better get the eggs now, or we will be late for school." She snatched up the egg basket and headed for the barn, stopping at the edge of the garden to smell the flowers on the elderberry bush. Humming a tune, she disappeared into the barn.

Aunt Sarah watched her go. "She seems happy here, but I wonder what John has in mind for the future. I hope the children don't have to face more heartaches." With a sigh, she filled her pail and carried it back to the house.

chapter fourteen

The Chest in the Attic

Brutus, Michigan: 1931

The school door opened. Laughing and shouting children spilled out across the schoolyard.

"Yippee!" Art yelled. "School is over! Here we go, Barney!" In a moment, he was on Barney and trotting briskly out of the schoolyard.

"I'll race you home," Joshua challenged. Daniel and the boys were off. Summer vacation had arrived.

Norma, Katie, Lydia, Magdalena, and Anna started for home, chattering as they went. "I can hardly believe that I'm done with school!" Lydia exclaimed.

"Next year, Aaron can come along to school," Anna rejoiced.

"Don't talk about next year yet," Magdalena groaned. "I'm going to enjoy summer first."

Norma's happy face sobered. Next year—would Dad let them stay here that long? He had said that they could go to school here *this* year. Now what? Determinedly, she pushed her troubled thoughts aside.

When they got to the end of the lane, Erma and Nellie were waiting for them. "Now you don't have to go away to school for a long time! Aunt Sarah told me. May I carry your lunch pail, Norma?"

Norma handed her the pail. "Look inside, Erma. I saved something for you. No, Nellie, you get down. Here, I'll help you get the lid off."

"Candy!" Erma exclaimed.

"Yes, the teacher gave us some, so I saved a piece for you."

"Yum." Erma happily popped the candy into her mouth.

June 26 came and went. Now Norma was eleven and Erma was five. Naturally, Norma thought of Mom. Did she think about her girls' birthdays?

The usual summer work kept everyone busy. Aunt Sarah and Uncle Peter put more responsibility on the Brenneman children. Raymond learned to feed the calves by himself. He helped hoe corn and make hay. With the bigger girls working away, Aunt Sarah taught Katie and Norma how to cook and make bread. Norma enjoyed helping with the laundry. How she liked hanging fresh wash on the clothesline. This time when the garden needed weeding, she knew which were carrots and which were weeds. Erma learned to set the table for meals. There were berries to pick again and peas to shell.

In spite of being busy, Uncle Peter and Aunt Sarah took time for the family. Somehow life seemed busy and relaxed at the same time. Norma loved the quiet evenings with the family, especially when Betsy and Mandy were home too.

Lydia had been working for Grandma Brenneman. Occasionally on canning days, Aunt Sarah sent Katie instead and kept Lydia home to help. One day Aunt Sarah suggested that Norma be the one to go help Grandma for a day. Norma felt a bit hesitant. Would she be able to do whatever Grandma asked her to do? But she knew that someday she might have to work for others, and this was a good start.

It didn't take long to run across the fields to Grandpa's house. Grandpa met her at the door. "Come in! Come in!" he said, holding the door open for her. "Just look who our helper is!"

Grandma smiled her welcome while drying her hands on a tea towel. "I'm glad you could come, Norma. This grandma is always glad for young hands to help."

Norma heard footsteps running down the stairs. With a big thump, Walter landed at the bottom of the steps. "Hi, Sis, it's good to see you! Grandpa and I are going to build a new coop for the chickens. We've been planning it for a while."

"Yes," Grandpa chuckled. "You know what I usually say—well planned is half done."

Walter and Grandpa headed out the door, but not before Walter gave a tweak to Norma's pigtail. "I miss you, sis!"

Norma enjoyed working in Grandma's neat and cozy kitchen. Together they picked and shelled a few peas. Then Norma carried water for Grandma, swept and scrubbed the kitchen floor, and shined the windows.

Lunchtime was quite different from Uncle Peter's, with only Grandpa, Grandma, Walter, and herself. Grandpa asked about Raymond and Erma and wondered if Aunt Sarah was keeping her busy. Then he told stories from his school days. When the meal was done, Grandpa made sure that she and Walter each got a pink peppermint candy. Soon Norma was skipping happily across the fields to Uncle Peter's house.

From then on, Norma took her turn at helping Grandma. One day when she came, Grandma was busy at her spinning wheel. Fascinated, Norma stood watching awhile before she set to work.

Norma enjoyed helping her grandparents because they were her very own grandpa and grandma. She felt a real sense of belonging there. Grandma needed her. She was not just a temporary addition to the family.

"Norma," Grandma asked one day when Norma was about ready to leave, "will you please go up to the attic and get me a braid of onions? They are hanging on the wall. I just used up the last one I had down here."

"Sure," Norma answered cheerfully. Grandma's attic was fascinating. Norma had never had reason to come up here before. The attic smelled of smoked hams and dried herbs. In one corner, Norma found the row of onion braids hanging on the wall. Carefully she took one down. Taking a moment to look around, she noticed an old cradle. Did Grandma rock her babies in it long ago? There were barrels and boxes and an old butter churn.

Suddenly she noticed something in the far corner of the attic. It was a rather familiar-looking chest. It looked like—but it couldn't be. It looked just like the chest that Mom used to have in the tarpaper shack. Suddenly she remembered the old doll that she wasn't allowed to play with. In her mind, she could picture the outgrown clothes and the old quilt. Then she remembered the fabric that Mom had thrown into the woodstove. Was this the same chest or just one like it? How could that chest have gotten here? Dad must have brought it. If she opened the chest, then she would know.

Should she? Norma stepped over to the chest. The old hinges screeched as she opened the lid. Oh well, Grandma couldn't hear well anyway. Then she saw the old quilt. It was Mom and Dad's chest! There on the top of everything lay a big, black book. A Bible! Carefully she opened the front cover. What she saw inside made her feel cold. Her heart began to beat faster. A paper lying inside the Bible said, "Papers of Separation for John and Alzina Brenneman." Her eyes skimmed the paper. There was her name! "The father, John, shall be in charge of the five children: Walter, Arthur, Norma, Raymond, and Erma. When the children reach the age of twelve, they may choose whether they wish to live with father or mother."

Slowly, she read it again. She closed the Bible and carefully lowered the lid on the chest. She forgot about looking at anything else in the chest. Neither did she look around in the attic anymore.

Forcing herself to smile, she took the onions to Grandma and said goodbye. Soon she was out the door and walking slowly across the fields. Seeing that paper made it all so real. She determined to tell no one what she had found—not even Katie.

Twelve years old—one more year. What if Dad decided they must go somewhere else? If only they could go to school here this fall. Then by spring, she would be almost twelve. Why would they want to leave here if Mom and Dad were separated? It sure didn't seem like Mom cared about them. And live with Dad? She couldn't imagine that!

Norma looked across the growing fields around her. She could see the school to her left and Daniel Brubacher's across the fields. Wilson Reed's and Uncle Peter's lay to her right. Cowbells tinkled in the distance, and a horse and wagon were coming down the gravel road. It was one of Wilson's boys with a load of hay.

Nellie came running out the lane to meet her. Norma squatted down beside Nellie and scratched her ears. "I don't want to leave here, Nellie. I wish I was twelve now. This is the best home I ever had." Nellie licked her chin and ran in the lane ahead of her.

Summer was coming to a close. Berry picking was done for another year. Soon it would be time to get the potatoes, cabbages, and carrots out of the garden. Uncle Peter would soon be threshing again. School time was getting closer. When would Dad come again and tell them if they should start school here? When the others started to talk about school, Norma said nothing.

Finally, one day, Dad's old Model T pulled in the driveway. Lydia called everyone for supper, but Norma wasn't hungry. She forced herself to eat a bit and hoped no one would notice.

Aunt Sarah did notice. When the men went to milk the cows, Aunt Sarah took Norma aside. "Norma, I think you would like to know that your dad asked me about keeping you children for this winter again. I was glad to say 'yes.'"

"Oh, thank you!" and Norma threw her arms around Aunt Sarah. Aunt Sarah held her close while a tear dropped on Norma's hair.

"Oh, I'm so glad! I must go tell Katie!" Norma pulled away and raced across the yard to the barn where Katie was feeding the chickens. She burst into the henhouse, and chickens went fluttering to the far side of the pen. "Katie! Guess what? Dad said we can go to school here again! I'm glad, glad, glad!"

"Me too!" Katie rejoiced as Norma grabbed her in a big hug, spilling chicken feed on the floor. Several chickens scurried in to grab the spilled feed but fluttered away in fright as the two girls danced about with excitement. "Watch out, Norma," Katie warned. "You almost sat on a chicken!" Both girls began to giggle uncontrollably at the thought until they heard Raymond calling for Norma.

"Oh, I better go now. Dad's probably leaving, and I must say goodbye," Norma remembered. Quickly she hurried out of the henhouse. "Not even Katie knows how happy I am," she thought. "When school lets out in the spring, I'll be almost twelve. That paper in the chest in the attic says that then no one can make me leave."

chapter fifteen

A Happy Winter

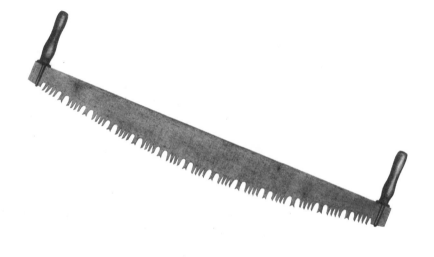

Brutus, Michigan: Fall 1931 to Summer 1932

The first day of school arrived again. This time there were only four school lunches to pack. Erma rejoiced that Lydia stayed home with her. Next year it would be her turn to go to school.

When the Reed children met them at the end of the lane, Anna announced happily, "Aaron can come to school now!" Little Aaron hurried to join the schoolchildren, but he shrugged off Magdalena and Anna's mothering and lengthened his stride to keep up with Daniel, Joshua, and Raymond. He gave a quick wave to his mother, who stood by the door seeing her youngest off to school.

Norma's heart was light. The cloud that had hung over her for so long was gone. Dad had given his consent for another school year. She liked school and her teacher. This year she knew the other girls and felt like she belonged. She even understood when some of the girls lapsed into Pennsylvania Dutch.

To her delight, the teacher assigned her to a double desk with Mary Evelyn. She smoothed the skirt of her new printed flour-sack dress and smiled at Anna, who was watching Aaron to make sure he knew what to do. Arthur grinned at Norma. She noticed Raymond happily examining his new desk and books. The teacher called the class to order. Another school year had begun.

The weather turned cooler. Norma was content. Uncle Peter's house felt like home. Life seemed secure and happy. Walking home from school, she swung her lunch pail and breathed deeply of the fresh, crisp air.

"The fields look all empty!" Raymond announced.

"Yes," Daniel agreed. "We got all our potatoes in, and now we have to cut corn."

"We are almost done chopping again," Joshua said. "Our silo will soon be full!" Norma looked down the road at the tall, wooden silo and thought of all the work it took to cut and chop the corn to fill it.

"Now Dad's going to start sawing wood for winter. He can make that two-man saw go faster than anyone else," Joshua boasted.

"He is fast," Daniel admitted, "but I know some other people that are fast too."

Several evenings later, Norma watched, fascinated, as Uncle Peter and Uncle Joe sawed up logs for firewood. Back and forth, back and forth the saw went. First Uncle Peter would pull the saw toward himself as it bit into the wood, and then Uncle Joe would pull the saw. Back and forth, back and forth. After a while, Uncle Joe stopped and gave Silas a turn, but Uncle Peter's small, wiry frame never seemed to tire. The stack of wood grew. It would keep them warm and cozy all winter. After the wood was split, the children had the job of carrying the smaller chunks to stack in the woodshed. Norma was glad to be part of this busy, happy family.

The first snowflakes excited the children as usual. Before long, the long winter started in earnest. The wind whipped snowdrifts high against the buildings and across the fences. Uncle Peter had replaced the wagon wheels with runners, and Aunt Sarah brought out the warm winter clothes.

One blustery winter day, the children were excited on the way home from church. "We hardly ever go to Grandpa's house for a meal," Katie declared. "Manasseh Kulps are coming too! I get to hold baby Mary Ann."

"Me too!" the other girls protested.

Grandma's kitchen smelled *so* good as Grandpa welcomed them all warmly at the door. After all the food was cleared away and Raymond declared that he was "full to the top," the girls discovered that baby Mary Ann was fast asleep. Aunt Sarah instructed them to find something else to play for now. They were soon playing a lively game of "Hide the Thimble." One person would hide Grandma's thimble while the others covered their eyes. The thimble had to be visible without their having to move anything. The first person to see the thimble called out, "I spy the thimble." That person got to hide the thimble next.

When Norma had found the thimble twice in a row, she let Erma have a turn hiding it. Uncle Peter whispered something in Erma's ear. When the children opened their eyes, no one could find the thimble. Erma jumped up and clapped her hands. "I hid it hard!" Finally Walter spied it fastened onto Grandpa's suspender clip.

When the laughter had died down, there was a cry from the bedroom. Baby Mary Ann was awake. After the baby was cared for, Manasseh's wife let each of the girls have a turn holding the baby. Erma just couldn't get done holding her.

"Here, Erma," Mandy said, "I'll make a baby for you." The winter shawls and coats were lying on the bed. Skillfully Mandy took Aunt Sarah's shawl and wrapped it into a roll. Then she took Erma's coat and cap and put it on the bundle. She took a white hankie from her pocket and tucked it across the face area. "Here, Erma, here's a doll for you."

Baby Mary Ann was starting to wiggle and protest. Erma handed her to Lydia and hugged to herself the unusual doll Mandy had made.

"Make one for me, Mandy," begged little Rachel Kulp. Soon all the shawls were used up as Erma, Rachel, Norma, and Katie played doll with their "shawl babies." Mandy and Lydia happily went off with the real baby.

Norma sat rocking her "shawl baby" and thought of the chest in Grandma and Grandpa's attic. She felt almost guilty that she didn't miss Mom so much anymore. It had been almost two years since she had seen Mom. Sometimes it was even a little hard to picture her. Erma rarely spoke of Mom, and Raymond seemed very content where he was. Mom probably had no way and no money to come, but it seemed to Norma that she could have written a letter. Surely by now she had found out where they were. Hugging her doll a little tighter, Norma thought, "I'm so glad I found that paper in the attic. This is where I want to be."

When Grandpa passed out peppermint candies before they went home, his blue eyes smiled warmly at her. She smiled back shyly.

Dad didn't come around much over the winter. The roads were hard to travel with a Model T. When spring came, Dad was back, and took the children to the English church. It had been a while since Dad took them to church. Norma looked forward eagerly to the English songs and Bible stories. She was a bit surprised to see Magdalena there along with her parents and family. Then she remembered that she hadn't seen them at the German services for a while. Magdalena and Anna smiled at her. It was good to have friends she knew here.

Mandy had been working at Manasseh Kulp's. She went to a different school and only came home occasionally. When school was out in the spring, Mandy got a job farther away from home. Katie sometimes helped out in other homes.

Now Aunt Sarah came to Norma. "Norma, you know that usually

when our girls are about twelve, they work away some, helping other people. Uncle Peter and I thought maybe this summer, since you are almost twelve, you could help out at Manasseh Kulp's sometimes. You know Manasseh and Amanda a bit, and we thought you could try it some. Mandy stayed over the weekends, but we thought it would be better if you come back home weekends for now. You would just do jobs like you do here at home and help take care of the children."

Norma nodded soberly, but her heart felt heavy. She didn't feel like she knew Manasseh's wife Amanda that well, and she would be away from Erma and Raymond all week. "If you think I should, I can try."

"Uncle Peter will take you on Monday and come for you on Friday afternoon. For right now, you won't go every week."

Monday morning, Norma put a few clothes in a bag and climbed into the wagon beside Uncle Peter. He was taking butter and eggs to Brutus. Then they would travel on to Manasseh's. It seemed very strange to go away without the rest of the family. Swallowing the lump in her throat, Norma waved bravely at Raymond and Erma as she rode out the lane. Manasseh's lived twice as far away from Uncle Peter's as the church house. It seemed a long way to Norma. After they passed the church, they were in country she had never seen before. She could only think of the miles between her and Erma, and the unknown ahead.

At Manasseh Kulp's home, little Rachel and Paul came running out to meet them. "Norma! I'm glad you came!" Rachel rejoiced. Norma's heart lifted a bit. Uncle Peter handed Norma her bag and said kindly, "I'll be back for you on Friday. Do your best!"

Soon Amanda was showing Norma where to put her clothes in Rachel's room. Norma was glad she didn't have to sleep in a room by herself. There were dishes to wash and laundry to hang outside. Rachel followed Norma around, chattering happily. Amanda loved to sing. Norma enjoyed hearing her singing in the kitchen.

But when bedtime came, Norma's pillow was damp with tears. Friday seemed far away. So did everything else that was comfortable and familiar. There was no Erma to put her arm around in bed. Was Erma crying for her?

Friday finally came. When Uncle Peter's wagon drove in the lane, Norma was delighted to see that he had brought Erma along. When she climbed into the wagon, Erma threw her arms around her. "Norma! I missed you so much!"

"I missed you too," Norma said, hugging her little sister to herself.

What was Peter saying to Amanda? "Next week we'll bring Katie. Erma and Raymond need to have a little time to get used to being separated from Norma." Norma hugged Erma a little tighter.

After that, Norma and Katie took turns helping Manasseh's. Norma was glad it was her turn to be at home on June 26. Not much was said about their birthdays, but she was glad to share the special day with Erma. "Now I'm twelve!" she thought. "I'm so glad Dad can't take me away now. Erma's not twelve, but Dad wouldn't take her without me, I'm quite sure."

Erma was six and talking eagerly of school. "Aunt Sarah said I can use Lydia's old lunch pail. I can hardly wait to walk to school too. Nellie's going to miss me."

With a smile Norma said, "It will be fun to take you along to school."

chapter sixteen

No, Dad, No!

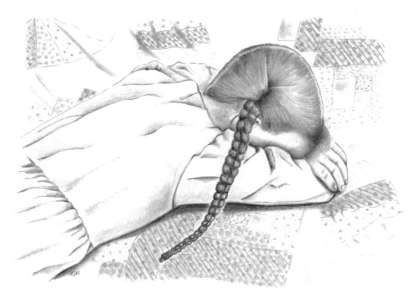

Brutus, Michigan: Summer 1932

Norma took a towel from the wash basket and shook it out with a brisk snap. She hung it on the clothesline and reached for another one. Someone was coming in the lane. Neighbor ladies didn't visit each other often. Who could it be? Maybe someone needed to borrow something. She reached for a washcloth. It looked like Abe Sauder's wife, Juliann. What could she want?

Before long, Juliann came out of the house and headed home. She didn't seem to be carrying anything. Soon Aunt Sarah came out and headed for the barn where Uncle Peter was cleaning out the pigpen. The towels flapped cheerfully in the breeze. Norma reached for a sheet and shook the wrinkles out. Then she pinned it carefully on the line.

Aunt Sarah was particular about the wash being hung up neatly.

Now Aunt Sarah came out of the barn. She walked over to Norma just as Norma hung up the last shirt. "Norma, it looks like you are all done. Did you see Juliann was here? Well, she brought some surprising news. She has company at her house. You would never guess who. Apparently your mom decided it is time to see her children. She hitchhiked up here and is at Abe's now."

Norma's heart started to pound. Her mind was in a spin. Now what?

Aunt Sarah continued, "Your mom is not comfortable coming over here, but Juliann suggested that you could come over there and see her."

Norma was quiet. Aunt Sarah stepped closer and put her arm around Norma's shoulders. "I'm sure you have mixed-up feelings right now, Norma, but I think it would be good for you children to go over there to see her. Why don't you hang up the next basket of wash to give yourself a little time to get used to the idea. Uncle Peter will talk to Raymond about it too."

"But—but what is she going to do? Does she want to take us away?"

"I don't know what she has in mind, but Uncle Peter and I talked about this. We thought it would be all right for you to go over there for a short visit." Aunt Sarah gave her shoulders a reassuring squeeze.

Norma sighed and picked up the wash basket. For so long, she had wished to see Mom, but now she didn't understand her own feelings. Her heart felt heavy with dread, but then old memories rushed back. Good memories of Mom in the kitchen, Mom baking pies, the old, familiar presence of Mom. Suddenly she wanted to dash across the fields and throw her arms around Mom. And yet—was she actually the same Mom? It was such a long time ago.

Norma was half done with the next basket of wash when Raymond came out of the barn and walked slowly over to the clothesline. His face looked troubled. "Norma, did you know that Mom is at Abe Sauder's?"

"Yes, Aunt Sarah told me," Norma answered.

"I sort of want to see her and sort of not," Raymond said, his voice quivering a bit. His foot kicked at a clump of grass.

"I know, I feel that way too, but—"

"Why didn't she come before?" Raymond interrupted. "Where was she? What was she doing?"

"I don't know," Norma answered. "Maybe she didn't have any money to travel or a way to get here."

"Why didn't she write or something? Now it's been so long I hardly feel like I even know her anymore."

"I know," Norma said, hanging up the last sock, "but she's Mom, so you better go change your clothes so you don't smell like the pigpen."

"I know, that's what Uncle Peter told me too." Raymond headed for the house. Norma followed. Aunt Sarah was combing Erma's hair.

"Norma," Erma piped up, "we are going for a walk to Abe Sauder's. Do you remember our mom? She's there. I hardly remember her. But I remember a little bit." Her cheerful face clouded over. "We didn't see her for a long time."

Abe Sauder's lived on a farm across the road from Grandpa's house. Three pairs of feet trudged the field. Norma had a moment of panic when she suddenly wondered what Mom would think of how they were dressed. They looked like three Mennonite children. She remembered Mom's reaction to the white cloth that had been in the chest long ago. Now Norma knew it was a cap like Aunt Sarah wore. Would Mom be upset with their long dresses, aprons, and pigtails?

Raymond interrupted her thoughts. "Norma, I'm kind of scared." His lips quivered.

This would never do. "Raymond, let's think of all the happy things we can remember about Mom. Remember the good pies Mom used to make? One time Mom made a cake for my birthday. Do you remember sucking icicles that we broke off the fence?"

Norma looked at Raymond. His face had brightened a bit. "I remember when you had a pet snake. I remember selling pies—I thought it was fun."

At Abe's house, Norma reached for Erma's hand. Her courage almost failed her. "Let's go over to that bush beside the house and peek in the window first," she suggested. The three children hurried to the shrub beside the house, where they could peek in and not be seen. There was Juliann, sitting at the kitchen table, and across from her was a gray-haired lady. *That* couldn't be Mom. Mom had black hair. Just then the lady smiled at Juliann. It *was* Mom! Her hair had turned gray.

"Come," Norma said. "We can't stay here. We have to go in." Slowly the children walked across the porch and knocked on the door. They could hear footsteps coming to the door. Then the door opened, and there was Juliann. A few steps behind her stood Mom.

"Come in! Come in!" Juliann welcomed them. Shyly the children came in. Norma looked up and met Mom's eyes. Mom's eyes had tears in them! Mom reached out her arm, and Norma went to Mom. She laid her head on Mom's shoulder, still clutching Erma's hand. Mom's arm went around her. It felt like Mom, even if it didn't look like her. Norma swallowed hard. Then Raymond was on the other side of Mom. He threw his arms around her. "Mom! We missed you!"

Erma stood quietly, trying to absorb it all. This didn't look like the mom she remembered faintly. Then Mom laid her hand on Erma's shoulder. "My, Erma, you are a big girl now. You must be about ready for school." Erma smiled shyly, and Mom gave her a quick hug.

Juliann brought cups of cool garden tea while the children sat and talked with Mom. Mom asked about school and life on the farm. Then it was time to go. Mom didn't say anything about taking them away from Uncle Peter's. She didn't even talk about seeing them again. With a quick goodbye, the children were soon running across the fields, back to Uncle Peter's house.

Norma thought about their visit. Mom didn't actually say that she had missed them. She didn't say why she hadn't come sooner or written to them. Mom did seem to care, and yet something was missing. It was all confusing to Norma.

Several days later, Dad drove in the lane. Norma looked out of the kitchen window and saw Dad and Aunt Sarah talking by the garden. Neither of them looked very happy. A dark foreboding filled Norma's heart. Something was wrong, and she was quite sure it had something to do with her. After a while, she looked out the window again. They were still talking. It almost looked like Aunt Sarah was wiping tears. Then Dad headed for the barn. He stayed for lunch. He and Uncle Peter did most of the talking. Aunt Sarah was quiet. Norma thought her eyes looked as if she had been crying.

After lunch, Uncle Peter sent all his children out to hoe corn. Raymond started to follow the others, but Uncle Peter called him back. "Your dad wants to talk to you, Raymond. You too, Norma and Erma." Aunt Sarah turned her back to them and started washing dishes.

Dad looked at his three children. "Well," he said slowly, "I've decided it's time for you children to live elsewhere. I've come to take you down to Indiana. I've got friends there who said they will keep you."

The children stared at him in disbelief. "But Dad!" Raymond cried.

"Now, no fussing," Dad said. "That won't change anything. We're going to get your clothes together and head off today."

Norma had stood in silent shock. She had never spoken up against Dad. Now she looked at Dad and said determinedly, "I don't want to go. I'm going to stay here."

Dad looked surprised, and then his blue eyes narrowed. "But you *have* to go."

Norma was trembling. "No, I don't have to go. I found a paper in the chest in Grandpa's attic that said if I am twelve, I can decide where I want to live. I just had a birthday, and I'm twelve. I will stay here." Her voice shook.

Dad's face looked hard and stern. "Very well, we'll get Raymond's and Erma's things and be gone then."

"Oh, Dad!" Raymond began to cry. Erma clung to Norma, crying. Suddenly it dawned on Norma what Dad was really going to do. "No, Dad, no!" she cried in anguish. Dad wouldn't really take Raymond and Erma from her, would he? "Please, no, Dad!"

Dad turned a deaf ear to the children's pleas. Aunt Sarah came down the stairs with two bags. Tears streamed down her face. Uncle Peter was blowing his nose. Raymond had thrown himself against Uncle Peter. Erma wouldn't let go.

Dad reached for the two bags, and Uncle Peter gently led Raymond to the car. Aunt Sarah put her arms around Norma and Erma both. They all clung to each other, crying. "Come, girls, we must go," Aunt Sarah said. She reached for Erma's hand.

Norma threw her arms around Erma. "Oh, Erma, I don't want you to go, but if he takes you away, just remember I will come and get you sometime." With one last sob, Norma let Erma go. Then up the stairs she ran and threw herself on her bed, sobbing. She couldn't bear to watch Dad take them away. How could he be so cruel? She heard Dad's car drive away. She only sobbed harder. Then Aunt Sarah stepped softly into the room. She gathered the weeping girl into her arms, and they sobbed together.

Finally the sobs subsided and Norma asked, "Why did he take them away? Couldn't he see they were happy here? Why? Why?"

Aunt Sarah blew her nose and wiped her eyes. "He told me he found out your mom was in the area. He didn't want her to take you away."

"But Mom wasn't trying to take us away," Norma sobbed.

"It doesn't seem that way, but your dad has the final say. I'm glad you stayed," Aunt Sarah said softly, giving her a squeeze. "When did you find that paper? I never knew."

"I found it last summer, and I was so glad for my twelfth birthday to come. But—oh, Aunt Sarah, I never guessed he'd take them away from me." And Norma began sobbing all over again. Aunt Sarah rubbed her back sympathetically.

When Uncle Peter told the other children that Raymond and Erma were gone, they were shocked. "How can he be so cruel?" Mandy demanded.

"We didn't even get to say goodbye!" Lydia said.

"What will I do without Raymond?" Joshua cried.

"I'm glad Norma stayed, but how will she stand it to have Erma gone?" Katie wondered.

Suppertime came. Joshua was found crying in the haymow. Suppertime was quiet and tearful. The table seemed empty. No one was hungry.

Norma dreaded bedtime. She couldn't stop wondering where Erma was. Angry feelings toward Dad made her feel like pounding her pillow and screaming. Instead, hot tears soaked her pillow until she heard Katie whisper, "Shall I come and sleep in your bed?" Norma nodded, and Katie crawled in and filled the empty spot where Erma should have been. The girls fell asleep holding hands.

chapter seventeen

Sometime I'll Get Her

Brutus, Michigan: Fall, Winter 1932

Tears fell into the dishwater. Norma wiped her eyes with the corner of her apron. She washed another cereal bowl and then wiped her eyes again. Where was Erma? Was she crying too? Would Dad ever bring her and Raymond back again?

Aunt Sarah moved quietly about the kitchen, mixing up bread. Katie had gone to Manasseh's, and Lydia was away too. Mandy was in the garden. Norma turned to Aunt Sarah. "Do you know where Dad took Erma and Raymond? Do you know when he'll bring them back?"

"Well—" Aunt Sarah paused with her hand in the flour bin. "He said he was taking them to Indiana. He mentioned taking Erma to some Mitchelen relatives. I'm not sure about Raymond."

"Oh, Aunt Sarah, do you think he didn't even keep them together?" Norma cried in dismay.

"I'm sorry, Norma. I really don't know. It didn't sound that way, but from the little I know of the Mitchelens, Erma will be well cared for."

Norma wiped her eyes again. "I thought—I thought—maybe I should have gone with Erma to take care of her, but if he would have put us in different homes, I guess it's good I stayed here. But, oh, I miss them so much!"

"I'm sorry, Norma, I know it's hard." Aunt Sarah wiped her eyes with the back of her floury hand, leaving a bit of flour on her cheek. "We all miss them too."

Norma washed the last dish and hung the dishcloth up to dry. She reached for the egg basket to gather eggs. The warm summer breezes dried her tears as she walked to the barn. Joshua sat forlornly on the barn hill with his arm around Nellie's furry neck. Even Nellie seemed to miss Raymond. Norma swallowed a lump in her throat. "Come on, Joshua. Why don't you help me with the chickens?"

Joshua came willingly enough. They worked together in companionable silence, feeding and watering the chickens and gathering the eggs until Joshua spoke up. "Oh, Norma, I miss Raymond so much. I keep thinking about him all the time, but I'm glad you're here."

The ache in Norma's heart eased a little bit. Joshua was like a brother. It was good to feel wanted and to know others shared her grief.

As the two children came out of the chicken house, Mandy called from the garden, "I have beans for you to snap, Joshua. Mom said you should help too." While they worked, Mandy did her best to tell stories and help them all think of other things besides their loss.

"Did you ever know that our house burned down one time?" she asked.

Norma looked shocked. "No, when was that?"

"Actually, it was long ago, before any of us children were born, but we've heard the story often enough!" Mandy answered.

Joshua nodded. "Tell it again, Mandy."

Mandy reached for a handful of beans. "Soon after Mom and Dad were married, Dad decided to build a new house. He worked hard to get it done before their first baby arrived. The house was done, and baby Henry came. He was named after our grandpa. He wasn't a healthy baby, and he died when he was just two days old."

"Poor Aunt Sarah," Norma said. "Her very first baby!"

"I wish he would have grown up so I could have him for a big brother," Joshua said.

"Anyways," Mandy continued, "only two weeks after baby Henry died, the house burned down."

"Oh, no," Norma exclaimed. "How did it happen?"

"There were some wood ashes in the woodshed," Joshua interrupted.

"Joshua, *I'm* telling the story," Mandy stated. "The ashes were saved to make soap, and I guess they weren't cooled, and they started a fire somehow. It was at night. The best way out for Mom and Dad was through the window. Quickly they threw their bedding and clothes out the window. Next they pushed a trunk out and then climbed out themselves.

"Dad's brother Henry was here as a hired man. Mom's sister Mattie was still here, helping since the new baby. Dad rescued both of them from the house while Mom ran stocking-footed across the snow to tell Grandpas. There was nothing to stop it. The new house burned down. They had to live at Daniel Brubacher's for a while until they could build again."

"First their baby and then their house," Norma said soberly.

"We had another brother after they moved into their next house," Mandy said. "They named him Jacob, but he only lived three weeks. Later they had Silas."

Thinking about Uncle Peter and Aunt Sarah's sorrows helped Norma. Other people had troubles too.

The summer days plodded steadily by. Constant reminders of Erma and Raymond were everywhere. Aunt Sarah quietly put away the school dress that she had been sewing for Erma. No word came to them of how the children were doing. Mom was still in the area and found jobs here and there working in homes in the community. Norma saw her occasionally.

Walter and Arthur had been shocked and angry when they found out that Dad had taken the two younger children away. "Hey, Sis, how did you ever manage to stand up to Dad and stay here?" Walter asked Norma one day when she was over helping Grandma.

Norma told him about the chest in the attic and the separation papers.

"I think I'll go have a look at those papers myself," he responded. "Where did you say they were? I'm sure glad you didn't leave too."

"I'm glad too, but Walter, do you think that we could somehow get them back if Dad doesn't bring them soon?" Norma asked.

"Indiana is far away, Norma. I'm afraid that for right now, we can't do anything. I often wonder how Raymond is doing. He was so happy here. Uncle Peter was so patient with him and helped him in a lot of ways."

The new school year was approaching. One evening at the supper table, Norma heard Uncle Peter and Aunt Sarah talking.

"Did you know Wilson Reed's little Anna isn't doing well?" Uncle Peter asked. "She gets some kind of spells. The doctor doesn't know for sure what's wrong with her."

"She just started school last year. That must be hard for Susannah," Aunt Sarah sympathized.

"Little Anna!" Norma thought. "She's such a special little girl. I hope she's better soon."

The excitement of the new school year was overshadowed by the absence of Raymond and Erma. Norma tried not to look at the spot in school where Raymond usually sat. She tried not to think of Erma trudging off to a strange school in a strange place among people she hardly knew. How Norma had looked forward to taking Erma along to school this year. It was a strange, empty feeling to have no one to take care of or to look out for.

And so she slowed her steps to walk beside Anna Reed, who came to school some days looking rather pale and drawn. "Here, Anna," she offered, "let me carry your things for you." Anna smiled at her gratefully.

When the fall threshing began, she thought of Raymond. How he had loved to watch the horses plodding round and round. Was somebody somewhere taking time to help Raymond, as Uncle Peter had? Was his teacher patient with him? When winter approached and the first snow arrived, she wondered if Raymond and Erma had warm clothes. Dad hadn't taken much along when he took them away.

One snowy December morning on the way to school, Anna announced happily, "We have a surprise! Our brother George is getting married." For the next two weeks until the wedding, Magdalena and Anna could hardly talk of anything else.

Christian Kilmer was showing interest in Betsy and was a regular visitor at the Brubacher home. Norma listened to the wedding talk on the way to school and watched Christian and Betsy as their friendship deepened. They looked so happy together. "I don't know if I ever want to get married," she thought. "I sure wouldn't want to have an unhappy home like Mom and Dad did. How would I know it wouldn't be that way? But then there is Uncle Peter and Aunt Sarah's happy home. Now wouldn't it be wonderful to belong to a home of my own like that! How can a person know how it will turn out?"

Christmas came. Norma couldn't help but wonder about Raymond and Erma. The hot chocolate and maple sugar candy weren't quite as good without them there. Grandpa's, Uncle Joe, Aunt Salome, and Martin and Mary Kilmer came for dinner.

The snow was extra deep. What fun the children had after dinner.

"Hey, Norma," Art said. "Guess what? I had a ride in the big snow-plow!"

"I'm afraid you're telling stories, Art," Walter chided.

"No, really I did," Art answered.

"How did that happen?" Norma wondered.

"Well, I was walking down the road, and along came the snowplow. The driver stopped and asked if I wanted a ride. I said 'sure'! So I climbed up in the cab, and down the road we went. It was sure fun!"

Joshua stared at him in awe. "I wish I could have a ride sometime!"

"Maybe if you stood out on the road sometime, he'd pick you up," Art suggested.

"You better not!" Katie exclaimed. "Art, you should know better than to tell him to stand on the road when the snowplow is coming."

"I'm getting wet and cold. Let's go in," Lydia suggested.

The rosy-cheeked children trooped into the kitchen. "Let's play 'Jing Hands Up,'" Mandy suggested. "Martin and Mary, will you help us?" They lined up on two sides of the kitchen table. Martin Kilmer, sitting across from Norma, produced a penny. Everyone on his side of the table put their hands under the table and huddled together to decide who got the penny. The penny was carefully hidden between someone's fingers. Then they chanted, "Jing Hands Up," and all hands came up on the table.

Three times they rapped the table with their knuckles and then carefully placed their hands in a row on the table—palms down and fingers close together. Norma's side had three guesses at which hand had the penny in it. If they found it, then it was their turn to hide the penny.

Norma quietly watched the other players. Joshua's eyes sparkled with excitement, but he didn't hold his hands still enough or the fingers close enough to keep a penny hidden. He didn't have it. Martin had a very innocent look, and Mary smiled sweetly. Norma looked closely at Walter and Katie, the other two on the other side of the table. Katie seemed distracted by something at the far side of the kitchen. Norma was pretty sure Katie had the penny hiding between her fingers—but which hand? Looking closely, Norma noticed that one hand was more relaxed than the other.

Betsy guessed Martin's right hand. He held it up for all to see—no penny. Mandy guessed Walter's left hand—no penny. Joshua wiggled excitedly. "You can't find it!"

"Norma, you guess," Lydia said.

Norma looked at Katie again. Katie quickly looked away. "I think it's in Katie's left hand," Norma guessed.

Katie frowned at Norma and then started laughing. She held up her hand for all to see the penny carefully tucked between her fingers.

"Now we hide the penny," Arthur rejoiced.

Norma's side huddled together. The penny was placed in Arthur's hand. Carefully, he tucked it between his fingers—carefully, so it wouldn't show on top.

"Jing Hands Up!" Up came the hands, and *rap, rap, rap* went their knuckles on the table. Then everyone carefully put their hands flat on the table.

Oh, no! Norma, sitting beside Arthur, clearly heard the penny in Arthur's hand hit the table. But no one else seemed to notice because they all guessed wrong. Norma's side got to hide the penny again. Back and forth the penny went from one side to the other.

Norma smelled popcorn. The game ended when Aunt Sarah set a big bowl of apples on the table and then two big bowls of popcorn.

It was a cozy family circle, but there were two missing. Norma caught Walter's eye and knew that he too was thinking of Raymond and Erma, so far way. When Grandpa and Grandma were ready to go home, they went around the circle, shaking hands with each one. Norma swallowed hard when Grandpa took her hand in both of his big ones and squeezed it gently. He knew, and he cared.

The ache in her heart just did not go away. Always she had looked out for Erma and Raymond—through happy days and bad days. She had done it when Mom and Dad fought and broke up. She had done it when they came to Uncle Peter's and everything was strange. Who looked after Erma now in a strange place? Who walked with her to school? Katie and Norma continued to share a bed. Did Erma have to sleep by herself? Did she cry at night too?

"Sometime," Norma whispered fiercely to herself, "I will go get her back!"

chapter eighteen

On Her Own

Brutus, Michigan: Spring, Summer 1933

Squeak, squeak. Norma scrubbed the kitchen window until it
sparkled. Katie was on the outside, cleaning the window. Norma
tapped on the window and frowned sternly. She pointed to a smudge
that Katie had missed. Katie opened her eyes wide and let her mouth
drop open in surprise. Then she made an ugly frown and scrubbed
diligently at the tiny smudge. Norma smiled a huge smile and nodded
vigorously. Both girls burst out laughing.

"Now, girls," Mandy chided. "You better get those windows clean,
or Betsy will be after you. Everything has to be just so-so because
Christian Kilmer is coming!"

Betsy came up behind Mandy and snapped her cleaning rag, giving

Mandy a little sting on the arm. Mandy was after her in a flash. Out the door Betsy flew, slamming the screen door in Mandy's face. Around the garden and past the windmill she ran, doubling back to make a circle around the elderberry bush. Away she flew toward the barn. Nellie joined the race. Mandy nearly tripped over her. Up the barn hill Betsy went. Scurrying into the barn, she slammed the door and leaned against it, puffing hard.

Mandy moved quietly back to the windmill and got a tin cup of water from the pump. Walking softly, she stepped up beside the barn door. Katie and Norma watched from the house. Mandy waited.

"Mandy, Betsy, we aren't going to be ready for the hymn sing if you don't get busy," Katie called loudly.

The barn door cautiously opened a crack. Suddenly Betsy screamed. "You!" she sputtered as Mandy ran laughing to the house.

The kitchen door opened and Aunt Sarah came out. "Girls, what's all the ruckus? I think it's time to get back to work. Betsy, you look like you put your head in the mop bucket."

Sheepishly the girls picked up their rags and began to clean, but not before Betsy muttered quietly, "You just wait, Mandy. You have it coming yet!"

Before long, the house was clean and shining. The yard was trimmed and the porches were swept. Betsy and Mandy had invited the young people for a hymn sing on Sunday evening. Carefully the girls guarded their cleaned house, scolding Joshua soundly and shooing him out the door when he tracked dirt in on the kitchen floor.

Norma was looking forward to the hymn sing. The young people sang English hymns. She hadn't been to the English church for quite a while, since Dad wasn't coming around anymore. She missed the English songs and teaching.

That night when Mandy slid her tired feet under the covers of her bed, she let out a scream. Betsy was on the other side of the room with her back turned, but a smile played around her mouth. Throwing the covers back, Mandy discovered prickly pinecones scattered between her sheets. She scooped up a handful of them and threw them across the room at Betsy. "Okay, you win, but just wait!"

On Sunday evening, Norma, Katie, and Joshua sat on the daybed in the corner of the kitchen, listening to the singing. The house was full of young people—the Brubachers, the Gregorys, the Kilmers, the Martins, the Ringlers. How Norma enjoyed that singing! She joined in singing some of the songs that were more familiar to her.

When they sang, "What a Friend We Have in Jesus," she listened carefully to the words. "Is there trouble anywhere?...Take it to the Lord in prayer." Would God listen if she prayed about Raymond and Erma? Did He see her aching heart? How she longed for Erma's sleepy little head resting on her lap just now. She swallowed hard.

What were they singing now? Norma didn't remember hearing the song before. "Amid the trials which I meet...Thou thinkest, Lord, of me." Later they sang, "Be not dismayed whate'er betide. God will take care of you."

"Uncle Peter and Aunt Sarah took pretty good care of me," Norma thought, "but—I said I would always take care of Erma, and I *can't!* When will I ever see them again?" The lump in her throat rose up to choke her. Quietly she slipped off the daybed and went outside. She clenched her fists. "I will not cry now," she whispered determinedly.

Afraid someone would come looking for her, she went to the pump for a cool drink. Slowly she walked back to the house. She sighed with relief to find out the singing was over.

Katie met her, bursting with excitement. "Norma, guess what? Martin just stepped in to tell us that he and Mary have a baby girl! Her name is Lydia. Lydia is so pleased to have the baby named after her, and guess what else—that makes me Aunt Katie. Don't I sound old?!" She giggled. Pushing her own hurts aside, Norma rejoiced with Katie. What fun it would be to have a little baby in the family!

Another year of school came to a close. Norma spent a morning helping Grandma make strawberry jam. She watched with interest as Grandma added a bit of cream to the dishwater when she was washing canning jars. "It makes the glass sparkling clean," she declared. Grandpa came and joined the circle, helping them cap the tiny wild strawberries.

"Well, Norma, I guess you just have one year of school left. I hear you will be helping Manasseh's this summer," Grandpa said.

"Yes," Norma responded. "This time I will be staying there for weekends too."

"I guess it seems pretty far away from here—about nine miles—but at least we will see you when we have church in the church house," Grandpa said, smiling.

"I'm glad for that too," Norma responded.

"I'm sure Amanda will be glad for you," Grandma said. "She has her hands full."

When Norma was ready to go home, Walter came across the yard. "Hey, Norma, how about if I walk you home? Seems like we hardly get to talk lately. How is it going?"

"Okay, I guess," Norma answered slowly. "But, oh, Walter, I miss Erma and Raymond *so* much! I just can't quit wondering if they are all right. I picture Erma crying herself to sleep, and Raymond—where is he? Does anyone have patience with him?"

"You know, Sis, sometimes I get so upset at Dad. I feel like he practically kicked Art and me out of our home, and then, what he put the rest of you through—I just can't think about it too much. I guess he brought Art and me up here from Grand Rapids because we were old enough to earn our keep and times were hard, but it hurt anyway. I just keep telling myself that at least he brought us to good homes, but this latest thing with Raymond and Erma just sets me off again. Art—he just sort of seems to take what comes, but me—" He stopped. "Sorry, Sis, I guess I just needed to unload, and no one else really knows how it was for us."

Norma nodded sympathetically. "Did you know I'm going to be at Manasseh's for the summer? It's hard to leave Uncle Peter's, but I guess I'm old enough to earn my own keep too."

"You've been at Manasseh's a little bit before, haven't you? Is it okay?" Walter wondered.

"I'll miss Katie. It's like losing another sister, but I will come back for school in the fall. Amanda Kulp is not as soft with her tongue as Aunt Sarah. Sometimes it hurts a little, but she sings a lot of the time. I like that. Manasseh is very kind, and it helps to have the children to take care of, like I always looked out for Erma."

They turned into the Brubacher lane. "Thanks for listening, Sis. I better head back now. I hope to see you on Sunday sometimes at least." With a quick wave, Walter headed back to Grandpa's home.

Norma packed her clothes to move to Manasseh's. Down among her clothes, she tucked her only treasure. It was a tarnished silver cream and sugar set.[1] She ran her finger over the leaves and flowers etched on the outside. Her mind was back in the tarpaper shack. There was a new tablecloth, and the family was all together, crowded around the table—Dad, Mom, Walter, Arthur, Raymond, Erma, and herself. The cream and sugar set was up on the shelf because there was no cream or sugar, but they were together and they were happy.

With a sigh, she tucked it down in her bag. How well she remembered her surprise when she met Mom at Gregorys and Mom handed the cream and sugar set to her. "I want you to have this, Norma," was what she said. Catching up her bag, she said a quick goodbye and headed out the walk.

Uncle Peter took her to Manasseh's. Six-year-old Paul and four-year-old Rachel came running out to meet her. Baby Mary Ann toddled after them. Amanda stood in the doorway. "Welcome here, Norma," she greeted her. "I guess you know where to put your things."

"Yes," Norma said. "What would you like me to do first?"

"Well," Amanda answered, "there's wash to hang on the line. Take the diapers first. We are almost out of them. Then there's the kitchen to clean up. Paul, Dad wants you to help him get beets and carrots for market."

Norma picked up the wash basket and headed for the clothesline.

[1]See sketch on page 147

Rachel followed her, chattering happily. Norma breathed deeply of the fresh, piney air and began swiftly hanging diapers on the line. "I want to give you the clothespins," Rachel begged.

"All right." Norma slowed a bit and waited for Rachel to hand her the clothespins. She gave Rachel a little hug as they went back into the house for more wash. It felt so good to be around little children.

There was always lots of work, and Norma liked to work. Besides, hard work helped her not to think of the ache in her heart. Amanda was easy to please because she was not quite as particular as Aunt Sarah was.

So the summer sped by. June 26 was a hard day for Norma. She and Erma had always had their birthdays together. The girls from church gave her homemade birthday cards, but she didn't even know where to send one for Erma.

It was always good to see Katie and the rest of the family at church every other weekend. One Sunday, Norma stood in a group of girls after church. "I don't like to sleep by myself, Norma," Katie complained. "I can't wait till summer is over and you come back. Of course sometimes I'm working out too."

Norma smiled—it felt good to be missed. "I miss you too, Katie."

"Well, I like having her in our neck of the woods," Alice Ringler spoke up. "We're too busy to see each other much, but sometimes we do things together."

Sometimes the Kulps would go out to visit the Ringlers' family of ten children. There was always fun and laughter at the Ringler home. Norma and Alice quickly paired up and became lifelong friends. It was good to have that kind of friend nearby when everything familiar seemed far away.

Norma liked the kind way Manasseh treated his children. He reminded her of Uncle Peter. She was a bit surprised to find out later that Manasseh had actually lived with Uncle Peter's before he was married.

One day Norma picked up baby Mary Ann and went to change her diaper. "Mia," Mary Ann said sweetly, pointing at Norma. "Mia?"

Norma laughed. "Yes, I guess I'm Mia since you can't say Norma."

Quickly Norma replaced the wet cotton diaper with a dry one. Carefully she put a diaper pin into one side of the diaper. The other pin just would not go through the cloth. Norma took it out and tried a different spot. Still it wouldn't go through. She pushed a little harder. Suddenly it slid quickly, and Mary Ann began to yell. "Waa!"

Quickly Norma pulled the pin out, but it was too late. A red pinprick showed on Mary Ann's soft baby skin. Mary Ann could not be comforted. "Waa! Waa!" Norma felt terrible. Mary Ann continued to scream. Amanda came hurrying into the house. She reached for her crying baby. Mary Ann's screams subsided a bit. "Waa, Mia. Waa, Mia."

"Whatever happened?" Amanda asked Norma.

"I'm sorry," Norma said, struggling to keep the tears back. "I pricked her with the diaper pin by accident."

"You must be more careful," Amanda chided.

How foolish Norma felt. Mary Ann soon forgave her, but Norma had a hard time forgiving herself.

September came, and Norma packed her bags and moved back to Uncle Peter's. It felt good to be home.

chapter nineteen

What's Next?

Brutus, Michigan: Winter 1933 to Winter 1934

Norma dangled a hair in Katie's sleeping face. Groggily, Katie rubbed her nose. Norma brought the hair down again and tickled Katie's forehead. Katie scratched her forehead and rolled over on her side. Norma put the hair on Katie's ear. Suddenly Katie lunged at Norma. Squealing, Norma rolled over and tumbled out of bed, but not before Katie's pillow thumped her on the head. Jumping up, Norma said, "Well, come on, sleepyhead. It's the first day of our last year of school, and there's work to do before we head out the lane."

"Doesn't it feel strange to think that we are the 'big girls' at school now?" Katie asked. "I don't feel that old."

"But remember, you are Aunt Katie now," Norma teased.

"Oh, yes," Katie groaned. "I guess I should get my old aching bones out of bed." Quickly the girls dressed and combed. Then they hurried to gather eggs and help Aunt Sarah in the kitchen.

"Joshua, tuck your shirttail in," Katie admonished as they started out the lane. They hurried to catch up with Daniel, Magdalena, Anna, and Aaron, who were started down the road. The boys went ahead, eager to choose their desks for the year. The girls came more slowly.

Anna looked pale and thin, but excitement shone from her eyes. "I'm glad it's school again. I hope I don't have to miss too much this year."

"Aren't you big girls glad it's your last year?" Magdalena asked. "I wish I was in grade eight. What do you think you will be doing next year this time?"

"Oh—" Katie grinned mischievously. "Watching you go off to school, I guess." Magdalena made a face at her.

"Next year," Norma thought. "What *will* I do when I'm done with school? Maybe Manasseh's will need me for a while, but then what? I can't just expect Uncle Peter's to always take care of me. Even their own girls work away." She pushed the troubling thought away, but just that quickly she thought of Erma. "Erma is starting grade two. I never even found out how she liked grade one. It's already more than a year since I saw her and Raymond."

"Sometimes I think it would be fun if we'd get a different teacher," Magdalena was saying. "Wanda Kuebler has been the teacher for ever so long, and she's strict!"

"This is only her third year," Katie said, "and she's a good teacher. You don't know what it's like when the teacher doesn't keep order— it's no fun!"

"I'm glad to have her for my last year," Norma agreed. "Oh," she thought, "I hope Erma and Raymond have a kind teacher."

The girls joined the group of children in the schoolyard. It was good to see the other girls again, especially Mary Evelyn, since they didn't see each other at church. Mary Evelyn and her sister Naomi didn't dress like the Mennonite girls, but no unkind remarks were ever made—Teacher Wanda saw to that. Norma and Mary Evelyn found seats close together and smiled at each other happily.

The routine of school, the busyness of harvest, and the comfortable familiarity of Uncle Peter's home were good for Norma. The longing for Erma was always there. It was like a deep wound that never healed. It was like the loss from death, but different. Where was Erma? Was she all right? Keeping busy helped, but suddenly, while holding Mary's baby, Lydia, she would be back in the tarpaper shack, holding her dark-haired little sister. Quickly she would wipe her eyes on baby Lydia's blanket.

Betsy and Aunt Sarah were busy sewing—comforts, bedding, tea towels, and such like. Christian and Betsy were planning a wedding. It was a family secret; the custom was to announce the wedding at a church service two weeks ahead of time. It would be held in Uncle Peter's home with only family and the young people of church attending. Afterwards a meal would be served. Mandy, Norma, and Katie were put to scrubbing the house spic and span. Then just before the wedding, there was food to make. The pie cupboard was stocked with pies. Pudding cooled on the counter alongside loaves of crusty bread. Aunt Sarah was busy frying chicken, and the girls were busy peeling potatoes. Finally everything was ready. Silas and Mandy were going to be the witnesses.

Norma didn't remember ever being to a wedding before. She watched Christian and Betsy's happy faces on their special day and wondered if there would ever be someone that she would be able to trust enough to marry, or if there would be anyone that would want her. Christian and Betsy looked so happy. Uncle Peter and Aunt Sarah were happy together too, but what about Mom and Dad? Their marriage didn't work. Never did she want a home like theirs had been.

Several weeks later, Katie and Norma woke up to hear the wind howling around the corners of the house. The bedroom was icy cold. One glance out the window told them it was a blizzard.

"I'm glad it isn't Betsy's wedding day today," Katie said.

"What would we ever have done with all that food if people couldn't have gotten here?" Norma wondered.

Aunt Sarah kept the schoolchildren home. Uncle Peter and Silas came in from the barn looking like snowmen themselves. The next day the sun shone. Silas shoveled a path to the road. The snowplow rumbled past. The children bundled up for the cold walk to school.

Magdalena and Anna were bursting with excitement. "Guess what the blizzard brought us," Magdalena began.

"Let me tell! Let me tell!" Anna interrupted.

"All right," Magdalena said.

"We got a new baby brother," Anna said happily. "His name is Irvin. We didn't have a new baby for a *long* time. Six years, I think. That baby was little Susie, and she got sick and died now we can't call Aaron the 'baby' anymore. I can hardly wait to get home from school again."

Just then Anna's brother Martin came out the lane on a horse. He stopped beside the girls. "Anna, Mother doesn't want you to walk to school in this cold. She said I should take you on the horse."

"We'll carry your things," Katie offered.

Carefully, Martin helped his little sister up on the horse behind him and went down the road to school. Norma noticed his kindness to his little sister. It reminded her of Uncle Peter and Manasseh. The girls met him coming back a lot faster than he went, his dark hair blowing in the wind.

Throughout the school year, Norma had occasional troubling thoughts about what she would do after school was done. It would be nice just to stay in the security of Uncle Peter's home, but she would be fourteen this summer. A fourteen-year-old was considered quite old enough to hold a job working in someone's home. She was old enough now to realize how much Uncle Peter and Aunt Sarah had sacrificed and skimped to make a home for her, Raymond, and Erma. Dad wasn't bringing any money to help out anymore either. Uncle Peter's had given her a home for almost four years. It was a scary thought to be on her own, but with Raymond and Erma gone, there was really no reason for her to stay.

Aunt Sarah came to her early in the spring. "Norma, Amanda Kulp wonders about you coming to work for them again when school is over. They have baby Isaac now too, you know. She thought they could use you until after the fall butchering is done. Does that sound all right to you?"

"I think so," Norma answered.

"I'd really like to keep you here longer, Norma, but it seems this is the right thing to do. We will miss you," she added, putting her arm around Norma's shoulders and giving her a little squeeze. "I'm glad that you can go to work for someone we know like Manasseh's."

"Thank you, Aunt Sarah—thank you for all that you have done for me," Norma replied.

"You are always welcome here, Norma."

The morning finally came when Norma packed her molasses pail for the last time and joined the other children on the walk to the little white schoolhouse. She felt a sense of satisfaction in finishing school days, but her future was too uncertain for her to have the same excitement the other girls in grade eight had.

They passed one of the Reed boys plowing the field in preparation for potato planting. It was Martin, and he waved cheerfully at the schoolchildren.

"Sometimes Martin lets me ride on the tractor with him," Anna confided to Norma. She gave a little skip to keep up with the others. Norma slowed her steps a bit. Anna seemed to be doing somewhat better today. Norma would miss her when she moved to Manasseh's.

Then it was time to pack her bags to move. It seemed final. This wasn't for a week or even a month. This was until Manasseh's didn't need her. And then what? Norma carefully tucked her treasured cream and sugar bowl between her clothes. She really didn't have a lot else to take.

Suddenly Katie was at her side. She threw her arms around Norma. "Oh, Norma, you will always be my *oga-bopt shvesta*,"[1] she said with a shaky laugh. "I wish you didn't have to go, but I guess I'm going to be working away too. Come back whenever you can." The two girls stood with their arms around each other and tears in their eyes.

"Thanks, Katie, you are a wonderful friend and much more than an *oga-bopt shvesta*[1] even if we did have fun calling each other that. Thanks for sharing your home and mom and dad and bedroom with me." She gave Katie another hug and then tearfully picked up her bags and hurried out to the waiting wagon.

Aunt Sarah stopped her at the door. "God go with you, Norma. Come home anytime."

"Thanks again, Aunt Sarah," she whispered. "Home," she thought, looking back at the house after she was seated beside Grandpa in the wagon. For four years, this had been a real home to her. Memories of tears and heartache, love and laughter washed over her. Uncle Peter waved from the barn. She was glad that Grandpa had needed to go to town and had offered to take her on to Manasseh's. They rode together in comfortable silence.

After a while Grandpa broke the silence. "This will be a change for you, Norma, but changes do come in life. Sometimes they are good changes, and sometimes they are hard. Just remember there's nothing so bad that there isn't some good in it. I'm glad that it's Manasseh's that you are going to. You know them, and they are good people."

"I'm glad too," Norma responded.

They drove in silence again until Grandpa began to reminisce. "It's been about twenty-nine years since we arrived in Brutus from Indiana. We came by covered wagon in 1905—took our good time coming, stopping here and there. We even spent a summer in central Michigan." Grandpa paused and his eyes grew misty. "I had already lost two wives, and your Grandma Lydia was new at mothering six children, so we took it easy. Lydia did very well, and my hard times turned into very good ones."[2]

[1] Pasted-on sister

[2] See page 409 for more history on this account.

Norma looked at Grandpa in a new light. She had known that Grandma wasn't the mother of Grandpa's children, but she had never thought of the sorrows Grandpa must have had.

"You will be more or less on your own now," Grandpa continued, "but remember, our door is always open to you."

"Thank you," Norma answered simply. It was comforting to know that while her place in Uncle Peter's home would not be the same anymore, her status at Grandpa's house hadn't changed.

"Well, here we are," Grandpa said as they pulled into Manasseh's lane. "It looks like the children are watching for you." Norma gathered her bags and walked to the house, accompanied by Rachel's chatter.

Life fell into a familiar routine at Manasseh's. There was always lots to do, especially with new baby Isaac now too.

Manasseh worked hard to make a living for his little family. The land in his area was not as fertile as the Woodland area, but he managed to raise produce to sell in Harbor Springs. Rachel and Paul were glad for Norma's help to scrub beets and carrots for market. Norma loved helping Amanda cut small bouquets of flowers from the rows of flowers in her garden. These were sent to market too.

Norma's birthday came and went, marked by a little bouquet of flowers from Rachel and a pretty pinecone from Paul. Naturally, her thoughts were with Erma most of the day. She dampened her pillow with tears, as loneliness and uncertainty about the future hung over her. "What will I do, and where will I work when Manasseh's don't need me?"

Norma awoke to the sound of beautiful singing. "His yoke is easy, His burden is light; I've found it so, I've found it so…" Amanda was singing in the kitchen.

Norma hurried to join her. The question of the night before came again. "Where will I go from here? Will God lead me?" she wondered. Then she remembered, "It's the Sunday for German services—Uncle Peter's will be there too!" German services were held in the church every other Sunday. On the Sundays between, Manasseh's family didn't attend church.

"Come on, Rachel, get up. It's Sunday, and I need to comb your hair," Norma said, giving Rachel a little nudge. Combing Rachel's kinky, curly hair was not an easy job. The job fell to Norma when Amanda was busy getting the babies ready for church.

Rachel was out of bed in a flash. "It's Sunday! We get to go to church! The sun is shining. I like to hear Mom singing. Tell me a story, Norma, so I don't think about the pulls when you comb," she begged. "Oh, I know, tell me the 'Twenty Froggies' poem that you learned in school."

"You'll soon know that yourself," Norma said with a smile. "Twenty froggies go to school, down beside the rushing pool..." she began, carefully working the comb through Rachel's hair.

In church, she found herself seated with the other girls her age— Katie on one side and Alice Ringler on the other. Katie gave her a friendly little pinch. She pinched her back, but there was no talking or whispering in church—that would have to wait.

After church, it didn't take the girls long to gather outside. "How's your job, Norma?" Katie wondered.

"Oh, it's all right," Norma answered. "I'm used to Manasseh's and they are used to me. That helps."

"Well, we sure miss you!" Katie exclaimed. "I'm so glad we get to see each other at church. I'm mostly helping Mom and Grandma since I'm the youngest girl, but sometimes I go away, and one of the other girls stays home to help. You should hear about Mandy's job. She's babysitting for people who have a store. She actually got to talk on one of those newfangled telephones!"

"Really?" Norma asked.

"Yes, she said it was kind of scary at first, but she likes to tease Joshua and me that she knows more than we do because we don't know what it's like to talk on the telephone. Do you ever get to see your mom?" Katie wondered.

"Not really," Norma answered. "I don't even know where she is right now. She moves around, working as a maid for different people."

"I heard she's working west of us at Ivan Sanford's," Alice spoke up. Katie opened her mouth to say something and then closed it tightly.

"I know, Katie," Norma sighed. "We are both thinking the same thing. Mom never tried to take us away like Dad thought. Raymond and Erma could have stayed. She hardly pays attention to me, but she is nice to me when I meet her somewhere. I didn't know she was working out our way."

Fall came, and Manasseh's were busy butchering. The future hung uncertainly over Norma. "What next? Where will I go?" Then Manasseh came to her. "Norma, Amanda really appreciates your help. She would like to keep you here several more months so she can get some winter projects done. Maybe by that time you will have another job waiting for you. Mahlon Martin's have shown some interest in you helping them sometime. How does that sound to you?"

"I'll be glad to stay," Norma answered.

"You know I didn't always know where I was going to live either when I was young," Manasseh continued. "I spent time at Uncle Peter's too. I'm sure something will work out for you."

"Thank you," Norma said gratefully. "Mahlon Martin's," she thought. "I don't really know them. I know they don't have children. That would seem strange. Oh, I just don't know."

I'LL SEE YOU IN THE MORNING

chapter twenty

Behind a Locked Door

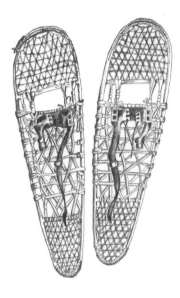

Brutus, Michigan: Winter 1934 to Spring 1935

Norma sliced potatoes into the sizzling frying pan. The kitchen smelled like the homemade sausage that was being kept warm on the back of the cookstove. On the table was one plate, a loaf of fresh bread, and a pat of butter. Quickly Norma fried the potatoes, then moved them back beside the sausage to keep warm. There was a stamping of feet, and the kitchen door opened. Mahlon came in, bringing a blast of cold air with him.

"Your supper is on the cookstove," Norma said, snatching up her coat. "I'm going to the Purple Inn."

Mahlon took an unsteady step toward her, but Norma was out the door and hurrying toward the inn before he could say much.

Time had run out at Manasseh's. She had to take the available job. Mahlon and Marjorie were a childless middle-aged couple. Marjorie had a pleasant personality. She spent some days working at the nearby Purple Inn.

One of Norma's jobs was to make sure Mahlon's supper was ready on evenings when Marjorie worked. Norma was plain-down scared of Mahlon. She was sure that when Manasseh had recommended this job, he had not known that Mahlon drank.

Running lightly down the snowy road, Norma soon arrived at the welcoming warmth of the inn. She found Marjorie in the kitchen. "I came to help you wash up dishes. Mahlon has his supper," she said as she plunged her cold hands into the warm dishwater.

"Thank you, Norma!" Marjorie said gratefully. "It's been a long day."

"Oh, it looks like you have help!" Nellie Purple said smiling at Norma as she carried a heaping platter of her famous chicken to the waiting diners.

"Yes," Marjorie answered, "and I am glad!"

When the diners were gone and the kitchen at the inn was sparkling

The Purple Inn

clean, Marjorie and Norma walked home together in the crisp night air. Quickly Norma washed up the few dishes from Mahlon's supper and excused herself to her room. Once inside, she carefully locked the door.

Slipping into bed, she thought, "What a contrast to Uncle Peter's and Manasseh's happy homes!" How she missed Katie and Mandy. It was like losing two more sisters besides Erma. A lonely tear slid down on her pillow.

While Norma missed the chatter of little children, working for Marjorie was relatively easy. How glad she was that Mahlon worked long days away from home. With more time on her hands than she was used to, Norma sometimes took walks when the work was done. Living in Brutus meant that occasionally she saw people she knew drive past while she was walking. Sometimes it was one of the Reed boys or Jesse Brubacher.

Once it was Uncle Peter himself. He drew old Ned to a stop and asked, "How are you doing?" She didn't tell him that she wanted to climb up beside him, go home, and be a little girl at his house again.

Then one day a car stopped, and a familiar voice called, "Norma!" The next thing she knew, Mary Evelyn's arms were around her.

"How are you, Norma? It's been so long since I saw you. Are you living here in Brutus? The last I heard, you were working out by Ayr at Manasseh Kulp's."

Norma returned Mary Evelyn's hug warmly. "Oh, Mary Evelyn, it's so good to see you! I've been working here at Mahlon Martin's for several weeks now."

"Is it good?" Mary Evelyn asked, searching her old school chum's face.

"Well—" Norma hesitated. She knew she couldn't hide anything from Mary Evelyn. "Marjorie is very nice, but—well, Mahlon—I'm scared of him. I'd never have come here if I knew that he drinks, but really, I didn't have a lot of choice."

Mary Evelyn's parents, Mose and Bessie, sat waiting patiently in the car while the girls talked. "Do they keep you real busy? Could you get away sometimes? I'd love to have you come to our house."

"Oh, Mary Evelyn, really?" Norma's heavy heart rose. "I'd love to get away from here a bit, but how would I get there? It's a little far to walk by myself, and it would have to be sometime when Marjorie is not working at the Purple Inn."

"Just wait," Mary Evelyn answered. She hurried over to the waiting car and leaned inside, speaking to her parents. Soon she was back. "It's all figured out. Dad says we can come and get you. He'll figure on doing some business in town then. When does Marjorie have off? Would you be able to stay a weekend?"

"Just let me run in and talk to Marjorie. She's at home today." And off Norma ran.

Bessie sat watching from the car. "Mose, there's something special about that girl. My heart just goes out to her. I never could understand how John and Alzina could just dump their children off like that. I sure hope Marjorie will let her come."

Before long, Norma was back, her face aglow. "She said 'yes,' Mary Evelyn! She doesn't work next weekend. Would that work for you?"

Soon it was all arranged. The evenings that she spent in her room with the door locked because Marjorie was working didn't seem so bad. There was something to look forward to.

By Friday afternoon, Norma had the house spic-and-span. The bread was baked. There was a pie on the table and pudding in the icebox. The laundry was folded and put away. She fairly skipped out the door when Mose Martin's Model T stopped by the road.

"Have a good time," Marjorie called after her.

Norma felt like a bird set free. The girls chattered happily. As the car chugged over the Maple River bridge, Norma thought, "I haven't been to Woodland since last spring, but it seems even longer." They were almost at Uncle Peter's when the car turned right and traveled a short distance to Mose and Bessie's house. Norma had rarely been to Mary Evelyn's house when she lived at Uncle Peter's, even though she had gone to school with Mary Evelyn.

Bessie welcomed Norma with a motherly hug. Norma smiled at her shyly. She glanced around the kitchen. It was a warm and homey place.

"Mom, do you think we could take a little walk before supper? Norma has never used snowshoes, and I'd like to show her how."

"Sure," Bessie responded. "Naomi and I will get supper, and then we'll let you and Norma wash the dishes. How does that sound, Naomi?"

"Sounds good to me," Naomi answered.

The sun shone brightly on the snowbanks as Mary Evelyn helped Norma put on the snowshoes. Then Mary Evelyn demonstrated how to slide the snowshoes over the deep snow with a somewhat outward motion. It was funny walking with such big feet. "Here I go," said Norma as her "big feet" tangled, and down she fell on her knees in the deep snow. After that, it didn't take long to get the feel of it.

"Let's walk back to the sugar bush," Mary Evelyn suggested.

"You must make a lot of maple syrup!" Norma exclaimed when she saw all the maple trees.

"You'd think that for sure if you were emptying sap pails," Mary Evelyn groaned. "I think we have over seven hundred trees. Dad likes to tell about the year we had a long season and he got a thousand pails of sap. He sold 343 gallons of syrup at $1.25 a gallon. I'm glad that was before I was born. But I do like maple syrup."

"I always liked gathering sap at Uncle Peter's, but we didn't have *this* much!" Norma said.

"We better head back for supper. Did I tell you what we are doing tomorrow?" Mary Evelyn asked. "I hope you don't mind working."

"Of course I don't mind working," Norma responded. "What are you planning?"

"Menno and Elias, my older brothers, are getting ready to cut our summer's supply of ice from back at the dam. Elias rigged up an ice saw with a motor. They want us to pack the ice blocks in the icehouse."

"It sounds like fun to me," Norma answered.

"Let's run," Mary Evelyn suggested, taking off in a dogtrot with her snowshoes.

"Hey, you! I'm just learning," Norma laughingly protested. Nevertheless she gradually picked up speed and managed to arrive at the house soon after Mary Evelyn.

"You're doing pretty good, Norma," Mary Evelyn congratulated her just as Norma tripped and went down. Rising up on her knees, Norma quickly threw a snowball that landed on Mary Evelyn's forehead. The snowshoes were off in a flash, and the fight was on. Around the outside of the house, laughing and shouting, the girls ran until Mary Evelyn rounded the corner and, forgetting the snowshoes, landed on one snowshoe while another came up and hit her in the face.

"Ow!" she yelled, and fell into a laughing, tangled heap. It looked so funny that Norma leaned against the side of the house, laughing.

"Some people get tangled up when they try to use snowshoes," she teased when she could get her breath. "Would you like me to show you the proper way to use them?"

Mose and his two boys were walking in to the house. The girls hurried to join them. It felt so good to sit around the table and listen to their relaxed conversation.

The dishes done, the girls retired to their room. As they snuggled down under the covers to warm up, Mary Evelyn asked, "Do you ever see your mom? What about Raymond and Erma? Have you heard from them?"

"Mom's around," Norma answered. "Sometimes I meet her in town, and she's always glad to see me, but she never seeks me out. I'm not sure where she's working now. Maybe she's still at Ivan Sanford's. As far as Raymond and Erma—Dad took them to Indiana. Aunt Sarah thought Dad took Erma to George Mitchelen's, and someone thought Raymond is at Walter Pletcher's. They are both relatives of some sort. I've never heard how they are doing, and it's been three years now. It's so hard, Mary Evelyn! I just can't think about it too much. I miss Erma so—*much!*"

"I'm sorry, Norma," Mary Evelyn sympathized. "I can't imagine how it must be." She squeezed Norma's hand under the covers.

The next morning, the girls were up early. "Please, Elias," Mary Evelyn begged at the breakfast table. "May we ride along to the dam and watch you cut the first load of ice?"

"Me too!" Naomi added.

"Well, really," Elias drawled, frowning at his sisters, "we were going to haul ice and not girls!" A twinkle lurked around his eyes. "But I guess maybe, since you will be packing ice all day, you should get to see where it comes from. You better bundle up good and take a blanket to sit on. It's going to be *cold*, and it's a little piece out to the dam. Don't make us wait. We are in a hurry to get going."

"Oh, good! Thanks, Elias!" And the girls scrambled to get ready. "Here, Norma, you can wear these heavier mittens. You'll need them to pack ice," Mary Evelyn offered. "Here's an extra old sweater to put under your coat."

Soon the big, flat wagon was rattling out the lane. Mose and Menno sat up front. Menno kept the horses going at a fast clip. The return trip would be slower with a loaded wagon. Elias and the girls rode on the back, with Elias keeping watch over his precious motor-powered saw that he had rigged up himself.

Soon the girls' cheeks were rosy red. "So you think you're going to cut ice faster and better than anyone else," Mary Evelyn teased her brother.

"Oh, we'll see," Elias said grinning. "It ought to be easier, anyway."

It seemed strange to Norma to drive past Uncle Peter's lane and not turn in. She noticed Joshua carrying a pail to the house. He probably had the morning's milk, but he was too far away to communicate with. Down the familiar road to school they went, and then turned off at the school and headed toward the dam.

The dam was a beautiful place, even in winter. The quiet beauty of it all was shattered by Elias starting up his motorized saw. Mose took a handsaw and cut a small hole in the ice. Then he and Elias sawed parallel to each other, making a long, narrow chunk of ice. Norma watched, fascinated. Uncle Peter's had no icebox, and she had not seen this done before. She noticed that Mose pretty well kept up to Elias even though he had no motor on his saw. Elias had to stop occasionally to tinker with it.

Menno took an ax and cut the long chunk of ice at the end. It rose a bit in the water. Mose took a long pole and pushed the chunk of ice toward the small hole that he had cut in the ice. The long, narrow chunk slid up on the ice, and Elias quickly sawed it into blocks. Menno picked up the blocks with the big ice tongs and loaded them on the wagon while Elias and Mose each began sawing another long, narrow chunk. As the chunks were pushed out of the water, the section of dark, cold water widened where the ice had been.

"Dad, do you want to try my saw?" Elias offered graciously. Mose smiled and said, "No, I'll just stick to the one powered by elbow grease."

The blocks of ice on the wagon rose higher until Mose said, "Menno, why don't you take the girls back and unload while we keep on cutting. Then you can have a turn at the saw."

The girls threw a woolen blanket on the ice and huddled together on the blanket to keep warm. It *was* cold. The water had not even dripped from the ice chunks. It just froze immediately.

Back in the icehouse, the girls set to work. There was no time to warm up in the house now. Menno needed to go back for another load of ice.

Menno pulled the wagon close to the icehouse door. Using a slanted board, he slid the blocks of ice off the wagon and into the icehouse. The icehouse floor had been covered with a thick layer of sawdust. Now the blocks of ice were placed on the top of the sawdust. Using their mittened hands, Norma and Mary Evelyn packed more sawdust around each block of ice.

As soon as the wagon was empty, Menno left for the dam. Norma and Mary Evelyn kept on packing sawdust all around and between the blocks until the job was done. The work had helped to warm them up, but they were still glad to run to the warmth of the house till Mose came, this time with an even bigger load of ice. Then back they went to pack sawdust around the next set of ice blocks.

"Where did you get all the sawdust?" Norma wondered.

"Dad hauled it from the sawmill at Pellston," Mary Evelyn answered. "You know what, Norma? I sure hope you can come to our house like this again."

"Oh, I'd love to," Norma responded. "It made my whole week go fast because I was looking forward to this. Do you think your mom and dad would care? I'd have to talk to Marjorie, though. If it wasn't for Marjorie, I'd just quit the job if I found another one. For right now, I'm stuck there."

"I'm sure Dad and Mom won't care. Dad's taking milk and eggs to town pretty often, so we could pick you up."

The girls worked hard, and by supper that evening, Elias announced, "I think one more day like this should about do it for cutting ice this year."

"Let's take a couple days' break, and likely we'll get another real cold day when the ice comes out 'dry,'" Mose suggested.

The next day was Sunday. Norma noticed something was different at Mose and Bessie's, but she wasn't sure at first what it was. Then she realized that Sunday was like any other day. They were not church-goers.

The girls were getting ready for the day. Norma combed her dark, curly hair, twisted it up, and pinned it neatly to the back of her head. She was growing up. She was outgrowing the dresses that she had while at Uncle Peter's.

"Here, Norma, why don't you try one of my outgrown dresses," Mary Evelyn suggested. "I'm taller than you. I think they might fit. Mom loves to sew, so I'm sure she wouldn't care if I gave you a dress or two. She'll just make more for Naomi if she doesn't have enough of my hand-me-down dresses."

Norma hesitated. "I am going to have to get dresses somewhere," she thought. "I don't really have the time or the means to sew dresses. I'd still need some help, even though Aunt Sarah taught me a lot about sewing."

"Just try it on once," Mary Evelyn urged. "Here, I think this one would look good on you," she said, handing Norma a pretty blue print. Norma took the dress and slipped it over her head.

"Perfect," Mary Evelyn exclaimed. It felt rather strange to wear something other than a Mennonite dress, even though the dress was made fairly simply and fit loosely on Norma's petite build. Norma looked at herself in the rather cloudy mirror. "You're not bad looking," Mary Evelyn commented.

Norma snatched up a pillow and threw it at her. "How about yourself, my beautiful blonde?" she returned.

"Just wear it for breakfast once and see what Mom says," Mary Evelyn returned.

Rather self-consciously, Norma entered the kitchen. Bessie smiled at Norma. "Who would have thought it would fit so well? You are certainly welcome to several dresses. Naomi will be glad if her dresses are not all hand-me-downs."

"Thank you," Norma replied. "I wasn't sure what I was going to do for dresses."

Elias puckered up his lips to whistle, but stopped when Mary Evelyn gave him a warning look.

The girls spent the morning helping Bessie with baking and cleaning. After lunch, they took another walk in the snowshoes. Norma found it quite easy this time. Then it was time for Norma to go back to Brutus.

Elias and Menno were going to the dance hall and said they could drop Norma off at Mahlon's. "Sorry I can't come along with the boys to the dance, Norma," Mary Evelyn said. "Mom says I'm too young yet."

"Thanks so much for the nice weekend," Norma responded. "And thank you too, Bessie."

Bessie hugged Norma. "You come again, Norma—anytime."

"Dad said we'll stop by and see when it suits for you to come again—after you talk to Marjorie. I hope you can come back soon." Mary Evelyn gave her a big hug.

"I hope so too," Norma replied.

"Did you have a nice weekend?" Marjorie asked when Norma arrived back at Mahlon's.

"I sure did. I learned to walk in snowshoes and watched them cut ice. Mary Evelyn and I packed it in the icehouse," Norma said enthusiastically.

"Maybe you can go again sometime," Marjorie suggested. "I think

Mose & Bessie Martin

it's good for you to get out."

Norma's otherwise lonely life was brightened by numerous trips to Mose and Bessie's home. Mose became a kindly father figure to her. Bessie taught her various household skills along with Mary Evelyn. The girls took every opportunity they could for outdoor fun. Mary Evelyn taught Norma to cross-country ski. Several times she and Mary Evelyn walked to Uncle Peter's and stopped in. Aunt Sarah welcomed her with open arms. When spring came, Norma and Mary Evelyn sometimes sat with their feet dangling in the Maple River and talked.

Still, the time between visits dragged along. Norma spent many evenings alone in her room. If only there would be another job available—but where?

Occasionally Norma would get letters from one of her school friends. One day in early April, she got a letter from Magdalena. Tears filled her eyes as she read, "Anna had been getting worse and worse. She had 24 hours of bad suffering, and now she is gone. We miss her so much." Norma bowed her head and wept. She had loved little Anna. She found herself crying, not only for Magdalena's little sister, but for her own—Erma.

One lovely spring evening, Norma walked leisurely along the road. A walk was a better choice than locking herself in her room. Then a car slowed. "Norma," a familiar voice called. It was Mary Evelyn with Elias and Menno. "Guess what? Mom gave me permission to go along with the boys. There's a square dance at the hall. Why don't you come along? It's close enough I can walk you home by the time Marjorie is home from the Purple Inn."

Norma *was* lonely. Maybe it wouldn't hurt to go this once. It would help to fill up the evening. She looked down at her dress.

"Oh, you look fine! Hop in," Mary Evelyn begged.

When they entered the door of the dance hall, Norma found herself among a loud and jolly crowd. Suddenly she thought of Grandpa Brenneman—and Aunt Sarah—never would she want them to know that she was here.

"Come on, Norma, I'll show you how," Mary Evelyn offered. "This isn't any harder than snowshoeing or skiing."

Norma watched the dancers swing each other around the dance floor. She saw several young men glance her way.

"No, Mary Evelyn," she said, backing against the wall. "I'll just watch this time."

In one corner she saw several young men standing together, drinking. The music played loudly. Once again she saw Grandpa's gentle, godly face. In her mind, she heard Betsy and Mandy's sweet voices singing, "What a Friend We Have in Jesus."

Then she saw another face—Dad's. Dad would be comfortable here. "Who do I want to be like? Who do I want to please?"

Mary Evelyn left her dance partner and came her way. "Ready, Norma?" she asked.

"No, Mary Evelyn, this just isn't for me. I'm ready to leave."

Sensing her discomfort, Mary Evelyn said kindly, "Okay, Norma, I'll walk you back. Let me go tell Elias where I am."

Stepping out of the dance hall, Norma took a deep breath. "Never again!" she said to herself.

chapter twenty-one

Petoskey

Petoskey, Michigan: 1935-1936

"**M**arjorie," Norma began hesitantly. "Do you think it would work for me to have off this Friday? I'd like to go along with Mose and Bessie to Petoskey. I guess I should tell you that I'm going to see about a job there. I like working for you, but—"

"I know," Marjorie finished for her. "It's Mahlon. I understand, and I'm sorry. I'll really miss you, but, yes, we'll make it work so you can go."

When Friday came, Norma dressed carefully. She looked at herself critically in the mirror. "I'm so glad that Mose found out about the job. He said the man is an insurance salesman and he doesn't drink. His wife is very particular. I hope I look good enough, and I sure hope I can tell if it's a good place to work."

As she stood by the window waiting for Mose and Bessie's car, she saw Walter and Grandpa come by on their way to the store. Walter saw her at the window and waved. She waved back. "Oh," she thought, "if I get this job, I'll be far enough away that I won't see Walter and Arthur very often. Why do there have to be so many partings for me?"

Norma was surprised and pleased to see that Mary Evelyn and Naomi were along when Mose and Bessie stopped for her. The three girls were squeezed into the back seat.

"I hope you can find a better place to work," Mary Evelyn stated.

"I hope I can be good enough for them," Norma responded.

"They better be satisfied with you!" Mary Evelyn declared. "After all, you had Mom and Sarah Brubacher teach you to work."

"Here it is!" Mose stopped in front of a neat little cottage. "We'll be just down the street at the general store. You can walk down there when you are done."

Bessie smiled at Norma as she got out of the car. "You'll do fine, Norma."

When Norma knocked on the door, she heard the sound of a running child's feet. A woman opened the door with a pleasant "hello." A little boy with black curls stared up at her.

"I heard that you are looking for a maid," Norma began.

"Just step inside," the woman welcomed her. "I'm Mrs. Smith, and this is our Bobby."

"I'm Norma Brenneman," Norma said, shaking her hand.

"Why don't you come in for a cup of tea, and we can get acquainted?"

Norma followed Mrs. Smith through a plush sitting room and a formal dining room to a sparkling kitchen in the back of the house. She perched on the edge of her chair as Mrs. Smith put on water for tea. Then slowly she slid back in her chair and tried to relax. Mrs. Smith was very pleasant in spite of the formal setting. Bobby peeked at Norma from behind his mother's skirt.

After they had talked for a while, it was decided. Norma would start work in two weeks. "I will expect you to serve us in the dining room and then take your meals in the kitchen," Mrs. Smith was saying. "Now let me show you around a bit.

"Here is the nursery," she said as they passed a sunny room with toys and a crib. "And this will be your room," she continued, opening another door to a small but very pleasant room. Looking into it, Norma thought it would be the nicest bedroom she had ever had.

"You will be free from Saturday noon until Monday morning. I'm sure a young lady like you needs some social life. The dance hall is within walking distance. I would expect you to have the house clean and food made for the weekend ahead of time."

"Thank you," Norma said.

"I hope you don't mind Bobby. He can be quite a chatterbox," Mrs. Smith said apologetically.

"Oh, no!" Norma answered. "I'm used to children, and I enjoy them."

"We hope to see you then in two weeks," Mrs. Smith finished, showing Norma to the door.

"I'm looking forward to that," Norma answered. "Bye, Bobby."

"Bye, bye," Bobby said. "Thoo come again."

Two weeks later, Norma moved into the little, cozy bedroom at the Smiths. The Smiths were happy with Norma's cooking skills, but Norma felt lonely and strange eating by herself in the kitchen. Bobby trailed Norma all over the house as she worked, chattering happily. Mrs. Smith spent a lot of her time reading books and having friends over for tea. She gave Norma very particular instructions on how to iron Mr. Smith's shirts and then fold them carefully and place them in his shirt box.

When the weekend came, Norma was at a loss. "What is there to do all weekend? Who is in Petoskey that I know?"

On Saturday afternoon, she wrote a letter to Aunt Sarah, telling her about her new job. Then she wrote to Alice Ringler. "It would be so nice to have someone to talk to," she thought. "All week, it's been basically only Bobby's chatter."

Norma walked to the post office with her letters. Then she decided to explore Petoskey a bit. As she topped a little rise, she uttered a cry of delight. There before her lay Lake Michigan in all its sparkling blue splendor. She quickened her steps, and sure enough, this road ended at a broad, sandy beach. She breathed deeply of the fresh air.

A faint memory stirred in her mind. Hadn't Mom brought them to Lake Michigan sometimes long ago when Erma was a baby and they lived in Petoskey? Yes, the memory began to come back—Walter, Arthur, and little Raymond playing in the sand and wading in the water. Mom and baby Erma were there. It was a happy family memory. Tears filled her eyes. "Oh, Erma, I miss you so! Will I *ever* see you again?"

Resolutely she turned back toward Smith's, but the sadness lingered. "What will become of me?" she asked herself. "I don't really belong at Uncle Peter's anymore. It's nice to go to Mose Martin's, but I'm just a visitor there. Walter, Arthur, Raymond, Erma, Mom, Dad, and me—we are scattered all over. Will we ever be back together? Wouldn't it be wonderful to have a family to go home to?"

A group of young men stood on the street corner. Norma walked faster and crossed to the other side of the street.

On Monday morning, Norma happily tackled the family laundry. "I'd much rather work," she thought. "I'm afraid these weekends are going to be awful long."

They were. More than once, for lack of something better to do, Norma took walks along the streets in Petoskey and contemplated her future. "What am I going to do with my life? I've been working here for over half a year—longer than any other job. What will I do if this job ends? Am I going to be somebody's maid for the rest of my life? Will I ever have a home of my own? Would anyone ever want me? How could I be sure it would be a happy home if I had the opportunity?"

The twenty miles between Brutus and Petoskey were not so easily traveled as Norma had hoped. Aunt Sarah, Katie, or one of her old school friends sent occasional letters. Norma treasured each one. Walter stopped in several times to see how she was doing, but otherwise the winter stretched on.

One Saturday the following June, there was a knock at the door. There stood Mary Evelyn, her eyes sparkling. "You thought I'd never come—right?" The girls threw their arms around each other.

"Come in!" Norma welcomed her. "I can hardly believe that you are here! I'm almost done with my work. Come on back to the kitchen."

Mary Evelyn settled herself on a kitchen stool and looked around. "You have it pretty nice here, don't you? Are you sure a humble country friend like me will do?" she asked mischievously. "Here, let me dry those dishes for you."

"Oh, if you only knew how glad I am to see you. This is a nice place to work, but I get awful lonely. How did you get here?"

Norma and Mary Evelyn

"Lizzie Sauder and I hitchhiked. Elias will come and take us home on Sunday. I couldn't miss your birthday, you know. Happy sixteenth!"

"Well, thank you! I didn't expect anyone to think of my birthday here. You hitchhiked! You must have been eager to come. Where's Lizzie?" Norma asked.

"Well, that's the good news. She came to see Rhoda Gregory. Rhoda works here in Petoskey, and I found out that there's a carload that comes out to Brutus to church some Sundays. That should help your loneliness, won't it? Especially if you can get a ride with them sometimes."

"Oh, yes!" Norma's eyes sparkled.

Bobby peeked around the corner of the kitchen door. "Come, Bobby." Norma reached for him. Bobby quickly ran to Norma, and she picked him up. "See, Bobby, this is my friend Mary Evelyn." Bobby hid his head on Norma's shoulder.

"I think I'm done for the weekend," Norma stated. "How about we walk to the lake?"

"Sure," Mary Evelyn said, hanging up her tea towel. "A walk to the beach will give us a chance to talk. So what are you going to do for your birthday?" she wondered as the girls started down the street.

"Well, I didn't expect anything from Mrs. Smith. She lives in her own world of books and leisure. I'm just the maid. Uncle Peter's never did much for birthdays, so I'm fine with that. I guess I was just planning to keep busy and try not to think too much about Erma. It's her birthday too, you know."

"I'm sorry, Norma," Mary Evelyn sympathized.

"Someday, I don't know how, but I'm going to find Erma and bring her back."

"Hey, Norma!" Mary Evelyn said. "This looks like a pretty nice dance hall we are passing. Maybe you wouldn't be so lonely if you came here sometimes. There's probably some handsome sailors that come here."

"You know I tried that once with you, and it just doesn't appeal to me," Norma answered. "I do love coming down to the lake. Look, there it is. Let's run!" The girls spent the afternoon wading, walking in the sand, and talking.

"I saw your mom in Brutus the other day," Mary Evelyn remarked. "She asked about you. I told her you are working in Petoskey. She has been working some for Amos Gregorys."

"You know, I never really know where she is. She never makes any attempt to let me know, either," Norma answered.

"Well, she did seem pleased that you had a good job in Petoskey," Mary Evelyn said.

"How do I make connections with the group that goes to Brutus on weekends?" Norma wondered.

"I know where Rhoda works because we dropped Lizzie off there. Why don't we walk by there on our way home?" Mary Evelyn suggested.

When they talked to Rhoda, she answered that she would be happy to have Norma along. "I'll talk to my brother John to make sure, but it's usually just John and me and some other boys," Rhoda said. "We usually go early Sunday morning and come back Sunday evening. I'll walk down to the Smiths and let you know."

"Say, Norma, maybe if you come on Saturday, you could spend time at our house," Mary Evelyn suggested.

"I'd like that!" Norma answered.

The next Sunday morning, Norma was ready and waiting when a carload of young people stopped for her. She got into the back seat with Rhoda and her brother John. "Good morning," Rhoda greeted her. It was a beautiful morning! The sun shone brightly. The lake sparkled, and Norma's heart was light. She sat back and listened to the stories and wholesome banter among the young people.

"Are you wanting to be dropped off somewhere, or are you planning to go to church with us?" Rhoda wondered.

"I'd be glad to go to church," Norma responded. "It's been a long time since I had the opportunity."

Memories washed over Norma as they drove into the churchyard. This was the same church that she had come to with Uncle Peter's every other Sunday when the services were in German. She remembered the cozy feeling of being securely tucked in the back of the wagon on a cold, snowy day, following Aunt Sarah and her girls into church, and seeing Grandpa Brenneman behind the pulpit.

But this was an English service. Cars filled the churchyard instead of horses and wagons. English church brought back troubling memories of coming with Dad. She remembered taking Erma's hand—they had both been little girls—and finding their way into church among strangers.

As the young people filed into the back of the church, Norma noticed Magdalena smiling at her. Looking around, she soon realized that a number of people from the German church were coming to the English church now—especially the young people. She recognized Reeds, Sauders, and Kilmers.

When the singing started, Norma joined in eagerly with "What a Friend We Have in Jesus" and "I Am So Glad That Jesus Loves Me." Deep in Norma's heart, a longing began to grow to know this Jesus—to really know Him as a friend.

Norma recognized Clyde Kauffman as soon as he rose to speak. Eagerly she drank in his message about seeking God's will for our life. "Does God really care for Norma Brenneman? Does God really have a plan and purpose for my life?"

After the service, Norma's lonely heart soaked up the friendliness extended to her. It was good to be among these young people. Norma noticed Rosetta Kauffman and Susannah Reed visiting together. Rosie Weaver wasted no time in coming to meet the young people. "Now I should know you," she said, taking Norma's hand warmly between both of her own hands.

"I'm Norma Brenneman," Norma answered.

Rosie's mouth dropped open, and she lifted her hands in surprise. "Well, Norma, you are no longer a little girl! You have grown up.

We are so glad to have you here. Are you working in Petoskey like Rhoda?"

"Yes," Norma answered. "I'm working as a maid for an insurance salesman and his wife. It's a nice job."

"So where is little Erma by now?" Rosie asked.

Norma sobered. "Dad took her to Indiana. I haven't heard from her for about four years."

"Oh, Norma!" Rosie said sympathetically. "I'm so sorry. I will pray for her."

"Thank you," Norma said simply.

Back at the Smiths that week, Norma's thoughts returned again and again to the Sunday morning church service. How can Jesus be a close friend? How does God show people what to do?

It was two weeks until English services again. Eagerly Norma awaited the trip to Brutus. This time Clyde spoke on the plan of salvation. Norma listened intently. Suddenly the pieces started to fall together.

Rosie Weaver

Never before had anyone explained so clearly what Jesus had done, and why. Soberly Norma knelt to pray with the rest of the congregation.

After the service, Norma overheard two women who were talking. Then she heard a condescending voice: "John Brenneman's daughter...Petoskey...Alzina..." Her heart sank. The old, uncomfortable feeling settled over her. "Maybe God feels like that about me too," she thought. "Maybe I really don't and can't fit in here either."

Just then, Rosetta Kauffman laid a friendly hand on her arm. "Norma, I missed talking to you the last time. We are glad you came and hope you can come again. Would you like to come to our house for lunch? We are having a few other young people too."

"I would be glad to," Norma answered.

Clyde and Rosetta Kauffman

Clyde welcomed the young people warmly. Norma followed the girls to the kitchen, where Rosetta bustled about. "Can we help you?" the girls asked.

"Well, I believe you can. I'm not used to having so many helpers," Rosetta replied. "Here, someone can put the potatoes in this dish, and someone could pour the water."

Norma took the water pitcher and began filling the glasses. Hearing a burst of laughter, she glanced up to where the young men sat visiting. She met the twinkling brown eyes of Martin Reed. Blushing, she hurried to refill the pitcher. "Norma, what is wrong with you?" she asked herself severely.

As everyone gathered around the table and bowed their heads for prayer, Norma felt the same peaceful, secure feeling that she had known at Uncle Peter's and Grandpa Brenneman's homes. She gave a quiet sigh of contentment. "The homes I've been in lately didn't have this. Just exactly what makes the difference?"

Norma looked across the table and met Martin's smiling eyes again. She smiled politely and then concentrated on the food on her plate. After all, Martin was five years older than she was. He couldn't possibly be interested in her—not *Norma Brenneman*.

The day passed quickly. Clyde and Rosetta had no children of their own, but they took a keen interest in each of the young people. When they were ready to leave, Clyde admonished them to study the Scriptures. "If you don't have a Bible, please help yourself to one," he encouraged them. "There's a stack there by the door."

Norma looked longingly at the stack, but she wasn't sure she had the courage to take one. Rosetta caught that look and pressed one into Norma's arms as she left. "Start in the book of John," she suggested quietly.

"Thank you," Norma whispered.

Clyde's message on the plan of salvation and the godly atmosphere of their home were never far from Norma's thoughts as she worked at the Smiths that week.

I'LL SEE YOU IN THE MORNING

chapter twenty-two

He Leadeth Me

Petoskey, Michigan: 1936-1937

Norma ran her hand over the cover of the book. A Bible of her own! Uncle Peter had a German Bible, and then there was Dad's big family Bible in the chest. What a contrast of feelings those memories brought!

Slowly she opened the Bible in her hands to a list of the books of the Bible. Rosetta had said, "Read the book of John." Running her finger down over the list of books, she stopped. "There it is." Turning to the right page, she tucked one foot underneath herself and settled down to read. Slowly she read, wishing that Clyde Kauffman were here to explain it all. Suddenly she stopped at chapter 3, verse 16. "For God so loved the world, that he gave his only begotten Son, that whosoever believeth in him should not perish, but have everlasting life." Clyde had read that verse on Sunday. Why hadn't Uncle Peter or Grandpa Brenneman explained these things? A great longing welled up in Norma's heart. "O God, I want to know and understand."

Soon it was time to make breakfast for the Smiths. Quickly Norma tied an apron on and hurried to the kitchen.

Now Norma looked forward to weekends instead of dreading the lonely times. She enjoyed learning to know Rhoda as they traveled together. Rhoda was glad for every chance she could get to go to Brutus. She was courting Urias Kilmer.

Norma looked forward to Sunday school classes and Clyde's simple, direct messages. Her hungry heart drank it all in. Rosetta and Rosie Weaver took special interest in Norma, and she was often invited to one of their homes. Occasionally when the carload left for Brutus on Saturday, Norma would spend time with Mary Evelyn. Then there

Norma at 16

were times that she spent the night at Grandpa Brenneman's. Walter welcomed her eagerly, and Norma enjoyed the love and sense of belonging that only family can give.

One Saturday evening, Norma stood waiting for her ride to Brutus. When the carload arrived, she noticed that Rhoda's brother John wasn't in the back seat. Instead, Martin Reed got out and opened the door for her to get in. Did Rhoda have a mischievous twinkle in her eye? Norma brushed the thought away. Martin got in beside her, and they were on their way to Brutus. The boys in the front seat were laughing and talking. Rhoda was reading a letter.

"How was your week?" Martin asked.

"Oh, it was good. I have a real nice place to work," Norma answered. She found herself telling him about her job at the Smiths.

"I was in Petoskey to get a tractor part for my father and was glad for a way home today," Martin said. "This is a bad time of the year for the tractor to break down, but this time I think it was to my advantage."

Norma felt the color rise up in her face.

"I was wondering," Martin continued. "I heard that you'll be at Gregory's this weekend. Would you mind if I stop in tomorrow afternoon? Maybe we could walk back to the dam, or something like that?"

Norma's head was spinning. Martin Reed was asking for her friendship! She knew him mostly as Magdalena's big brother. She remembered him gently helping his little sister Anna up on the horse to take her to school. "Do I want this? Can I trust him? Doesn't he know I'm John Brenneman's daughter? Doesn't he know I'm not part of the Mennonite church?"

He was waiting for an answer.

"Why, yes. Yes, that would be fine," Norma answered.

"Well then, I'll look forward to that," Martin said.

Ever so carefully and slowly, Rhoda gave Norma a little nudge in the side. Slowly, Norma moved her foot and discreetly brought it down on Rhoda's toe.

Norma had a hard time concentrating on Clyde's message this Sunday morning. Rosie Weaver thought Norma looked extra happy when she shook her hand. Norma herself could not quite believe it was true—Martin Reed was coming to visit *her*.

After lunch with Rhoda and her family, Norma visited with them nervously. Rhoda's friend Urias was coming too. When the boys arrived, the two couples decided to walk to the dam together.

Conversation flowed easily, and Norma found herself relaxing and enjoying the beauty around her—the wildflowers along the road and the waterbirds attracted to the sanctuary at the dam site. Martin asked her about the various jobs she'd had. She described the busy life at Manasseh's, the fearful times at Mahlon's, and the pleasant but rather lonely times at the Smiths.

"I'm always glad for the weekends when I have a ride here to church," Norma said.

"How about if I come and see you Saturday evenings when you can't come here?" Martin asked.

Norma looked at him in surprise, and then she blushed. "Oh! Why, yes, I'd like that."

"This time I won't need a tractor part for an excuse to come," Martin added mischievously. They laughed together. "I'm sure Urias will let me borrow his car since I don't have one yet."

Urias and Rhoda had beat them back to the house. Norma smelled popcorn. "Just come on in for a bite to eat," Rhoda welcomed them both.

"Would you like to ride to church with us tonight?" Urias asked, looking at Martin. And so it was that when Martin and Norma rode into the churchyard together, the news was out.

Rosie Weaver smiled and said a prayer for the girl she had come to love. "I'm afraid there will be some disapproval," she said to herself. "Not everyone knows her like I do."

The next Saturday afternoon when Martin knocked at the Smiths' door, Bobby beat Norma to the door. When Norma arrived, Martin was squatted down, talking to Bobby. "Norma!" Bobby said turning to her. "'Ere's a man here, and I yike 'im."

"Shall we take a drive or a walk?" Martin asked, smiling at Norma.

"Oh, let's walk!" Norma responded. "We can walk down to the lake. If we walk far enough, there's a breakwater that we can walk out on."

"That's fine with me," Martin answered.

Lake Michigan held memories for both of them. Norma told her early memories of coming here with Mom and her siblings. Then she told him of Mom and Dad's separation and about the paper in the chest in the attic. "That's why I'm still here—because I chose to stay. I really didn't think Dad would take Raymond and Erma away from me. It is very hard."

"I'm sorry, Norma," Martin said sympathetically. "But I am glad you chose to stay," he added, smiling at her.

Marty at 22

Martin told her how they had gone to the lake as a family. Little Anna had collected pretty seashells, and when they got home, she put them in a little glass dog that had come filled with candy. Very soon after that, she had gotten very sick and died.

"I'm sorry, Martin. I always loved Anna. When Erma was taken away, it helped me to look out for Anna on the way to school. I was always used to taking care of someone."

Before they knew it, they were at the breakwater. It was a long stretch of rocks built out into the lake to make a shelter for the little boats to dock.

"Shall we walk out to the end?" Martin asked.

Marty and Norma during courtship

"I'd like to," Norma agreed.

The wind whipped color into their cheeks, and the seagulls screamed overhead. Norma breathed deeply of the fresh air. Martin soon discovered what a nimble-footed girl Norma was. She had no problem keeping up with him. They walked the rocks to the end of the break and back.

"Norma," Martin began slowly as they headed back the beach toward the Smiths, "I thought maybe I should let you know before you hear it elsewhere. My parents aren't real happy about our friendship." Norma's heart froze. "They don't really know you since you've left Peter Brubacher's, and they know you are not with our church. I knew that when I asked you, but I'm quite sure that their feelings will change with time. I wish I didn't have to say this, but I want you to be prepared for some talk. It doesn't change my feelings about you."

Norma looked at him with troubled eyes. "It's not really new for me to have people talking about me, but I don't want to be the cause of trouble between you and your parents. I've always admired your mother. Is there anything I can do to make a difference?"

"I'd say just be yourself," Martin answered. "Like I said, I think it will just take time."

"You know, I think I really do want to be part of your church sometime, but there's so much I don't know and understand yet. Uncle Peters lived their faith, but they didn't talk about it or explain it. I couldn't understand the German at church. Rosie Weaver is a big help to me, though," Norma said. "Clyde and Rosetta are real understanding too."

Just then a car pulled up beside them and slowed to a stop. Mary Evelyn leaned out the window of Elias's car. "So—what we heard about you is true! Congratulations!"

Norma blushed. "What brings you here to spy on good people?"

"We came in to the dance hall but stopped by the Smiths to say hi. Bobby told us, 'Dat ere man tookt you away.'" Everyone laughed.

"Bobby's quite a talker," Norma answered.

"Well, we best be going. Best wishes to you." Mary Evelyn waved goodbye.

"Did she ever try to get you to go with her dancing?" Martin wondered. "I know you two are good friends."

"I went with her one time in Brutus," Norma answered. "I didn't last long, and I decided never again."

"Just wait until I tell Magdalena that," Martin thought to himself. He didn't trouble Norma with the rumor that she and Mary Evelyn hitchhiked to Petoskey to dance with the sailors. Norma had never seemed like that kind of girl to him.

"There's Bobby watching for us," Martin said as they neared the Smiths. "I guess I should head back to Brutus. I'll look forward to seeing you next Sunday when you come for church. Maybe sometime we could drop in at my home a bit. I'd like them to learn to know you better."

"That sounds okay to me," Norma responded. But a shadow hung over her anticipation of the next weekend.

The next weekend, Martin and Norma, along with a number of other young people, ate Sunday lunch at Clyde Kauffman's home near Brutus. Clyde found a moment to assure Martin and Norma of his prayers as their friendship developed.

Norma's lonely heart soaked up the devoted attention Martin gave her. She soon realized that the kindness she had observed him giving to his little sister Anna years ago was a real part of his character.

After visiting awhile, Martin and Norma decided to take a walk through the little town of Brutus. The carload of young people would pick them up on their way back to Petoskey. Because it was Sunday, businesses were closed. The hitching rail in front of Evans's grocery store stood empty. Nellie Purple waved to them from the porch of the Purple Inn.

"Let's walk out to the artesian well and get a drink of water," Martin suggested.

"Sure," Norma agreed.

Turning south at the crossroad, they walked until they saw a stone well built up by the side of the road. The round well had a section several feet higher on the back with a pipe protruding from it. Clear, cold water poured out of the pipe and dropped down into the well below.

"You're first," Martin offered when they got to the well. Norma leaned over the edge of the well and drank deeply of the refreshing water. Then Martin had his turn. They stood talking by the well when John Kilmer's car drove up with the load headed to Brutus.

"It looks like it's going good," Rhoda teased when Norma climbed in.

"The weekend seemed too short." Norma said. She was learning to love the young man with the laughing eyes and boyish grin.

There were times, though, when old memories came back and doubts and fears troubled her. "How do I know that we could have a happy home together? I don't want a home like the one I grew up in. I

Artesian well at Brutus

don't ever want my children to be hurt like we were. Is Martin really as nice as he seems? He seems so very different from Dad. Could we have a home as happy as Uncle Peter and Aunt Sarah's? After all, I'm only sixteen—how do I know?"

"Please, God, don't let me ever have an unhappy home like Mom and Dad's," she prayed.

One Saturday when Martin drove to Petoskey to see Norma, he suggested that they drive back to Brutus and do some visiting at Woodland. Then he could bring her back to Petoskey Sunday afternoon. Norma was sure Grandpa would put her up for the night.

They had a pleasant but short visit with Uncle Peter's. Aunt Sarah told her Betsy and Christian had just had their second little girl. Norma noticed that Joshua was growing fast. She realized that Raymond must be growing fast too. But her mind kept going to the coming visit with Martin's family.

Next they drove across the road to Wilson Reed's. It felt strange to come to the Reeds as Martin's girlfriend. Knowing the family didn't really approve of their friendship made Norma nervous. Martin's older brother George was working in the yard with his little son Harold. As they drove in the driveway, a look of disapproval spread over George's face. Norma felt like turning around and running away.

As they got out of the car, little Harold piped up innocently, "This is my daddy's shovel!" The shovel handle reached far above his head, but he was trying hard to help his daddy. Norma and Martin smiled at him. Norma felt herself relaxing a bit. Susannah and the girls treated Norma pleasantly enough, but Norma could feel an undercurrent of tension. She felt relieved when she and Martin headed out the lane for Grandpa Brenneman's house.

Grandpa welcomed them warmly. It seemed very strange that Grandma did not come to welcome them too, but Grandma had passed away a year ago already. "May I stay the night if I make you breakfast?" Norma asked mischievously. "Certainly, certainly," Grandpa said, "breakfast or not."

When Martin left for home, Walter carried her bag upstairs to her room. "Well, as I heard, Martin was seeing you, but I was anxious to hear it from you. Are you happy? Is he good to you? You know I want the best for you. I don't want you to end up with an unhappy home like Mom and Dad."

"I know, Walter. I thought about all that a lot. Sometimes I've felt scared just thinking about it, but I've learned to pray about it. Martin is very kind and good to me. He makes me very happy. He's not like Dad at all. I know he could just be pretending, but I've seen him relate to his sisters. He really is kind, Walt."

"I sure hope so, Sis. You know I care about you a lot," he said rather awkwardly, rubbing his toe against the polished floor.

"I know you care. You've always looked out for us the best you could. Changing the subject, do you ever hear from Dad or Mom?"

"Not Dad. I think he stopped in here once when I was away. I hate to say this, but I'm pretty sure he's married again. He'd be ashamed to bring a second wife to Grandpa's, and with Mom in the area, I think he's staying in the south. I sure hope he pays some attention to Raymond and Erma, wherever he put them."

"Oh, Walter, what makes you think he remarried?" Norma asked in dismay.

"Well, you know people always talk. I was in the general store, and there were several men talking. They didn't see me. One of them was Owen Kilmer. You know he's a good friend of Dad's. Owen seemed to think Dad had remarried."

"Oh, Walter, will the hurts never end?" Norma wondered sadly. "What about Mom?"

"She's working here and there for people. I don't see her often."

"I haven't seen her in a long time, since I'm in Petoskey. How about Art?"

"He seems happy at Uncle Joe's," Walter answered. "Sometimes we get to work together in the fields, chopping wood or something like that. Well, I should let you get to bed. I wish you and your beau the best," he added with a playful grin.

"Thanks, Walt. Good night."

One Saturday, Martin and Urias showed up in Petoskey in a horse and sleigh. They picked up Rhoda and Norma, headed back to Brutus, and went on to the dam.

"Did you ever skate, Norma?" Rhoda asked.

"Just a little when I was with Mary Evelyn," Norma answered.

"Well, I brought skates for you, and now you will get a chance. The dam is a great place to skate. You wait till you see Martin skate!"

While the girls were still putting their skates on, the boys took off, chasing each other across the ice. Rhoda was right. Martin skated forward and backward and twisted and turned, trying to keep away from Urias.

Soon the boys were back. "Take it slow and easy until you get your ice feet," Martin suggested, offering Norma his arm for support. Slowly at first, and then soon with more confidence, Norma glided over the ice.

"You're doing pretty good," Martin said, smiling down at her.

"It's going better than the first time I tried snowshoes," Norma said laughingly. "Thank you for the help."

"My pleasure!" Martin replied. What fun they had! The air was crisp, and the sun made the snow sparkle on the trees.

Then back to the Gregorys in the sleigh they went to warm their toes and drink a hot drink before they left for Petoskey. Martin drove the sleigh on the way back. Wrapped in blankets and sitting next to him, Norma thought she had never been so happy in her life. How could it be that this young man wanted her—in spite of her past and no matter what others thought. For now, all the hurts of the past were put aside as she glanced at his wavy brown hair blowing in the wind and watched his skillful hands guiding the horses. Then she caught his eye on her and blushed.

"It was a very nice afternoon, Norma," he said.

"I enjoyed it too," she agreed.

As winter's chill gave way to budding trees and the breath of spring, their friendship deepened.

Norma was reading her Bible faithfully. Her relationship with God had deepened also. As she sat reading one day, her heart overflowed with thankfulness to God for peace and forgiveness. Suddenly a phrase jumped out at her: "Even as Christ forgave you, so also do ye." An uneasy feeling settled over her. "Forgive, of course. I want to forgive people. Who would I not forgive?" Then it hit her—Mom and Dad! All the hurts of her childhood washed over her. The arguing and fears, the separation and tears, abandonment and anger, loneliness. Mom basically ignoring them. Dad taking Raymond and Erma away. People talking. Even the Reeds' attitude toward the friendship she shared with Martin. It was all rooted in Mom and Dad's choices. "O God, how can I forgive them?"

"As Christ forgave you." The answer was before her in black and white.

Norma struggled for days. The hurts were still very real. Mom still ignored her. Dad had remarried. Never would their family be together as before. People still talked, and Raymond and Erma were still gone.

Martin noticed a soberness about her and hoped he hadn't done anything wrong. Rosie noticed too. She prayed.

On Sunday morning, Clyde got up and announced his text: "'Forgive, and ye shall be forgiven.' First of all we want to look at some misunderstandings about forgiveness. Forgiveness is not ignoring our hurts and just pretending they never happened. Forgiveness is facing our hurts and choosing with God's help to forgive. When you choose to forgive, it releases you from carrying those hurts with you all your life. Forgiveness is freedom! When we begin to understand how much Jesus forgave us, the more we understand that we need to forgive others."

As they knelt to pray, Norma whispered, "Yes, God." Peace flooded her heart. She wiped tears from her eyes as they rose from their knees. With deep feeling, she helped to sing, "Have Thine Own Way, Lord."

Martin noticed the light in her eyes and relaxed. Rosie thanked God.

One morning after church, Norma approached Rosetta. "I've been reading the Bible that you gave to me, Rosetta. I think I would like to have a head covering to wear at least for church.[3] Can you help me to get one?"

"Surely!" Rosetta responded. "I've been happy to see you growing in the Lord. Do you feel like you really understand why we wear a head covering?"

"Yes, I do," Norma answered. "Clyde explained it so well the other Sunday in church. That's what helped me to decide. I went home and read I Corinthians 11, where he had preached from."

Norma had told Martin what she was thinking. He smiled his approval when she showed up in church with a head covering. Rosie Weaver met her coming into church and shook her hand warmly. "God bless you, Norma."

Norma joined in the singing with a full heart. "He leadeth me, O blessed thought…" Deep in her heart, she knew she had the approval of those she admired most and of God above. What could be better?

---

[3] The church conference that Brutus was associated with encouraged head coverings for worship and prayer but didn't require them all the time.

chapter twenty-three

A Home to Call My Own

Petoskey, Michigan: 1937

Norma tucked a stray curl under her head covering and hurried to the door. "Here dey come!" Bobby announced from his post by the door. "Bye, Norma!"

"Bye, bye, Bobby," she answered, blowing him a kiss before she hurried out the door.

It was a glorious Sunday morning. Blue skies and fluffy clouds greeted Norma as she hurried out the walk. The red tulips lining the walk nodded their goodbyes as she slipped into the car beside Rhoda.

"Brutus, here we come!" Rhoda announced as the carload of young people headed north.

"It sounds like poor Brutus had quite a time this week," John said from his place at the steering wheel.

"Why do you say that?" Harvey asked from the back seat.

"Didn't you hear?" Levi wondered in surprise. "The Purple Inn caught fire, and they lost it all."

"Really!" Harvey exclaimed.

Norma turned to Rhoda. "I didn't hear that either. What happened?"

"Apparently," Levi was saying, "a fire started in the kitchen. No one knows why. When Nellie walked into the kitchen from serving people, the whole wall was on fire. Alanson, Pellston, and Petoskey fire departments came, but it was too late. The people are okay, but the inn was a total loss. Evans's store burned too, and Zach Frye almost lost his barn. The fire companies were kept busy trying to save the nearby buildings. The wind changed direction, or they would have probably lost the railway station."

When they reached Brutus, the car slowly turned left at the cross-road. Smoldering ruins lay on either side of the road. Rhoda commented, "A lot of people drove to Brutus for Nellie's good chicken. The inn will be missed."

Norma was thinking about what a welcome refuge the inn had been to her during her troubled days at Mahlon's.

When they pulled into the church parking lot, Norma's heart beat a little faster as she saw Martin standing among a group of young men, his hat cocked jauntily to one side of his head. He saw them coming and tipped his hat and grinned at her.

The afternoon found Martin and Norma walking along the road to the dam. The sun shone warmly, and wildflowers waved in the breeze. An oriole burst into song nearby. As they neared the dam, a wood duck fluttered up out of the water. Martin picked up a stone and sent it skipping across the water.

"You know, Norma, I've been busy hauling cedar fence posts, but that's coming to a close for now," Martin said. "I'm thinking the best work this summer is going to be in the south. I heard of a job that pays well picking cherries."

"When would you go, and how long would you be gone?" Norma asked in concern.

"Well, that depends on a lot of things," Martin began. "I really don't want to leave you, Norma. I thought maybe the best answer is to take you along as my wife. How does that sound to you?"

Norma's heart beat quickly. A feeling of panic seized her, but it was quickly swept away when she looked into his warm brown eyes.

"Oh, Martin, how? I mean, yes, I will go with you, but how can we work that all out?"

"All you have to do is say 'yes,' Norma. I'll take care of the rest," Martin said happily.

"Yes, Martin," she said, looking up at him, "but I have one request."

"Whatever you say, my dear," Martin responded.

"Well, I would like if we could go south and get my little sister Erma to come and live with us. Then I am content."

"I'll be happy to do that, Norma. I know how hard it is for you. It might need to wait a few months until I go south for a load of fence posts again."

"Thank you, Martin. Oh, thank you," Norma responded. "Now let's talk about us."

"Well," Martin said mischievously, "now that you have said 'yes,' I'll have to tell you that we will have to live in a tent for a good part of the summer when we go south."

"I'll live anywhere with you, Martin," Norma responded, her face radiant.

And so the plans were made. Martin would talk to George Weaver, a preacher in Petoskey, to see if he would marry them, because Norma was not formally a church member and the policy was to have only members' weddings at the church.

"Let's ask Urias and Rhoda to be our witnesses," Norma suggested. "I'll have to give the Smiths notice that I am leaving." Then her face clouded. "What will your family say, Martin?"

"Don't worry, Norma," Martin assured her. "They are coming to appreciate you like I thought they would. I'll talk to them."

When Martin arrived in Petoskey the next weekend, he told Norma, "I talked to George Weaver, and it suits him for July 3. Urias said he and Rhoda will be our witnesses. That's only several weeks away. Is that enough time for the Smiths to get a replacement for you?"

"Oh, yes," Norma answered. "I talked to Mrs. Smith. She said she's very happy for us. Bobby's not happy, though." She laughed.

"Norma, I have very good news for you," Martin said. "I told my parents our plans. Mother would like to serve a wedding meal for us at my home and invite Walter and Arthur too."

"Oh, Martin, I'm so glad. That is so nice of them," Norma exclaimed.

"And guess what else," Martin added. "Father said we can borrow his Ford if we want to take a wedding trip. He also offered us the little apartment at their house until we go south. We'll find something else when we come back."

"Really! Oh, I'm so happy. Where would we go on a trip?"

"I thought it would be nice to go to Sault St. Marie if that suits you," Martin suggested. "It would be a nice trip, and I'd like to show you the ship locks."

"I've never gone on any trip like that!" Norma said. "I think the only trip I remember is when Dad brought us to Brutus. That wasn't a very nice trip, but this sounds wonderful!"

Norma's seventeenth birthday came, and with it thoughts of Erma. Erma would be eleven. What did she look like now? A number of years earlier, Uncle Joe had traveled to Indiana. When he came back, he had showed her a picture of relatives at a reunion. There among the children was Erma! Norma had gazed longingly at the little girl peeking from the back row. That had been several years ago.

This time, with thoughts of Erma came a sudden joyous thought. Erma was coming! "I said I would get her sometime," Norma remembered. Now Martin was making that possible. She hugged the thought to herself. How she loved Martin for understanding!

July 3 came. Norma stood in front of the mirror. She adjusted her royal blue dress and tucked a stray hair into place. Picking up her bags, she took one last look around her cozy little bedroom at the Smiths. Then she went out and shut the door.

Bobby met her by the front door. "Oh, Norma, I'm gonna mith you. Thath a pretty dreth."

Norma bent to hug him and then hurried to the door. Martin was here. Love and admiration shone from his face. "I like your dress," Martin said. As he reached for her bags, he said with a twinkle in his eye, "It looks like you didn't change your mind."

"Oh, no," she answered happily. They stopped to pick up Urias and Rhoda and then drove across Petoskey to George Weaver's home.

Pastor Weaver spoke briefly and then pronounced them husband and wife. "As long as you both shall live." Norma looked at Martin. "Yes, I will love him all my life," she agreed. This was a promise to God. Side by side they would face the future. No more lonely days wondering just where she belonged. Norma had found her place. They dropped off Urias and Rhoda, and Martin joyfully took his little wife home.

The next evening, the kitchen table in the Reeds' house was stretched out and laden down with good food. Mashed potatoes and fried chicken—Martin's mother, Susannah, had done her best. Martin and Norma took their place together at the table. Walter and Arthur arrived scrubbed and dressed in their best.

The Reeds gathered around the table too. They were all there, even Emma and her husband William with little Alvin and a new baby, Eunice. George lifted Harold onto a stool and sat down beside his wife, Elizabeth, who held baby Anna Mary on her lap. Daniel, Magdalena, Aaron, and little Irvin gathered around. Susannah sat down beside Wilson with one-year-old Esther on her lap. Norma looked around. "I actually belong in this circle," she thought.

Everyone bowed their heads in prayer. Then happy chatter broke out. After a time, Magdalena rose and refilled dishes. Then it was time for dessert. Susannah handed baby Esther to Wilson and then carried lemon meringue pies to the table. She handed the first one to Martin.

He looked at Norma with a twinkle in his eye. "Let's see, I think you don't care for this kind, do you?"

Norma looked at him in surprise. "Did you know this is my favorite kind?"

He laughed. "Mother found out from your Aunt Sarah, and she insisted we have this kind."

Norma looked quickly at Susannah. Susannah was smiling at her. "Why, thank you!" Norma exclaimed.

Just then she heard the children talking. "She's part of our fami-

Marty and Norma on their wedding day

ly now!" Irvin said to Harold. Noticing her emotion, Martin reached under the table and squeezed her hand. She smiled back at him tremulously.

Little Esther toddled around the table and stopped by Norma's chair. She reached up her arms. Norma drew the little girl onto her lap and hugged her to herself.

After the meal, she joined Magdalena and Susannah doing dishes. The men sat around the table talking. "So, Martin, where is this cherry picking job that you heard about?" George questioned.

"It's just a little north of Saginaw, close to the bay. The name of the town is Kawkawlin," Martin answered. "I'm hoping we can pick up another job on the side. There's a place nearby called Ken's Cabins. They'll give us a place to set up our tent."

"Are you getting one of those big tents that Mose Martin rents out?" George asked.

"Yes, I looked at them. I think he got them from a girls' camp, and they're nice and roomy," Martin replied.

"Sounds like you are in for an interesting summer," Magdalena said to Norma.

"I'm looking forward to it," Norma said. "It will keep me busy cooking with a makeshift setup. I'm used to cooking, but not in a tent."

"I'll send some canned meat and vegetables with you if you'd like," Susannah offered.

"That would be really nice of you," Norma answered.

Several days later, Martin and Norma chugged out the lane in Wilson's '32 Ford and headed north. "That's the road west for the Beaver Island Ferry," Martin pointed out. He was enjoying himself showing Norma many things she had never seen before.

At the Straits of Mackinac, they took the one-hour ferry ride across. It was Norma's first boat ride. "See, over there is Mackinac Island." Martin pointed from the ferry railing. "Sometime I'd like to take you there."

The drive north on the upper peninsula to the Soo Locks was beautiful. Watching the huge lake freighters move through the locks held a fascination of its own. At last the happy couple headed for home. They stood on the ferry looking out over the water when Norma asked, "Do you have any idea when we can go for Erma? I was thinking it would be nice if she could start school here this fall."

"I think that should work out," Martin answered. "The cherry picking will last from the end of July into August. We should be able to come back up north for a load of fence posts and go bring her back before school."

"Do you have an idea where we are going to live?"

"Well, I thought I'd check for a place to rent in Pellston. Almost anything will be better than a tent," he teased.

"Actually, I think it's going to be kind of fun to live in a tent this summer," Norma answered.

"I knew I picked a plucky little wife," Martin said, smiling at her.

Several weeks later found them settled into their makeshift tent home. They picked cherries and cooked over an open fire. When Norma closed her eyes at night after day after day of picking cherries, she

Marty picking cherries

Marty in their tent home

Marty doing laundry for the campground

saw buckets of round, red cherries. But she and Martin were young and healthy, and this was paying work. Work was scarce and the pay was none too high.

One day Martin popped into the tent where Norma was washing their dishes. "Guess what, Norma? The owner here at the campground needs someone to clean cabins and wash the bedding. Do you think we could take that on too? It pays fairly well, and we could work at it together."

Norma was not afraid of work. "Sure, it sounds good to me," she responded. And so there was little time to spare, but when the job was done and they headed north, Martin felt good about the cash in his pocket. These were Great Depression times. Jobs in 1937 were hard to come by. Martin's father, Wilson, had lost one of his two farms. Before coming to Brutus, Norma had felt the realities of the Great Depression more than Martin had. There were not a lot of handouts for a young couple starting a household. But Martin still had his truck, and soon they would go for a load of fence posts.

First they went house hunting in Pellston. "Someone told me the Hamners have a little house they might rent out," Martin suggested. "Let's check there first."

Mr. Hamner showed them to a little red tarpaper shack. When they stepped inside, Norma was pleased to see the hardwood floors in the living-dining area. An old cookstove took a good share of the tiny kitchen in the back of the house. Two bedrooms and a small lean-to completed the house.

"What do you think, Norma?" Martin asked. "It's just a tarpaper shack, but it's better than a tent."

"I'm satisfied," Norma answered. "It's not the first time I lived in a tarpaper shack. The other one wasn't as nice as this, and this one will be a happy home. And look, Marty, this smaller bedroom can be for Erma!"

And so it was decided. They moved their meager possessions into the little red tarpaper house. Norma looked around with satisfaction.

The cream and sugar bowl from Mom and Dad's house sat on a little shelf in the kitchen. Beside it were salt and paper shakers from Bessie. Gifts from many other friends were scattered about the house—gifts from Aunt Sarah, Martin's family, Clyde Kauffman's, Rosie Weaver, Elsie Gregory, Manasseh Kulp's, and many others. "Oh, Martin, I'm so happy," Norma sighed. "At last I have a home to call my own."

Loading fence posts. Marty (22) on top of load.

chapter twenty-four

Together at Last

Brutus, Michigan: 1937

Norma straightened the curtain and smoothed the blanket on the bed. She looked around at the little bedroom. Would Erma like it here? How much did she remember of Brutus? She had only been six years old when Dad had taken her away. Almost half of her life she had lived in Indiana. Would she have trouble adjusting when she moved back?

With some difficulty, Uncle Joe had gotten the address of the Mitchelens where Erma stayed. Norma had sent off a letter letting them know when she expected to arrive and asking them to let her take Erma. A return letter assured them that, yes, Erma remembered her sister. The Mitchelens gave their consent for the move.

"I said I would get her back someday," Norma whispered. "Oh, I can hardly wait."

Martin had gone north to get a load of fence posts. Norma chose to stay home and get everything ready for Erma's arrival. When Martin arrived with the loaded truck, she was ready.

"It looks like you split wood for the cookstove while I was gone," Martin commented.

"I had to have something to do to make the time go faster." Norma smiled, then she laughed. "Mrs. Hamner didn't like it, though."

"What do you mean?"

"Oh, she apparently didn't think I should be splitting wood. She said, 'What are you doing? If my husband didn't keep wood split, I'd put his kettle of potatoes outside the door!' I just laughed and told her my husband would split wood, but I needed something to do. She frowned and shook her head and went inside."

Martin laughed too. "She doesn't know what kind of a busy little wife I have. Are you ready to go?"

"Yes, I sure am, but Marty, I'm both excited and a little scared. What if Erma doesn't really want to come? We don't know how good she had it at Mitchelens."

"Don't worry, Norma. I think she's going to be mighty glad to see her big sister. She will have only good memories of Brutus," Martin reassured her.

Nevertheless, by the end of five hours of driving, Norma felt as if her stomach was tied into a knot. When Martin suggested they stop and get something to eat, she just shook her head. "I'd rather pick up Erma first," she explained.

With the fence posts unloaded, they hunted up the address Uncle Joe had given them. Stepping out of the truck in front of a modest little house, Norma suddenly heard the front door bang open. A small figure flew across the yard and threw herself into Norma's arms. "Norma, you came!" Erma said with a sob in her voice. Laughing and crying, both girls clung to each other. Martin turned away, blew his nose, and wiped his eyes.

"Oh, Norma, it's been so—long," Erma said, giving Norma an extra squeeze.

"I know," Norma agreed. "You have grown!" she exclaimed, drawing back to take a good look at Erma.

"Well, you have grown too," Erma giggled through her tears.

"I guess I was only a little older than you are now, the last time you saw me," Norma agreed. "Did the Mitchelens tell you that I got married? Remember the Reeds that lived across the road from Uncle Peter's? Well, this is Martin Reed, and we got married in July."

Erma smiled shyly at Martin. "I think I remember the Reeds a little bit. Didn't you walk to school with them?"

"Yes," Norma answered. "There were Magdalena, Daniel, Anna, and Aaron. Martin is their older brother. Come now, let's go meet the Mitchelens. I see they are coming to meet us."

George and Opal Mitchelen welcomed Martin and Norma warmly. "Well, I must say," Opal said with her one arm still around Norma's shoulder, "no one can deny that you two girls are sisters!"

George was asking Martin about the trip and his fence post job.

"Come on inside," Opal welcomed them. "The men will come when they are ready." As they entered the cozy kitchen, she added, "Will you stay for lunch?"

"Thank you!" Norma answered. "But we'd like to get home by evening, and we have about a five-hour drive."

"Well then, let me at least send some plums and cookies along with you. Erma, if you go out and get plums and put them in a bag, I'll get the cookies," Opal suggested. Erma let go of Norma's hand and hurried willingly out the door.

"Opal," Norma began, "I want to thank you for taking care of my little sister. I can see she was well taken care of. I hope you understand why we wanted to come and get her."

"Now, never you worry about that!" Opal responded. "I well remember Erma's tears when she came here." She paused to gain control of her emotions. "I heard your name a lot. She's been reasonably happy, but there's no doubt that she lived for this day."

"Do you—do you know where Raymond is and how he's doing?"

"Yes," Opal answered. "He's with Walter Pletcher's—another cousin. He seems to be happy. Your dad gives him more attention than he probably gives to the rest of you."

"I wish we could take him too," Norma sighed. "I'm glad to know he's happy. Thank you again, Opal."

Erma's bags were packed and sitting by the front door. "Well, good-bye, Erma," Opal said, gathering Erma into her arms. A tear rolled down Erma's cheek. "Write to me, Erma, and be a good girl," Opal said, smiling through her tears.

"I will," Erma promised.

Erma followed Norma out the door. "Oh, Norma, I'm so excited! Are we going to ride in the truck?"

"Yes. Is that okay?"

"Sure, that will be fun." Erma took a little skip in spite of the bags she was carrying.

George Mitchelen gave Erma a little pat on the back. "Now you be good," he said with a little catch in his voice.

Martin, Norma, and Erma climbed into the truck, and with a wave they were off. The five-hour drive seemed a lot shorter on the way home as the girls chattered away, catching up on the last five years.

"Where are we going now? I mean, where do you live?" Erma wondered as they neared Brutus.

"Actually, we have a little house in Pellston," Norma answered. "We need to go past Brutus to get there."

It was dark by the time they arrived at the little house in Pellston. Erma was more sleepy than hungry, so Norma saw her to her room and made sure she was settled for the night. Bending over to give her little sister a hug, Norma said, "Good night, Erma. I'm *so* glad you are here!"

"Good night, Norma," Erma whispered sleepily.

Stepping out and closing the door, Norma took a seat beside Martin at the table. "Oh, Marty, I don't know if I can begin to explain to you how much it means to me to be able to take care of Erma once more. Thank you again."

Marty took her hand in his. "After today, I think I understand better. I'm glad she's here too."

Norma's days were busier now with Erma there. Together they baked and cooked and tended the little garden Norma had planted. Erma laughed over Norma's story of pulling up Aunt Sarah's carrots. "I really didn't know much about country life, but it looks like Opal must have taught you to garden," Norma observed.

"Yes, Opal was good to me and taught me a lot," Erma answered. "But I really missed you. I felt alone with strangers. Once in a while I saw Raymond, but that made me miss you more. How far away is Aunt Sarah? I'd like to see her again sometime, and Arthur and Walter. And Norma, what about Mom—is she really living near here?"

"You might like to know that Walter and Arthur are coming for Sunday dinner," Norma answered. "I want to take you to visit Aunt Sarah sometime too. If we go in the car, it doesn't take long to get there, but it's too far to walk. Sometime when we stop in at Marty's parents, you and I will go across the road and visit her. Grandpa Brenneman would like to see you too. He was glad to hear that you were coming."

"I hardly remember him," Erma said, "but didn't he give us pink peppermint candies?"

"That's right, he did," Norma agreed.

"But Norma, what about Mom? Do you ever see her? Whatever did happen to our family? I was too little to understand, but now I have lots of questions. I've heard people say it was Mom's fault because she was unfaithful to Dad. I wonder about a lot of things. Do we have another grandma besides the Grandma Brenneman that isn't living anymore?"

"I don't really know about our other grandma. If she's living, she's in Canada, I think," Norma answered. "As far as our family, it's not a nice story. I'm not surprised that you heard that it was all Mom's fault since you were living with Dad's relatives. It seems like Dad planned the separation to make it look like Mom left him. His family thought that for a long time. I think Mom and Dad were both at fault. But Erma, you deserve to know. Let's go sit in the shade while we talk."

And so, for Erma's sake, Norma relived the days of trouble before Uncle Peter's, the separation, the tear-filled days when Dad left them at Uncle Peter's, and then the anguish when he took Erma and Raymond away. "I think Uncle Peter's family all took their turns crying over that," Norma added. "We missed you so much!"

Erma listened wide-eyed, with tears occasionally spilling down over her cheeks. "But Norma! Why? Why did Dad take us away? It seems so mean!" Erma exclaimed.

"Some things we'll just never understand, Erma," Norma answered. "I was told that when Dad found out Mom was in the area, he was afraid Mom would try to get us."

"But Norma, you said she didn't! She doesn't even pay much attention to you. I could have lived here all this time, and Raymond could be here too. He just loved Uncle Peter! He told me so when we saw each other sometimes. Oh, Norma, it makes me so mad!"

Wiping tears, Norma pulled Erma close to herself. "I understand, Erma. I felt that way too sometimes, but it doesn't help at all. I ask God to help me to forgive Mom and Dad. It's not easy, but it sure makes you feel better to forgive than to be angry. Just telling you all this brings back my feelings of anger too, but God can help me to forgive again.

"Come, Erma," she said, catching her by the hand and pulling her to her feet. "We better make supper. Marty will be home soon. Tomorrow we want to take you to enroll in school. It's about school time, you know."

When Sunday came, it was with a deep sense of satisfaction that Norma walked into church with Erma at her side. "Norma, I kind of remember this. Didn't we come here with Dad?" Erma whispered.

"Yes," Norma whispered back. "And here comes Rosie, as usual."

Rosie met the girls warmly. "Erma, I'm so glad that you are here! What a big girl you are now." Erma smiled at her shyly.

With a contented heart, Norma sat beside Erma and shared a songbook. Now there would be no more wondering where Erma was and how she was doing. As their voices rose together in song, Norma reached out and squeezed Erma's hand. Erma smiled at her and squeezed her hand back.

Now that Norma had a home of her own and Erma was there too, Walter and Arthur both made occasions to drop in. Sometimes they came for supper and sometimes just to visit or play dominoes.

One day there was a knock at the door. When Norma opened it, there stood Mom, smiling at her. "Well! Hello, Mom. How are you? Would you like to come in?"

"Sure," Mom replied. "I have a job here in Pellston, and I thought I'd drop in and see you."

"Can I make you a cup of tea?"

"That would be nice," Mom said with a smile.

As they sat at the table drinking tea, Norma thought it felt a little strange and awkward to sit and visit with Mom in her own home and on an adult level. They talked about Mom's job, and Norma told her about their cherry picking job. Then Norma hesitated a bit. "Did you know that Erma came to live with us? She's in school right now."

"No, I didn't," Mom answered, "but I'm glad that you girls can be together again."

Mom's visit was short. Once again, Norma's feelings were a bit mixed up. Mom seemed so impersonal. She made no mention of wanting to see Erma. "But she came to visit, so she must care some," Norma concluded.

After that, Mom took to dropping in now and then. To Erma, she was basically a stranger. Mom didn't seem like a mother to the girls, but rather like a friendly neighbor. Yet underneath there was the binding knowledge that this *was* their mother.

The Great Depression continued. Martin had no work. To Mrs. Hamner's approval, he kept the wood chopped and split for the cookstove. Norma was pleased when he spent time helping his father about the farm and came home with potatoes or meat on butchering day.

Norma went along to help Susannah sometimes. Susannah always had plenty to do, even in the winter. Magdalena was out of school now, but there were growing boys to cook for, and her own toddlers and grandchildren were underfoot. Often Norma went home with a jar of preserves or a bottle of cream.

Martin helped cut ice blocks from the dam for the icebox. Sometimes the boys went ice fishing, dropping their lines through holes they cut in the ice. They pulled a little shanty out on the ice for weather protection. How everyone enjoyed the fresh fried fish in winter!

Occasionally Norma and Erma slipped across the road to visit with Aunt Sarah in her friendly kitchen. She welcomed them warmly. Aunt Sarah was missing Mandy's cheerful presence. Mandy had just gotten married to Aaron Shirk and had moved to Pennsylvania. Uncle Peter's had hoped to keep their children in Michigan to support the dwindling German-speaking Old Order church.

Martin and Norma traveled from Pellston to the English church at Brutus as often as possible. When baptismal services were held in the fall, Norma was among the class. Clyde and Rosetta breathed a prayer of thanksgiving, and Rosie Weaver's eyes misted over as Norma said her vows.

Norma's heart overflowed. "A home of my own and a church where I belong! What more could I wish for?"

chapter twenty-five

Not My Baby!

Brutus, Michigan: 1938-1939

Norma looked dreamily out the window at the budding trees. Spring was here at last! Carefully she folded the stack of soft, white diapers and neatly arranged them in the drawer next to a pile of tiny clothes. It wouldn't be long now until she and Marty would hold their firstborn in their arms. Marty was excited too. He watched over her safety and well-being with great tenderness. Susannah had supplied her with scraps of fabric and feed sacking, which she had happily sewed into little garments and diapers. She was interrupted in her dreaming by Marty slamming the back door.

"I have good news for you!" he announced. "You know my brother George has been wanting to try his hand at farming? Well, Father and

Mother have rented a house here in Pellston not real far from us so George's can farm for a while."

"Oh, Marty, that will be so nice to have Mother and Father nearby, especially right now!" Norma responded. "Erma can help me some when she's not in school, but it might be nice to have the help of someone more mature, like Magdalena, right at first."

"Another thing I like about it," Martin added, "is that if I'm off on the truck hauling fence posts or if we go south in the fall to help harvest sugar beets, you will have someone nearby."

"When are they moving?"

"Before too long," Martin answered. "Mother has been packing, and it's not like they have to move everything, since it's family."

"I'm so glad!" Norma said. "Are you really going to go south this fall to haul sugar beets?"

"It looks that way. Father would like to get several men to go with us. He wondered about Arthur going along to help shovel beets."

"Oh, I think Art would be glad to do that," Norma responded.

Wilson's were in the process of moving when, late in April, little Bobby made his appearance. Martin and Norma named him Robert Roy, but "Bobby" he was for now. Round-faced and sturdy, with a head of dark, curly hair, he reminded Norma a bit of the little Bobby at the Smiths, but this Bobby was theirs to keep.

Bobby knew how to let his needs be known! Norma was glad for the experience she had working for Manasseh's when they had a baby. She loved to watch Marty cuddle his little son. As she sat and rocked Bobby, new feelings of mother love and protection welled up within her. She would never allow this baby to know the heartache and pain that she herself had known. She held him closely to herself and wondered in a new way how Mom and Dad could possibly have deserted their family.

Erma, of course, loved playing little mother. Reluctantly she allowed Walter and Arthur a turn to hold Bobby when they stopped by. For the Brennemans, Bobby added a new and happy dimension to their lives.

Norma felt even more a part of the Reed family when the Reeds came to see Bobby, enthuse over him, and welcome him into the family.

For the first time, Norma found herself wishing that Mom would stop by. She wanted to show Mom her baby. It didn't take Mom long to come. Holding Bobby in one arm, Norma met her at the door. "Come in, Mom. I'm so glad you came."

"Norma, what a nice baby you have!" Mom said, reaching for Bobby and settling into the rocking chair. Norma tried to sort out her own feelings as Mom crooned to Bobby. Was Mom remembering happier days and babies of her own? She was taking obvious delight in her new role as a grandma.

"You know," Mom said unexpectedly, "it doesn't seem so long ago that I was showing my mom my first baby. Walter was a dark-haired baby too, but he didn't have the curls Bobby has."

Norma seized the opportunity. "Do you ever hear from your mother? Grandma Ruffert is in Alberta, isn't she?"

"Yes, she's in Mayton, Alberta, but we haven't kept contact," Mom answered.

"Grandpa Ruffert's name is Henry, isn't it?" Norma probed.

"Yes, he died the year before you were born. My mom's name is Frances, like your middle name, but she's called Franny. She was happy that I used her middle name for yours. Erma is named after my sister. I don't know if my sister ever found that out because we were back in Michigan by that time. Your baby's middle name is Roy. Did you know I had a brother Roy?" Mom asked.

"No, I didn't know that," Norma answered. "We just liked the name."

"Well, my brother Roy was quite the Roy," Mom said, laughing to herself. "One day he was supposed to rock the baby's cradle. He didn't want to sit upstairs and rock it, so he just tied a piece of rope to the cradle and dropped it through a knothole in the floor. Then he sat downstairs with the rest of us and pulled the rope to rock it."

Mom laughed again, and Norma joined her. It was unusual for Mom to reminisce.

Bobby began to cry. Mom stood up and handed him to Norma. "Well, I best be going," she said. "I suppose he's hungry. Take care of that nice baby."

Marty, Norma, and Bobby   Marty and Bobby

Fall came, and the men made plans to go south to Saginaw to haul sugar beets. They were taking several trucks and a few other men to help. It would be a fairly well-paying job at a time when jobs were scarce. Art was glad to go along. The men took one of Mose Martin's big tents because they weren't sure about lodging.

The several weeks they were gone seemed long to Norma. Marty had never gone away like this before. Six-month-old Bobby was a good source of entertainment. Erma was home from school in the evenings, and Susannah dropped in regularly to check on her. Together they wondered how the men were faring.

Then the men were back with stories to tell. Everyone gathered at Wilson's to talk. "We tried living in the tent, but that wasn't the most comfortable after a hard day's work," Marty related, scratching his head.

"We found a cabin the second night, and that was pretty good," Wilson added. "When we came back the following night and those cabins were full, we stopped at the edge of town by a park and tried to decide what to do." He paused, scratching his head. "Then someone saw a sign that said twenty-five cents a bed. We thought that sounded better than sleeping in a tent or the truck." He looked at Marty and laughed.

Marty took up the story. "Well, several of us went in to look at the room. Father went up to the bed and lifted the sheet. You should have seen—bedbugs ran everywhere!"

"Oh, no!" Susannah exclaimed.

"Well, we got out of there and slept in our truck," Marty continued. "The next day, we found a room by the railroad tracks. It was ten cents a day with meals. It was pretty nice and comfortable, but Art, you should tell them about our first night there."

Art scratched his head and grinned. He loved to tell a story. "Well," he began, "we got all settled down to bed, so glad we didn't have to sleep in the truck again. We were all sound asleep when the flier came through. We were right by the tracks, you know. Did that thing ever raise us up out of our beds! We didn't know what was going on! I think Marty must have jumped a foot!"

"Now, Art!" Marty chided. "You are just supposed to tell *true* stories. Anyway," he added, laughing, "we got used to it and eventually slept right through when the train went by."

"What I'd like to know," Magdalena spoke up, "is why do you all keep scratching your heads?"

The men looked at each other. "You know," Marty began, "that one fellow that was helping us had head lice. Do you think we—"

"Oh, no!" Susannah exclaimed again.

"Stay away from me." Magdalena backed up against the kitchen wall. Norma reached out to take Bobby out of Marty's arms.

Then Susannah took over. When she was done, all the men had fresh haircuts. Their scalps looked pink, and the smell of kerosene hung in the air. Even Bobby had his head examined thoroughly.

In spite of the difficulties they had had, Martin was very happy to go and pay their bill for flour and sugar at the grocery store. The job had paid well.

One day in December, Walter stopped by. He reached for Bobby and tossed him into the air. Bobby giggled happily. "Sis," Walter began, "I thought you might like to know that Dad's in the area. He's by himself," he said, reading her thoughts. "I don't think he'd bring another woman here. Anyway, I wanted to let you know so you're not too surprised if he stops in to see his grandson."

Sure enough, on Sunday afternoon, someone knocked at the door. Marty and Norma went together to answer it. Here was Dad, his hair thinner and now gray at the temples, but still Dad.

"Hello, Dad," Norma greeted him.

"Just come on in," said Marty.

"Thank you," Dad responded a little stiffly. "I was in the area and thought I'd stop by to see you. I heard you were married, and now your grandpa told me you have a little fellow."

"Yes, he's sleeping, but I'll get him," Norma offered. "He's about ready to wake up anyway."

"Have a seat," Marty said, motioning to the rocking chair.

"Thank you, I believe I will," Dad said, settling into it.

Norma took a moment in the bedroom to get on top of her mixed-up feelings. Then, breathing a prayer, she gathered the sleeping baby into her arms. Bobby sighed and snuggled up against her. She went back into the kitchen where Marty and Dad sat visiting.

"He's a fine little fellow," Dad said when he saw Bobby.

"Would you like to hold him?" Norma asked. "He's not shy."

"I'd be much obliged." Dad said.

Norma put Bobby in Dad's arms. She couldn't help but think about the fact that Mom had sat in the same chair holding Bobby not very long ago.

Dad looked down into Bobby's sleeping face. Bobby stirred and then opened his eyes. He stared wide-eyed at Dad and broke into a smile.

"Well, well," Dad chuckled. "You have a smile for Grandpa, do you?" Then Dad quickly wiped his eyes. Did Dad actually have tears? Norma couldn't be quite sure.

Norma knew that Erma would soon be home from playing over at Wilson's. Surely Grandpa would have told Dad by now that she was here. How did Dad feel about that? Just then she saw Erma coming. Excusing herself, she stepped outside to meet her.

"Erma, I just wanted to let you know before you come in. We have company. It's our dad. Remember, I told you he was around."

"Yes," Erma answered slowly. "I'm kind of scared, Norma. I hardly know him. Does he care that I'm here? Will he want to take me away again?"

"Don't worry, Erma, he will not take you away," Norma said, trying to still the misgivings of her own heart. "Just come in and say hi. Marty understands. He'll do most of the talking."

Hesitantly, Erma followed Norma into the kitchen. Marty was saying, "It looks like Erma's home. I guess you heard she's living with us now?"

"Yes, I did," Dad answered. "Hello, Erma."

"Hi, Dad," Erma answered, pulling a chair into the circle and perching on the edge of it.

"I'm sure you have a good time with this baby here," Dad said, smiling at her.

"Oh, yes, I do!" Erma said brightening.

"You're getting big enough to be a helper to Norma too, I guess."

"She sure is," Norma agreed. "Will you stay for supper, Dad?"

"Thank you, but your grandpa is expecting me back soon. I really appreciate your offer, though."

"I have an idea, Norma," Marty suggested. "Why don't you get your Brownie camera that you are so happy with and take a picture of Dad and Bobby before he leaves?"

"Sure," Norma said. "If Dad doesn't mind."

"I'd be much obliged." Dad said.

"I didn't guess how much she would enjoy taking pictures when I got her that Brownie," Marty said to Dad as Norma went to get the camera.

Dad seemed very pleased to pose with Bobby. Then Marty took a picture of Norma and Bobby.

Dad and Bobby

Norma and Bobby

"Take care," Dad said as he got into his car and left. Norma breathed a sigh of relief.

"He certainly was pleasant enough," Marty commented.

"But I was scared," Erma said. "I'm so glad he didn't take me away again."

"Don't worry," Marty teased. "You're stuck with us now."

"I'm glad," Erma returned quickly.

One day, Erma sat on the floor playing with Bobby. Norma was busy ironing. "You know, Norma," Erma said, "I wish we had a grandma that we could visit. The other girls at school talk about going to their grandma's house."

"I'm sorry that you don't remember Grandma Brenneman," Norma replied. "Why don't we each write a letter to our Grandma Ruffert in Alberta and see if she will answer."

"I'd like that," Erma said enthusiastically. "You should send her a picture of Bobby."

"That's a good idea," Norma replied.

And so letters were sent off to Alberta in hopes that they would actually reach the only grandma that the girls had. Would it reach her, and would she write back? "We'll just send it to Mayton, Alberta, and hope for the best," Norma said.

It was a warm, rainy day in April when Martin came home and announced, "The smelt are running. Father, George, Daniel, and I want to go fishing. Mother thought maybe you'd like to help clean and can some at their house. Father wants to smoke some too."

"Sure," Norma agreed. "Erma, I'll need you to babysit Bobby. It's a big job cleaning smelt."

"I don't know if I ever had smelt," Erma said. "Is it a kind of fish?"

"Yes," Martin answered. "They come up the rivers in the spring after a warm rain, and we wade in hip boots and catch them in nets. They're just little fish, but they are good!"

The men had fun netting the fish. Then everyone gathered at Wilson's for the tedious job of cleaning the small fish. Susannah fried smelt for supper. Even though an amazing amount disappeared at suppertime, there were still plenty to can and smoke.

As Norma helped Susannah pack fish into jars for canning, Susannah said, "This will be real handy to take along to Saginaw. It sounds like you and I get to go along and cook for the men when they haul sugar beets."

"Yes," Norma replied. "Bobby's over a year old now. I think it sounds interesting as long as there are no bedbugs or lice."

Susannah laughed. "Father wants to go early enough to locate a nice cabin for us to share. He will make sure no one has lice. That man who had lice last year isn't invited again. I think Levi Martin and the Eby boys are going along to help. It sounds like we'll be busy cooking with that many men."

Before the Reed caravan of trucks and a car headed south, a neighbor walked up. "News from across the ocean," he said. "Germany has attacked Poland, and I just got word that Britain and France have declared war on Germany." World War II had begun. As the men headed south, the war was heavy on their minds. Would the United States get involved? How would that affect them?

This time Wilson and Marty were early enough for one of the company cabins. After the men declared it fine, Susannah did a double check for bedbugs. Only then did Norma let Bobby down to run around. Although the place was crowded, they all made do. Other cabins stood nearby, many of them occupied by Mexican migrant workers.

Between tending Bobby and helping Susannah cook, Norma was kept quite busy. One day she took time to take Bobby and walk out to see the men shoveling beets into the trucks. The men worked hard and fast. The more beets they hauled, the more pay they got. At $1.25 a ton, they could make twenty dollars a day!

It didn't take the Reeds long to decide to convert their trucks to dump from the side. The waiting line to unload at the sugar beet factory was shorter for side-dumping trucks. A Caterpillar sat idling in the field to help the loaded trucks get out of the river-bottom fields. Then the trucks sped off to the factory to be unloaded. With six men, the Reeds kept the trucks going night and day.

Norma waited until Marty's truck was loaded, then waved as he drove past. He put his head out the window and waved back at them. "Truck, truck," said Norma to Bobby. "Tuk, tuk," he echoed happily.

Norma and Bobby walked back toward the cabins. A Mexican lady sitting outside her cabin smiled a toothy grin at them. "Pretty baby. *Sí! Lindo!*"

"Thank you," Norma said, smiling. She stopped and put Bobby down close to the cabin so he could run around a bit. The lady got up and came closer. She ran her fingers through Bobby's curly hair. "Pretty. Pretty."

Suddenly Norma felt uncomfortable. Smiling politely, she picked Bobby up and went inside to help Susannah.

Several days later, Norma took Bobby outside again. Susannah's little Esther ran along. The same woman stood outside her cabin, watching. Then she approached Norma. "Pretty baby! I take home and bring back next year?"

Norma looked at her in amazement. "No, you can't take my baby!"

"Yes. *Sí! Sí!* I bring back," the woman said.

"No!" Norma responded. "Not my baby!"

"I know where baby sleeps," The woman said with a grin. "I like baby."

Tight-lipped, Norma caught Bobby up in her arms and took Esther's hand. Turning her back to the woman, she hurried into the cabin.

"What is wrong?" Susannah asked, looking at Norma's stricken face and trembling hands. When Norma told her, Susannah was upset.

Loading sugar beets at Saginaw

"You get a hammer and nail that window beside his bed shut! Wait till the men hear about this."

The men were incredulous. "You mean she was serious?" Wilson asked. Marty took one look at Norma and knew that she thought it was for real.

"She's a bad lady!" little Esther piped up.

The window was indeed nailed shut securely and Bobby kept inside, but it didn't take the men long to decide that Marty would take time off work and take the women and children home. Magdalena came along back to cook for the men.

A few weeks later, the beets were done. Marty found a house at Ayr, a small community close to Manasseh Kulp's. Norma had reluctantly said goodbye to the red tarpaper shack in Pellston with all its memories. They could not afford to pay rent on the house while they were gone. Norma settled into her next house at Ayr happily. Electricity had just been put in west of Brutus, and she was glad for the convenience.

One day Bobby disappeared. She had been hanging up wash while he played in the yard. Now suddenly he was gone. Frantically she called him, searching behind all the bushes in the back yard. Then she hurried to the front yard. "Not the road!" she thought. As she rounded the house, she saw a truck stopped on the road. Her heart lurched. Just then she saw a man standing on her porch holding Bobby. Bobby looked at her and then pointed to the road. "Tuk, tuk."

The man laughed. "He was walking up the middle of the road saying, 'Tuk, tuk.' So I stopped and brought him in."

"Thank you! Oh, thank you!" Norma gasped, reaching for Bobby. With a laugh and a wave, the man was gone.

Holding Bobby close, Norma half sobbed, "Oh, Bobby, I knew that Mexican lady couldn't be around here, but—oh, I'm so glad you are okay!"

The next time Bobby played outside, Norma tethered him to a tree. The house was just too close to the road. Even though it wasn't a busy road, Bobby was just too fast and too busy.

chapter twenty-six

Runaway Truck

Brutus, Michigan: 1940

Norma spooned the pancake batter into the sizzling pan. Erma put five plates on the table. Bobby climbed up on a chair and looked out the window. "Dere's Daddy!" he said, climbing down and running to the door. Marty came in the door carrying a large chunk of wood. A rush of cold air followed him.

"Step back, Bobby. It's hot!" he said, opening the stove and carefully adding the chunk of wood. After he closed the stove he turned to Norma. "That should keep us warm for a while. It's cold out there!"

"It sure smells good in here!" Art declared, bringing another blast of cold air in from the outside and stamping snow off his boots.

Norma stacked finished pancakes on a platter and added more batter to the pan. "That stack of pine knots is a comforting sight to me when the cold wind blows."

"It was a big job last fall, tramping all over that burned-off area to get them, but it was worth it. What I like," Marty added, "is how nicely they fit in the stove. And they burn hot. You know, Art, I hope I told you I really did appreciate your help to collect them."

"You know what I'd appreciate about now?" Art asked with his eyes on the stack of steaming pancakes.

"That's not hard to guess," Norma said, setting the pancakes on the table and adding a jar of maple syrup.

"Come on, Bobby, pancake time," Marty said, picking Bobby up and putting him on a stool. Everyone gathered around for the main meal of the day. No one seemed to mind that pancakes had been on the menu yesterday, the day before, and the day before that. It would also be on the main menu tomorrow. It was food to eat, and it was good.

Even though money was scarce, Marty and Norma had welcomed Art into their home. He'd been working on the upper peninsula and smashed his ankle. Willingly Norma had taken him in and nursed him back to health. He really had nowhere else to go.

"Art, I have a job coming up this fall," Marty announced. "I think it will keep a number of us busy. You are welcome to go along."

"Where's this?" Art wondered.

"Beaver Island," Marty answered. "You know that's here at the northern end of Lake Michigan. There's a job cutting and hauling logs for pulp. They need to be cut and hauled to the boat to be ferried to the mainland."

"Sounds good to me," Art said. "When do we start?"

"Oh, not till August, but I wanted to get you lined up too," Marty answered.

"Norma, do you like the idea of living in a little cabin on Beaver Island?" Marty wondered. "There are cabins available for us while we are on the job."

"Would we still rent here?"

"Well, there's more to it," Marty answered. "I don't know if I told you yet, but George's have decided definitely to move to Pennsylvania this fall."

"Really?" Norma exclaimed.

"That means Father and Mother will move back on the farm," Marty continued. "George asked Father and me to take the truck with their furniture to Pennsylvania. So I thought if you and I move into the apartment at Father and Mother's, you and Mother could help each other out while we are gone. Then when we come back, it will be time to go to Saginaw to harvest beets again."

"Well, the Beaver Island idea sounds all right," Norma said. "I'd rather be there with you, especially if you are going off to Pennsylvania soon after that. How long would you and Father be gone?"

"I'm not sure, but I'd guess we'd be back in two weeks," Marty said.

"But Marty, I really don't feel good about going to do sugar beets after what happened last year. What do you think?" Norma wondered.

"Father and I talked about it and thought maybe you women should stay home this year. You and Mother will both be worried if that Mexican lady is there like she said she would be. We'll maybe get Magdalena or someone else to do the cooking. We have to take care of our Bobby," he said, giving Bobby's curly head a pat.

"I'm glad you understand." Norma said.

The summer flew by. Mom was working in the Ayr area. Since Norma had her own home, Mom seemed more comfortable dropping in to chat. It was a time for Norma and Erma to get reacquainted with Mom. Norma couldn't help but contrast her own happy home and marriage, the peace of God in her heart, and the church family they enjoyed, with Mom's empty life. Here and there Mom found housekeeping or cooking jobs and lived with the people she worked for. She really had no home of her own. Norma pitied her. At least when Mom came to their house, she had a sense of belonging. These were her children—Norma, Art, and Erma. Walter dropped in occasionally too. Bobby brought sunshine to them all.

One day Mom sat at the kitchen table with a cup of tea. Norma sat down at the table, and Bobby climbed onto her lap. "Mom," Norma began, "I never told you, but Erma and I decided to try writing letters to Grandma Ruffert in Alberta."

"You did?" Mom asked in surprise.

"Yes, and she answered us several months ago. She's doing fine and she asked about you. I sent her a picture of Bobby and me. She even sent a picture of herself."

"That's nice," Mom said. "I'm sure she liked seeing Bobby."

"Did you want more tea?"

"No, thanks. I guess I best be going. Bye, bye, Bobby," and Mom was soon out the door. Did Mom have no feelings for the family she had left years ago in Alberta? She hadn't even asked to see the picture of her mother. How pleased Erma had been to be able to tell her friends that she had gotten a letter from her grandma in Alberta.

August came, and everyone geared up for the job on Beaver Island. Household things were moved to the small apartment at Wilson's. Norma packed to live temporarily with less conveniences.

Lake Michigan sparkled a lovely blue as trucks and family were loaded on the *H.M. Stewart* to be ferried across the tip of the lake to Beaver Island. Bobby was excited about the big boat. Marty and Art were anticipating a paying job.

"I wonder what the cabins will be like where we stay," Erma said.

"I just hope they are clean!" Norma answered.

They found the situation doable. Marty and Art began loading logs as the loggers cut them, taking them to the ferry.

Norma and Erma set up housekeeping and were kept busy cooking and doing laundry. Erma was fourteen and a very capable helper. Also Bobby needed constant watching so he didn't wander off.

One day Art rushed into the cabin. "Norma, Marty says he'll be home late. You might want to walk down to the lake and see what happened."

Norma stopped folding laundry. "Is Marty all right?" she asked anxiously.

Grandma Ruffert (Alzina's mother)

Elmworth. setember 4. 1939.

Dear Norma I will now anser your nice letter I should have ritten before but I have always so much to do well I hope you are all well and wish yous God blessing and how Is the baby gitting along we are all fine we have afel raney weather and In the summer It was afel dry and the cutworms where very bad I thought true would not have no garden at all I sure looks like rain

well now and he will grow up grad and strown well I think I have to close I wont to write to you sister Emma I did not do It the last time hoping this will find you all well as It leaves us well I am getting quite old I will be 79 years old the 3 of November next I am real well I am daing all the house work well this will be all send my very best love to yous all and to you mother bye by from you Grandma

mrs Ruffert

and parts of her letter

"Oh yes, he is, but you should have seen! That whole boat tipped right over!" Art exclaimed.

"Whatever do you mean, Art?" Norma asked incredulously.

"Well, the trucks kept bringing logs and loading them on the ferry," Art replied. "The ferry was about full, but I guess the load was uneven. Suddenly the ferry flipped right over and dumped the logs into the lake. Then the ferry righted itself again. What a job we have, fishing logs out of the lake. We're going to be at it a long time even if there are a bunch of us. Marty wanted you to know where he is."

Later, as Norma stood watching the men walking over the floating logs and pushing them back to the ferry with long poles, she was glad that Marty was an excellent swimmer. Remembering his surefootedness on ice skates, she thought that would maybe help him now too. Nevertheless the job was dangerous. After watching a while, Norma gathered up Bobby and headed back to the cabin with a prayer for Marty's safety. The logs were reloaded carefully, and the men finally arrived back at the cabins, safe but exhausted.

By the end of August, the job at Beaver Island was drawing to a close. Norma found herself dreading Marty's trip to Pennsylvania. It seemed so far away, and two weeks was a long time not to hear from Marty. Finally trucks, household, and family were loaded on the ferry,

The *H. M. Stewart*—ferry to Beaver Island: 1940

and they all headed back to Brutus. They stood on deck enjoying the cool breezes coming off the lake.

"Arthur and Erma, did I ever tell you that I drove this ferry by myself one time?" Norma asked.

"Really?" Erma exclaimed.

"Now tell me about this," Art said with a laugh.

"It was that time Bobby and I went back to town for more groceries," Norma said. "On our way back, it was just the captain and Bobby and me on the ferry. He offered that I could take the wheel. He told me to just aim for one point on the shore and keep it lined up with that, so of course I had to give it a try."

"Was this the second time the ferry upset?" Art teased.

"Well, Art," Marty defended Norma, "you have to remember that this plucky little lady learned to drive first with a truck. Now she has piloted a boat. She now qualifies for a car. When we get home, I have plans to buy that '36 Dodge someone offered me."

"Oh, Marty, you didn't tell me that!" Norma exclaimed. "Then I will have a car if Mother or I need to go away while you are gone to Pennsylvania or Saginaw. Mother doesn't drive, you know, and I don't like to ask for Father's car."

"Guess what I heard!" Art said mischievously. "In honor of Mrs. Reed's driving accomplishments, the main road in Brutus was paved while we were gone."

"Oh, Art!" Norma laughed. Then she added, "Did they really pave the road?"

"That's what I heard," Art affirmed.

Norma settled gratefully into the apartment at Wilson's farm. By spring they were expecting a little playmate for Bobby. George's were busy getting ready to move. Norma kept their four preschoolers and four-year-old Esther on her side of the house some days so Mother and Elizabeth, George's wife, could pack.

Departure day came. Norma and Bobby stood with Susannah and the other Reeds at the end of the lane and waved goodbye. Susannah wiped her eyes. She was saying goodbye to two sons. Daniel was almost twenty and was planning to stay in Pennsylvania with George's for a while. Pennsylvania seemed far away and unknown.

Wilson and Daniel were traveling in the truck with George's belongings. They also had quite a few bags of potatoes that George had harvested that summer. George and his family were traveling in their car. Marty was driving his truck as far as Saginaw. There he would park it until the men went to haul sugar beets.

"Well," Susannah said matter-of-factly as the last truck drove out of sight, "I guess the way to make the time go fast is to keep busy."

Two weeks later, Wilson and Marty drove in the lane. They were met by excited children and happy, relieved wives. Sitting around Wilson and Susannah's kitchen table, they told their adventures.

"You tell the story, Marty," Father suggested. "But first I must say George's and Daniel are settled safely in their house in Pennsylvania."

"Well," Marty started, "we got through Indiana and Ohio all right. We were doing pretty good on the Pennsylvania mountains. We had a tag axle, but that extra set of wheels had no brakes on it."

Norma and Susannah exchanged worried looks.

"We were headed east on Route 30, still going through the mountains, when all of a sudden we heard a terrible clanging and rattling coming from our truck. We pulled off. We knew by the sound that the rear end had gone out. George's weren't that far ahead of us, so they soon figured out we had trouble and came back. With the tools and parts George had along, he got it fixed up, and we were on our way. Daniel rode with George's then, because it was pretty tight with three men in the truck. We all agreed that George's should just go on ahead and not wait for us with the truck. It was quite a trip for them with four little children.

"So we were grinding up the hills and gearing down on the way down because we didn't have enough brakes. The next thing we knew, we hit fog. Right when we were coming out of the fog, we saw a sign that said, 'Danger—Curve.' Now we were going downhill."

Susannah drew a sharp breath. Norma sat tensely squeezing her hands together.

"Father said to me, 'Marty, maybe we better jump!' I said, 'No! Then we'll both be killed!' So Father geared down, and we got around the corner—and then the clutch went out! We tore down the mountain, blowing the horn the whole time, and on through a town called Cashtown. We finally turned off at a school and got it stopped."

Norma let out her breath.

"We took the clutch out, and Father hitchhiked to Gettysburg for another clutch while I stayed with the truck. We were glad George had left tools with us. We got the new clutch in and drove to town. By then we needed gas, but we had used our money for the clutch. So we got some potatoes off the truck and sold them for gas money. The man that bought the potatoes asked us what we were going to do next. It was evening. Were we ever tired! We hadn't eaten much, so we were hungry. He offered us a bed for the night. Then he made us supper: eggs and bacon and the whole works. Was it ever good! We knew George's and Daniel were expecting us that evening. It was Saturday, but we had no way of contacting them. They didn't know where we were until we arrived Sunday noon."

"Norma, it sounds like it's good you and I were praying!" Susannah said. Norma nodded. "What do you think of Pennsylvania?" Susannah asked the men.

"It's nice farming country," Father answered. "The winters aren't as hard as here."

"Yes, it's nice," Marty agreed, "but I don't really think I'll ever move there."

"Marty, I didn't get to tell you yet, but I found out that Uncle Peter and Aunt Sarah plan to follow their married daughters to Pennsylvania in December," Norma said.

"It seems like the German-speaking church here at Brutus is really dwindling," Marty answered. "I'm not surprised that they are moving, but I know Uncle Peter really wanted to keep his family here.

Deacon Henry Martin's moved last fall and then when Bishop Daniel Brubacher's decided to go back to Ontario, that just didn't leave much left."

"I feel bad for your Grandpa Brenneman," Susannah spoke up. "Most of his family is gone, and Peter's leaving will be hard, I'm sure."

"Yes," Norma answered, "it's hard for him, but he's committed here and doesn't want to move anywhere."

"I'm thinking I'm ready to find a bed," Marty said, standing up and stretching. "The trip home was much easier with an empty truck, but it's been a long day."

"I agree," Wilson said, yawning.

Several weeks later and all too soon for Norma, it was time for the men to head south to Saginaw to harvest beets again. Once again Norma and Susannah kept busy to make the time go faster. Norma remembered admiring Susannah as Magdalena's mother. Now as they worked together, Norma's admiration and appreciation for Susannah grew. Susannah was like the mother Norma never had.

After several weeks the men were back with cash in their pockets. The job had paid well.

Erma was done with school and old enough to hold a job. Carefully Norma screened the jobs available working in homes. She wanted to make sure Erma did not have a situation like the one she herself had faced at Mahlon Martin's.

chapter twenty-seven

Two Telegrams

Brutus, Michigan: 1941 to Spring 1943

"Oh, Marty, this is wonderful!" Norma exclaimed, standing on the threshold and surveying the spacious house in front of her. "Can we actually afford to rent this?"

Marty looked at her happy face. "It's all settled. When can you be ready to move?"

"Oh, anytime," she answered. "Look at that open stairway and the open hall with the bedrooms going off of it. Just think, we'll have more room. With Art and Walter staying here sometimes and Erma coming home weekends, it will be so nice! We can get all nicely settled in before the baby comes. This full porch across the front of the house will be nice for Bobby to play. Thank you, Marty!"

"My little wife deserves the best," Marty said. "This time we won't have Mother and Father living here in Pellston when the baby comes. But Erma says she will help."

The days of March were coming to a close and spring was just around the corner when little Betty Jane made her appearance. The young mother held her new baby close and looked into the little red face framed by long, brown hair. A little worry dampened her joy. Would people think she looked nice? What would they say?

"I love you anyway," she whispered into the baby's ear.

Marty was thrilled to have a little daughter and totally unconcerned about little Betty's looks. "She's fine, Norma. You should have seen the red faces of some of my little brothers and sisters when they were newborn. That hair will be the envy of many a mother with bald-headed babies."

Norma laughed down her worry and enjoyed Bobby's enthusiastic welcome for his little sister. Nevertheless when the Reeds came to see the new baby, Norma's apprehensions returned.

Susannah and Magdalena vied for turns to hold Betty. "What a lovely little girlie you have, Norma," Susannah said sincerely. Norma's worries melted away. In fact, she laughed at her worries as Betty lost her newborn look and became a lovely little girl with soft brown curls and hazel eyes.

Since they had moved to Pellston, Mom couldn't get there right away, but when she did come, she seemed to take great delight in her little granddaughter.

When Betty was old enough for Norma to go to church again, Rosie Weaver came eagerly to meet Norma. "Oh, Norma, let me see your baby," she said, peeking under the blanket at Betty. "What a sweet baby you have! God has given you a gift to raise for Him."

Rosetta crowded close for a peek too. "You have a nice little family," she added.

Norma sat holding her baby in church. She looked across the aisle at Marty balancing Bobby on his knee. "Thank you, God," she whispered. "I am so blessed." She lent her clear soprano to join in the song, "Oh happy day that fixed my choice on Thee my Savior and my God…"

With two children to care for, summer was almost gone before Norma realized it.

"Norma, Father and I have been talking about hauling sugar beets again. The job pays well, and we really need that," Martin said one day. "We thought maybe you and Mother could go along this year. That Mexican lady never showed up, and I really like to have you and the children with us. Do you think we could manage it? Father thought we could get two cabins this time. That would make it a little easier for you with Bobby and Betty. What do you think?"

"I think I'd rather go with you than be left behind," Norma answered. "It will be harder with two children, and a second cabin would be nice. We were so crowded before, and with extra men in and out, it's hard to keep children on any kind of a schedule. I guess that means we give up this house, though, doesn't it?"

"Yes, I'm afraid so," he said. "We can't afford to rent it when we don't live here. We'll find something when we get back."

And so it was that when they returned from sugar beet hauling with enough money to hopefully see them through the winter, they had no house.

"Marty, I heard Abe Sauder's house is empty and available right now. Aren't you looking for a place?" one of the men wondered.

"Yes, we are," Marty answered. "Shall we check into it, Norma?"

"Oh, I'd like living right across the road from Grandpa Brenneman," Norma answered enthusiastically.

So it was arranged, and Marty and Norma moved in with their little ones. It was a smaller house than their last one, but they would make do. "I'll use a baby buggy for Betty's bed," Norma decided.

But several mornings later, when Norma got Betty out of the baby buggy, she noticed a scattering of red spots across the baby's arms and face. "Marty, look at this. I'm afraid Betty has the measles," Norma said.

"Maybe we better take her to the doctor. We don't want to spread it all over," he answered.

The doctor examined Betty, then looked at Marty and Norma quizzically. "Did you move recently?"

"Well, yes," Marty answered, "we did."

"I think what we have here is nothing but bedbug bites," he stated matter-of-factly.

Norma stared at him in horror.

"I guess we know what to do about that," Marty replied. "Thank you, Doctor."

When they got home, Marty threw the mattresses out the door. Norma scrubbed and scoured everything.

Not long afterward, Marty came and said, "Norma, how would you like to move to Petoskey? I found work for the winter."

"Well, that's a lot better than when you have nothing to do," she answered. "What is the work?"

"It's at Maple Butcher Block Company," Martin answered. "They cut up boards and glue together different sizes of butcher blocks."

"Wherever you go, I go," Norma answered.

So they packed up again and moved to Petoskey. Norma wasn't sad about leaving this house behind. She just couldn't quite forgive those bedbugs for biting her baby.

Marty liked his work. Mostly the blocks were made of maple, although some pine was used. "Norma, you should have seen! Some of those boards were a foot wide and three inches thick and sixteen feet long! What a shame to cut them up for butcher blocks!" When winter storms came, Marty was glad to be working inside. Mostly he was just glad for a job that helped feed his growing family.

December 7 brought the shocking news that Japan attacked Pearl Harbor. The next day the U.S. entered World War II. Uncertainty hung over everyone. All men between the ages of eighteen and thirty-seven were required to register. Anyone whose number came up would need to serve until six months after the war ended.

Clyde Kauffman admonished his congregation to pray for the government, pay their taxes, but to follow Jesus' teaching to "resist not evil." No one knew for sure what tests might face those who refused to fight.

When Marty's job in Petoskey came to an end, Marty and Norma moved their little family back to the apartment on Wilson's farm. Marty found work here and there. He hauled fence posts for a while and helped his father with the potato crop. By the end of the summer, the truck was parked in the shed with no work. How were they going to make it through the winter?

One day Mary Evelyn's brother Elias knocked on their door. "Marty, I hear you are out of work. I'm headed for Detroit. They say there are lots of jobs there because so many fellows are in the service. Do you want to go along?"

Marty looked at Norma. "We'll talk about it, and I'll get back to you soon," Marty answered.

"Norma, we are going to have to do something," Marty said after Elias left. "We have the whole winter ahead."

She nodded soberly.

"I really hate to leave you," he continued. "What if I go with Elias and check the situation out. Then I'll come back by bus and get you and the children if I get a job."

"That sounds like the best we can do," she answered. "I hope we don't have to live right in the city."

"I'll do the best I can," he replied.

Marty and Elias were off early the next morning. The following evening, Marty was back. "It was no problem getting a job," Marty said. "I have a job at Bulldog Electric, and I rented a house. I'm sorry it is in the city, but I had to be close to my work. I think you'll be all right."

It wasn't the cool fall breeze that made Norma shiver when they pulled up in front of their apartment in Detroit. She looked at the cracked sidewalks, the shabby houses, and the crowded neighborhood. Marty saw her look.

"I'm sorry, Norma, it's the best I could do. I think you'll like the house inside."

She did like the house inside. "But Marty," she said slightly mischievously, "I think one of the best things about this house is that big lock on the door."

"Well," he said, "I'll lock the door when I go to work and take the key. If anyone knocks, you don't have to answer, because I'll have the key to get back in."

Glad for a job, Marty went off to work. When Marty was home, they learned to know the pleasant neighbors in the other side of their house. But Norma couldn't relax. Noises from the street kept her on edge.

One day Norma had a letter to mail. She picked up Betty and took Bobby by the hand. "I'm going to let you and Betty play at the neighbors, Bobby, while I quickly take this letter to the mailbox." Norma started off bravely down the street. Suddenly a fire siren started up nearby, startling her. As she turned to watch the fire engine, Norma noticed a man staggering across the sidewalk and coming straight toward her. He was drunk.

That was enough. She turned around quickly, gathered up Bobby and Betty, went into the house, locked the door, and pulled the shades down. Marty's words of comfort when he came home were interrupted by shouting from the street. Norma did *not* like Detroit.

After six weeks in Detroit, it was time to go home for Christmas. Daniel had come home from Pennsylvania. He had been working for Susannah's brother Paul. He was full of stories and painted a pretty nice picture of Pennsylvania—rich farmlands, milder winters, and available jobs. "The Mennonite church there is different from the Mennonite church here," he stated. "At least, where George's attend."

"In what way?" Marty wondered.

"I think it's more Scriptural," Daniel said. "George thinks a lot of their bishop, J. Paul Graybill. The Lancaster Conference is quite involved in local mission work. They also hold to the church standards.

All of the ladies wear their plain dresses and head coverings all the time, not just for Sunday like a lot of them do here. Some Mennonite farmers raise tobacco, but there's a lot of talk against raising it or using it."

Susannah said, "That sounds like a good thing. It seems like the church here is sliding the other way."

"Yes," Marty agreed. "Clyde tries to hold to the standards of the church, but not everyone listens."

Marty and Norma took time to stop in to visit Grandpa Brenneman while Marty was in Brutus. Grandpa's days were long, and he was happy to see them. Reaching into his pocket, he held out his hand. "Here, Bobby, would you like this?" Sure enough, Grandpa still had pink peppermints in his pocket. He soon had Bobby leaning against his knee.

Betty was an active toddler. When Norma corrected her, Betty set up a loud and determined cry. Norma picked up Betty and slipped outside to Grandpa's woodshed. There she disciplined Betty and stilled her crying. Coming back into the house, she looked at Grandpa apologetically. "I'm sorry," she said.

"That's all right," Grandpa said kindly. "Just make her listen."

Norma smiled at him gratefully. How often she thought back to Grandpa's kindly encouragement as she struggled with Betty's determination.

Norma was happy for Marty's decision to go back to Detroit and leave her in Brutus for several weeks. Even though it was winter, she spent all the time she could outside in the fresh, clean air. Bobby and Esther loved when she played with them in the snow.

One day Norma and four-year-old Bobby stood in the yard watching for first-grader Esther to come home from school. In the distance they saw a snowplow arching snow high into the air. Just then they saw Esther running in the lane. When she got closer, they could see she was gasping for breath and her eyes were wide with fear.

"What's wrong, Esther?" Norma asked in alarm.

Esther and Bobby

"Irvin—Irvin—he said—the plow—would—would cover me!" she half sobbed. Bobby's eyes got big.

"No! No!" Norma comforted. "Irvin shouldn't say that. The man in the plow will be very careful when he sees schoolchildren walking home."

Marty and Daniel headed to Detroit by train. Marty had a job there, and Daniel would go on to Pennsylvania.

"What do you think, Marty? Don't you want to move to Pennsylvania?" Daniel questioned.

"I don't know," Marty answered slowly. "I never thought I'd want to, but a man has to have work. Norma sure doesn't like living in Detroit. I can't blame her, but I don't want her in Brutus while I'm in Detroit. You say there are plenty of jobs in Pennsylvania?"

"That's right!" Daniel answered.

"Well, I'll tell you what," Marty said. "You find a job and a house for us, and we will seriously consider moving to Pennsylvania."

"Sounds good," Daniel responded. "Expect to hear from me."

The time in Detroit stretched out long for Martin. No Norma when he came home from work. No little feet running to meet him. Then the telegram came. Marty stared at it. HOUSE AND JOB WAITING—DANIEL.

When the weekend came, Marty headed north to Norma. His family greeted him joyously. Marty urged Norma to return to Detroit for a while. "I just can't live without you, Norma," Marty said.

"I missed you too, Marty," Norma answered. "I do want to trust God to take care of us, but I don't look forward to Detroit."

Only after they were back in Detroit did Marty tell her about Daniel's telegram. "What do you think, Norma?" he asked.

"It would be a big change," Norma said soberly. "It looks more appealing from Detroit than from Brutus."

"Why do you think I waited until we were back here to tell you?" Marty asked, his eyes twinkling.

"Marty!" Norma scolded. They both laughed. "Really, there's a lot to think about," Norma said soberly. "Did he say what job he was going to look for?"

"When we talked, he mentioned working for a limestone quarry, but really, almost any job will do," Marty answered.

"What do you think about the differences in church?" Norma wondered.

"I've already made a change," Marty said, smiling at her.

"What do you mean?" she asked looking at him in surprise.

"Well, you know, I sometimes had a smoke when I was truck driving. I've quit, Norma. I'm done with tobacco, and I'm glad."

"Oh, Marty, I'm glad too!" she said happily. "You know I never did like that."

"Would you have a problem with the changes in dress that you would need to make?" he asked kindly.

"No, Marty, I wouldn't," she answered. "I've thought about it before this. Your mother and sisters wear head coverings and plain dresses for everyday. It makes sense. It is more consistent, and I am willing."

"I'm sure there might be other changes and adjustments too," he said. "But I think it will be a better place all around to raise our family."

"I would hate to leave Grandpa Brenneman and Erma and even Mom. I feel kind of responsible for my mom somehow. As long as she has a good job and a place to stay, she's okay, I guess. Erma's kind of on her own now, but I'd hate to be far away. What will your parents say?" Norma wondered.

"I don't know. It was hard for Mother when George's left. Let's pray about it," he suggested.

"That sounds good," she agreed. "I want whatever God wants."

Several weeks later another telegram arrived. This one was for Norma from Petoskey: GRANDFATHER DIED THURSDAY MORNING. FUNERAL SERVICE EXPECTED TO BE HELD MONDAY AFTERNOON. WE HAVE LET THE BOYS KNOW. ERMA BRENNEMAN

Dear Grandpa Brenneman was gone! Tears filled Norma's eyes, and memories played through her mind. Grandpa—faithful church leader and friend to all. Grandpa—to Norma he was one place of security and belonging that never changed. He was like an anchor in the tumultuous and changing scenes of childhood and youth. One objection to moving to Pennsylvania was taken away. Grandpa would not have to experience one more departure of family and friends. His lonely days were over. How glad Norma was that she and Marty had taken time to visit Grandpa.

This telegram signified closure. With Grandpa gone, the Old Order German church was no more. Grandpa was the last minister here, and most of the members had moved away. But the telegram also opened up new doors for Norma.

"What are you thinking about the move to Pennsylvania?" Norma asked Marty one day. Together they had prayed much about the decision.

"I was wondering how you were feeling by now," he answered.

"Whatever you decide," she answered. "I'm willing to go."

"Thank you, Norma," he said. "I was feeling like that is the best thing to do, but I wanted your agreement. I've been thinking if I send Daniel a telegram telling him that we will be there to start work at the beginning of April, that gives us time to wind things up here. I need to give notice at my job. Then too, I thought we need to tell my parents before too long."

"Yes, I don't look forward to that," Norma said.

"I'd really like to stick to this job as long as I can for the money. How about if we pack up here by the end of this month and tell Father and Mother our plans. I better get that telegram off to Daniel."

chapter twenty-eight

The Big Move

Brutus, Michigan: 1943

Norma pulled Betty's busy little hands away from the door latch and gave her a toy. "Bobby, move over a little bit so I can shift better," Marty instructed.

The truck was packed with their things. Norma had cleaned out their apartment and, without a backward look at Detroit, they headed north.

"Norma, I think you would do a better job at telling Father and Mother of our plans than I can," Marty suggested.

"Well, Marty, I think you should tell them. They are your parents."

When the truck pulled into Wilson's lane, the family came out to meet them. "What a nice surprise!" Susannah greeted them.

Bobby and Betty were soon out of the confines of the truck and running around.

"What do you have on your load, Marty?" Wilson wondered, looking at the tarp covering the load.

"I'll explain that to you later," Marty answered as the group moved to the house to get out of the chilly February air.

"Magdalena, let's add some plates quickly," Susannah instructed. "Surely they are hungry after all that driving. I'm glad you got here before we ate."

After supper, Susannah suggested, "Let's go visit in the sitting room." Magdalena brought a dish of peanuts and a plate of crackers to munch on. There was an air of expectancy.

Finally Marty said, "Norma has something to tell you."

Norma gave him a look of resignation. "We have a surprise," she began. "We came to tell you that we have our household things packed up and we are planning to move to Pennsylvania."

Susannah's mouth dropped open, and her hands went up. "You are? Well, we are moving to Pennsylvania too! We have our sale bill all drawn up for the farm!"

Now it was Marty and Norma's turn to be surprised. Soon everyone was laughing and sharing their plans. "Here we were, both dreading what the other ones would say!" Susannah laughed. "It won't be nearly as hard to see you go since we know we will be coming later. It could be a while, though, until we get the farm sold and all."

Norma filled the next two weeks preparing for the move. One of the things she wanted to do was to sew herself enough plain cape dresses for Pennsylvania. Susannah was happy to give her a hand. Together they worked and talked of their move to Pennsylvania. "What about your family?" Susannah wondered.

"Well, Erma will stay here for now," Norma answered. "I expect she will follow us when her job ends. I worry about my mom, though. As long as she has a job working in someone's home, she has a place to live. If that runs out, I'm not sure what she would do. It seems like she enjoys dropping in to see us. Somehow, I feel responsible for her."

"I can understand that," Susannah sympathized. "She really has no one but you children and a few friends."

"Walter and Arthur are both expecting to go into the army. It's all they can talk about lately. How I wish they wouldn't," Norma added.

"Do you hear from Raymond or your dad?"

"Not much," Norma answered. "We've talked about at least stopping to see Raymond on our way east. I'm not sure if that will work out."

Norma took Betty and Bobby to visit Mose and Bessie. Most of their children were married and gone, but Bessie greeted Norma with a motherly hug. "So you are going to leave us too? It seems so many of our neighbors are moving away," Mose commented.

"I know," Norma answered, "but you know jobs are easier to get in Pennsylvania. It seems strange to see Uncle Peter's and Daniel Brubacher's houses occupied by other people, though. Grandpa's house is empty too now."

When Norma rose to go, Bessie pressed a small box into her hand. "It's just a few salt and pepper shakers from my collection. I want you to have them. Mose brought a small jug of maple syrup. Do you think you have room in your load to take a little bit of Michigan along with you?"

"Why, thank you! I'm sure we do," Norma replied. "And thank you for being parents to me when I needed it."

As they walked back to Wilson's, Norma looked in at Uncle Peter's house. The big swing hung still under the maple tree. The windmill turned lazily in the breeze. A dog sunning himself on the barn hill raised his head and barked at them, but it wasn't Nellie. Uncle Peter's had moved over two years ago. Memories and nostalgia washed over her. Suddenly she realized all that she was leaving behind.

But, she reminded herself, life moves on. She quickened her steps. Marty would be home soon!

When Marty slowly drove in the lane, Norma took a closer look at the car. What was she seeing? Straps covered the bumper and crisscrossed the hood. Quickly she looked to see how Marty was.

"Doesn't look so good, does it?" Marty said, getting out of the car.

"Whatever happened? Are you all right?"

"I'm fine, but as you can see, the car's not. I had an accident in a snowstorm. I tied the bumper back on and limped her home."

"Oh, Marty, I'm so glad you are okay, but can we fix the car? What about moving to Pennsylvania?" she wondered.

"I've been thinking about that. I guess we'll have to tow it behind the truck. I can probably get George to fix it in Pennsylvania," he answered.

Car that was towed to PA

Sunday dinner was spent with Clyde and Rosetta. Rosie was there too. Norma remembered a gathering of young people in Clyde's home when she had met the smiling eyes of Martin Reed across the table. Now he sat at her side with Betty on his knee and Bobby beside him.

Clyde looked fondly at the young family. "Marty, I understand that you will be attending a more conservative church in Pennsylvania. I want to encourage you in that."

"Thank you," Marty answered. "We are willing to make the changes and feel it will be good for our family."

"I agree," Clyde said. "We wish you the Lord's blessing as you go.

I wish things were a bit different here."

When it was time to leave, Rosie put her arms around Norma and smiled at her tearfully. "Norma, I am so glad for the direction your life has taken. I will be praying for you."

"Thank you, Rosie. Thank you for all your encouragement and prayers in the past," Norma answered.

Moving day arrived. It was March 29 and Betty's second birthday. The truck was loaded, and the car was hitched up behind. Norma had food and supplies for several days stashed in the truck cab. There would be no sleepovers until they were there. Motels were just not in their budget. Wilson's waved as they pulled out the lane. "We hope to see you in a couple months."

As the truck hit the paved road and headed south, Marty said, "It's not Pellston or Petoskey or Saginaw or Detroit. This is the *big* move. Pennsylvania, here we come."

Bobby bounced up and down with excitement. "When will we get there? I can't wait!"

"Oh, Bobby, not for a long time," Marty answered. "It will get dark two or three times before we get there."

Bobby's eyes got big. "But where will we sleep, and what will we eat?"

"You will sleep right there on the seat or maybe on the floor. Mama has food along. Don't worry about that," Marty said patiently.

Hours later after darkness had descended, Norma stirred in her sleep. She shifted the sleeping Betty in her arms.

"Norma, I'm going to pull over and sleep a bit," Marty said quietly. Quickly Norma pulled sleeping Bobby's feet out of the way as Marty shifted down. She put her head back against the seat again.

After sleeping awhile, Marty was ready to go on. Fortunately Bobby and Betty slept reasonably well in spite of the conditions. Norma didn't. She dozed when she could, and otherwise tended, fed, and entertained the children. She thought of Raymond when they entered Indiana, but with the car towed behind them, it was no time to visit him. When the children grew restless, they stopped to let them run a bit. Then they got back into the crowded truck cab, and on they drove.

"I'm sure glad I traveled this with Father when we took George's things to Pennsylvania," Marty said. "At least I know the route and know what to expect. They say, though, that now there is a nice section of toll road in Pennsylvania instead of a road winding through the mountains. I hope they will let us on, towing the car."

"I hope so too," Norma agreed, reaching out to pull Bobby's hand away from the gear shift.

Bobby watched Marty shift down as they came into a small town. "Daddy, I can do that for you," he offered.

"No," Marty answered, and then added sternly, "You must never touch that stick when we are driving, or the truck won't work right. You must get big first."

Bobby nodded soberly and asked, "Will we be there soon?"

"No," Marty answered. "Remember, we said it will be a long time."

Bobby sighed, "What can I do?" Norma handed him a toy car. Soon he was driving it over the back of the seat and down Norma's arm.

"Take a look up there!" Marty said.

Norma looked up to see a "Welcome to Pennsylvania" sign. "Yay!" she cheered.

"It will take us quite a while to cross Pennsylvania yet," Marty warned. "I just hope they will let us on the turnpike."

Marty pulled up to the tollbooth and hopped out as someone came over to their truck. Carefully the man examined the connections between the truck and car. Finally he said, "I'm sorry, but I can't let you on the toll road. You don't have a good enough towing system. I'm concerned about your lights. You'll have to take Route 30."

Disappointed, Marty went back to the cab. "Just what I was afraid of," he told Norma. "They don't like our setup. That means we travel Route 30 through the mountains."

There was no choice, so over the mountains they went—uphill and downhill. It was quite a change from the flat roads of Ohio and Michigan. Norma tried to doze. She closed her eyes rather than look at the high dropoffs they were driving along. Many of them had no guardrails. She shifted children and tried to keep them happy. Marty just drove, barely stopping—to Norma, it was a wild ride.

At last they were out of the worst mountains. "Well, Norma, you certainly aren't a complainer," said Marty, putting a kindly hand on her shoulder. "How's my little wife holding up?"

She smiled at him. "Probably at least as good as you are. When did you sleep last?"

"I'm not sure, but guess what; a couple more hours and we should be at George's house."

"It will be so good to get out of this truck!" Norma said.

When the travel-weary little family pulled up in front of George's house in the little town of Blue Ball, George stepped out on the porch to welcome them. Eager little faces pressed against the house windows, looking out at the new arrivals.

"Welcome to Pennsylvania," George said. "When did you leave?"

"We left on the 29th," Marty answered.

"Let's see. Today's April 1," George said. "That's about three days. Long trip, isn't it?" he asked, shaking Norma's hand.

"I'm afraid I have a bit of a disappointment for you," George continued. "We wanted to keep you here until you get your house set up, but our children have chicken pox. I doubt if you want that right now."

"No," Marty and Norma agreed together.

"I thought I'd show you to your house and help you get unloaded and set up beds," George suggested. "Your house is only about ten or fifteen minutes away."

"Sounds good," Marty said, yawning and stretching.

Bobby and Betty set up a wail. Neither wanted to get back in that truck. "Just a short ride this time," Norma assured them.

Before long they were pulling up in front of a house in the little town of Terre Hill. "Half of the house is yours," George said, showing them into a house sitting close to the sidewalk. A porch ran along the front

House at Terre Hill, PA

of the house. "Shall we get started unloading, Marty?"

It didn't take long to bring their few possessions into the house. "Marty, did you see the back yard?" Norma exclaimed. "It will be so nice for the children to play! What an improvement over Detroit—and over the truck cab," she said with a laugh.

George set a few groceries on the table along with some soup that Elizabeth had sent along. "Now you all settle in and get some sleep. We'll be back later to show you around. By the way, Ivan Martin says you can start work whenever you are ready. We'll let you follow us to church on Sunday."

"Thanks a lot," Marty said, yawning.

Happily Norma bathed her children and tucked them into bed for the first time in three days. It felt so good to be clean and to stretch out in their own beds!

The next day Norma busied herself arranging her house and doing laundry from the trip. Betty and Bobby played contentedly in the balmy spring air while she hung laundry to dry in the back yard. When she took them for a walk, Norma was impressed by the extreme friendliness of the neighbors who stopped to chat with her.

George had come and taken Marty to introduce him to his new employer. When Marty returned, he reported to Norma, "Ivan Martin is a nice Christian man. I think I'll enjoy working for him. There's steady work because the government is giving lime to the farmers right now to help boost their production. Just imagine, Norma—no more moving here and moving there to try to get a little work."

"It sounds too good to be true," Norma agreed. "When was the last time we lived in a house for more than a year? I'll be happy to stay right here for a long time."

"There's one thing I'm sure going to have to get used to," Marty added. "It's these crooked roads. I never realized how nice it was in Michigan to have everything laid out in squares. I hope I can find the places where I am to spread my lime."

There was one more thing Martin had to get used to. One day Ivan Martin stopped him at the quarry. "Marty, are you holding onto some paychecks instead of cashing them? It makes it hard for me to keep records."

"I'm sorry, I guess I am," Marty answered. "I'm just not used to checks. I always dealt with cash." When Marty got home, he took the checks out of the drawer and went to the bank.

A steady job brought enough money—in fact, more than they were used to. It wasn't long until Marty bought Norma a gas stove to replace the wood-burning cookstove.

Sunday morning, Marty and Norma drove to George's house and followed them to the little church along Route 23 at Churchtown where George and his family attended.

"I wonder how many churches there are in this area," Marty commented as he slowed down to pass several horse and buggies. "George says there are other Mennonite churches close enough for us to drive to, but they have come to like this one and thought we might too."

George was right. Marty and Norma were welcomed warmly. The sermons reminded them of Clyde Kauffman's sermons. They felt their souls were fed.

"Did you notice, Marty?" Norma asked as they left church later.

"There's a lot more consistency in church application of modest dress. I like it. I feel so at home here."

"There's a lot of emphasis on mission work and reaching out in the community too," Marty answered. "I like that. I really feel, Norma, that God wants us here."

"I'm content," Norma said, smiling at him.

chapter twenty-nine

The War Touches Home

Pennsylvania: 1943-1945

Bobby was counting the days until his fifth birthday. But before his birthday came, he had a surprise. A car pulled up in front of their house. The car door opened and Bobby stared. "Esther! Grandfather! Grandmother! Mama, look who's here!" he shouted.

Marty and Norma came hurrying out of the house. "Welcome to Pennsylvania!" Marty greeted his parents. "You folks must have made good time. We didn't expect you quite yet."

"Well," Wilson answered, "the farm sale went well. William Eby's bought the farm. Mother and Magdalena were packed and eager to get here."

"How was your trip?" Marty wondered.

"Oh, pretty good," Wilson answered. "I drove the truck, and Aaron and Magdalena drove the car."

"We stopped for a motel in Ohio," Susannah added. "That helped a lot. They had a nice tub with hot water in the motel. Esther just couldn't get done talking about that. She never saw one before."

With the busy summer days behind her, Norma waited eagerly for the arrival of her little one. One crisp day in mid-October, Marty called Dr. Martin. The doctor wasn't there long until he delivered a big, healthy boy. Marty cuddled his newborn son. "This little fellow is the first to have his mama's black hair. Shall we name him Richard Wayne?" he asked Norma.

"Yes, I still like the name, but let's call him Dickie for now," Norma answered. "Richard is such a big name for a baby."

Little Dickie thrived. Norma happily tended her three little ones. "I wish I could show Mom my baby," Norma thought. "I think he looks like her babies. She'd love that."

The war was still going on. Everyone was issued war ration cards—meats, butter, sugar, oils, coffee, and canned goods. Gasoline was also rationed, so visits to Wilson's were kept to a minimum.

Marty worried about the draft. What if he were called? One day he discussed it with Ivan Martin, his employer.

"I think you are okay," Ivan answered. "We are hauling lime for the government, you know." Sometime later, Ivan came to Marty again. "Marty, I'm not so sure after all. There are so many people being drafted, I'm starting to worry that even I might have to go."

Marty talked to his father. Wilson spoke with Harry Shenk, a farmer living near him. "You know, Harry, I'm thinking Marty should see if he could get a farm deferment. I'd hate to see him leave Norma and their three children."

"Well," Harry answered, "why don't you send him on down to me? I have a big enough operation; I can put him to work. We even have a guest house where they can live until they find something else."

So about a year after they had moved into the house in Terre Hill, they were moving again. Norma didn't complain. "It's not a big sacrifice to make so I can have my husband at home. Another good thing is that we will be much closer to Father and Mother," she rejoiced. The Harry Shenk farm was located not far from the town of Morgantown near Loag's Corner.

This time they were not even in town. Bobby and Betty loved the freedom they had—no nearby street and lots of places to roam freely. Marty was back to his boyhood occupation of doing field work and milking cows. Harry Shenk certainly did have work for him. Marty helped six other men milk ninety cows by hand.

About a month after they arrived on the farm, Marty came in one morning with the mail. "Look at this, Norma!" he said, holding up an official-looking envelope. "I guess we moved none too soon."

"What is it?" she asked. "Is it a really a draft notice?"

"I'm afraid so," he answered. "It comes from Michigan. It says I am to report at Detroit. Now what do I do?" He sat down at the kitchen table with the paper in front of him. "Wait a minute. What does this say? Here in the fine print it says, 'Unless impossible; then contact local draft.'"

"Why don't you ask Father about it?" Norma suggested.

"Sounds like a good idea," Marty agreed.

At Wilson's suggestion, Marty called the local draft board. He was informed they had just closed the draft for that month. Temporarily relieved, Marty and Wilson talked to Bishop J. Paul Graybill.

"I'm glad you want a way out of military service," J. Paul said. "That is Biblical, but it's not always easy. Some of our young men are going into noncombatant service. I don't encourage that. Some are going to CPS camps to give community service. Since you are on a farm, you should be able to get a farm deferment," he told Marty. "Write a paper stating our belief. Get Harry Shenk to write a paper explaining his need, and then send them both in."

Marty did that, and thirty days later his farm deferment came in the mail.

"Norma," Marty said, "do you realize that if we had stayed in Michigan, I would have had no way of getting a deferment like this?"

"I'm so glad that God led us here," Norma agreed.

When Marty's number came up again, he took the train from Downingtown to Philadelphia for his physical exam. He had his deferment papers in hand. Neither of his brothers had passed the physical, but Marty was declared sound of health. On the strength of his deferment paper, he gratefully took the train back to Downingtown and his family.

Sitting around the supper table one evening, Marty looked at Norma with a mischievous twinkle in his eye. "Since you are so efficient at this moving business, how would you like some more practice?"

Norma looked at him reproachfully. "You know, the more children we have, the less excited I get about moving."

"Well, remember Harry said we could live in this guest house until we could find something else. I think I found it."

"I hope it's not too far from the farm," Norma said hopefully.

"No, actually it's just down the road about a mile at Loag's Corner. How about if we go have a look at it?"

"Let me get the dishes out of the way first," Norma said, starting to clear the table.

"I think we could just walk down there if you put Dickie in the baby buggy," Marty suggested.

It was a pleasant family walk. Bobby and Betty ran ahead along the tree-lined road, kicking up fallen leaves. When they reached the house, Norma liked the big cherry tree shading the yard. The kitchen faced south to let the sunshine in. And the house was conveniently located. Bobby would soon be in Grade 1. The school bus would pick him up at the house.

The move was made before school started. Norma stopped in at the Central School to meet Bobby's teacher. She was quite pleased with Mrs. Gundy. It was good to know Bobby would be in the hands of an experienced teacher. He was a lively boy and needed a firm hand.

Norma smiled to herself as she remembered a previous day when Bobby needed discipline. Marty had sent him out to get a switch. Bobby had chosen little switches before, and they carried a sharp sting. This time he came across the yard dragging a two-inch-thick branch about fifteen feet long. Marty hid his smile and instructed Bobby to go for something smaller.

Marty and Norma took seriously the responsibility of teaching and training their children. As Norma saw her firstborn off to school, her prayers followed him. "Be a good boy, Bobby," she said, waving from the front porch.

Mrs. Gundy had no complaints. Bobby did well in school, but out from under her watchful eye, sometimes his hot temper flared up.

One day Marty came home from the Shenks. "Bobby, could you tell me why Tommy Shenk came home with a bloody nose today?"

Bobby looked down. "Well, yeah. He took my seat on the bus," he said hotly, "so I hit him on the face."

Marty looked at Bobby sternly. "Is that the way we settle arguments?"

"Sometimes the big boys do," Bobby answered.

"Well, *we* don't!" Marty said firmly. "I'm going to punish you and

House at Loag's Corner

then you are going to walk down to the Shenks and tell him you are sorry."

"But Daddy, it's starting to get dark."

"The best time to take care of it is now. Maybe you will remember the next time not to hit people."

As Bobby started down the road to the Shenks, Norma said, "He's pretty little yet, Marty."

"He'll be fine, and he'll probably never forget the lesson," Marty said.

Norma watched from the window until she saw Bobby returning. It was quite dark now. His feet flew down the tree-lined road, and his eyes were wide.

Marty was waiting for him on the porch. He put his hand on Bobby's shoulder. "Bobby, we want you to grow up to be a good boy."

Norma had her struggles with three-year-old Betty too. Betty loved to bite—anyone and anything. It wasn't from teething, and it wasn't usually in anger, so why did she do it? Norma punished, she prayed, she tried everything. Someone even suggested that Norma bite Betty to show her how it felt.

Marty had brought a little dog home for the children. Penny liked to lie by the cookstove. One day Norma heard the dog yelp. Bobby came running to her, horrified. "Mama, do you know what Betty did? She bit Penny's tail!" Norma looked at him in shock. No matter what she did, determined Betty bit anyway.

One day Norma caught Betty opening her mouth to bite Dickie. Quickly Norma put Betty's hand in her own mouth. Tears filled her eyes after she bit herself. Never again did Norma have to correct her for biting.

Living in the country had its disadvantages. Any major snowstorm left them snowbound. The county's snowplows were kept busy on main roads, and the local farmers could only plow so much with their tractors. Neighbors banded together to help each other when necessary. Nevertheless, Norma liked the snow. It reminded her of Michigan and pleasant days at Uncle Peter and Aunt Sarah's.

One morning, one-year-old Dickie whimpered in his bed. When Norma bent over to get him, she gasped in alarm. "Marty, this baby is hot! Feel him!"

Marty put his hand gently on Dickie's forehead. "You don't even need a thermometer to know he has a fever. I've never felt anyone that hot. He needs to see a doctor."

"I wonder what I should do for him right now," Norma worried.

"I'll go over to Harry Shenk's and phone Dr. Martin," Marty decided.

Norma was busy sponging Dickie's head with cool water when Marty came back in the room with a troubled look on his face. "Norma, did you look outside this morning?"

"What now?"

"It looks like about two feet of snow out there, and it's still coming down," he answered. "I'm afraid Dr. Martin won't be getting through for quite a while. The roads are all snowed shut."

Tears filled Norma's eyes. "Marty, what shall we do?"

"Let's pray," Marty said huskily. Together they knelt and committed their baby to the Lord.

When they rose from their knees, Marty said, "I think I should go to Harry's and see if I could get ahold of the doctor, at least for advice."

"Marty, feel him now," Norma said hopefully. "I think he is a lot cooler."

"We prayed, you know," Marty said. "I think he feels quite a bit cooler too. Shall I wait a bit?"

"Why don't we, since the doctor can't get through anyway," Norma replied holding Dickie closely in her arms.

"I'll go clear the sidewalks," Marty said.

He was still shoveling when Norma opened the front door. "Marty, come quick!" she said, panic edging her voice. Marty hurried inside.

Norma was wrapping multiple blankets around Dickie. "Marty, something is very wrong! Now he is too cold. Look, he is almost blue," she sobbed.

"Norma, I hate to leave you right now, but I guess the only thing to do is to get to Shenk's and try to call the doctor. I'll be back as soon as I can." Norma nodded wordlessly.

By the time Marty got back, Norma had peeled the layers of blankets off Dickie. "He's getting hot again, Marty. He's so hot I can feel the heat when I get close to him even without touching him."

"Norma, I talked to the doctor. He can't get through here, but if we figure out a way to get him to the Lancaster hospital, he will meet us there. Harry Shenk said he will start clearing the lane. Then he'll drive ahead of us with the tractor until we get to better roads. The Shenks offered to take care of Bobby and Betty. The doctor suggested packing him in ice to keep the fever down. I talked to my parents to let them know what's happening. Mother suggested you could use snow for ice. She said she'll come over to the children as soon as she can get through. If you can get ready to go, I'll put chains on the car."

When Marty came in, Norma had a pile of blankets, some clean cloths and a bucket for snow. Mrs. Shenk knocked at the door. Norma let her in and gave sober-faced Bobby a hug. "We are taking Dickie to the doctor. Grandmother will come for you after a while. Be good for Mrs. Shenk."

Slowly, slowly they worked their way through the snow-filled roads. When they got to main roads, the going was better, but still very treacherous. Marty drove and prayed. Norma tried to keep Dickie as comfortable as possible. One moment she was bathing his head with cloths dipped in snow. Soon she was wrapping him in blankets as his body temperature dropped too low. It was nearly two hours later when they pulled up to the Lancaster hospital.

"You take him in, Norma," Marty said. "I'll park the car and come."

Dr. Martin was waiting for them. Dickie was extremely hot when Norma handed him to the doctor. Experienced hands packed ice around him to get the fever down. Dr. Martin gently examined and probed and tested. At last he turned to the concerned parents.

"I think what we have here is pneumonia of the blood. It's not very common. With the war in progress, it's quite possible that the germ was brought back from overseas. We have a fairly new drug called penicillin. It's been proven to help a lot of things that we couldn't cure before. I can't tell you yet how your baby will be affected by the high fever. He may have some lasting effects. First we will get this under control."

Several days later, Marty and Norma gratefully took Dickie home. There were no obvious effects from the high fever. As he grew, though, Norma noticed slight differences from other children. Dickie was a bit slower to learn and develop. School was difficult. At times he was frustrated by his inability to keep up with others his age. Norma thanked God that he did not stay an infant all his life, as he might have, but could go on to lead a reasonable life.

Bobby and Betty chattered about their time with Grandfather's while Dickie was in the hospital. "I helped Grandfather milk," Bobby piped up. "I went with Grandfather in the truck too. We saw a sign with numbers on it. Grandfather said, 'Look at that, Bobby. Now they are trying to tell us how fast we can drive our cars.' What did he mean, Daddy?"

"That was a speed limit sign," Marty answered. "We didn't have them in Michigan. Here there are more cars, and the government tells us how fast we may go, so it is safer."

"He didn't sound too happy," Bobby observed.

"That's because he's just not used to it," Marty answered.

"Do you know what else?" Bobby added. "Grandfather said he had some men picking tomatoes for him in the summer. He said they were prisoners from Germany. Why did he have prisoners?"

"There's a war right now, Bobby," Marty explained patiently. "Wars are not nice. Some people get hurt and the government keeps some people as prisoners. The government said our farmers could use some of the prisoners for farm work. Grandfather knows some German, so he could speak to the prisoners."

"Uncle Walter and Uncle Arthur are in the war, aren't they?" Bobby wondered.

"Yes, they are," Marty said soberly.

"Marty, did I tell you that Uncle Peter's Joshua went as a noncombatant?" Norma asked.

"What's that?" Bobby wondered.

"It's someone who goes to the war but won't hurt people. They just help the army in other ways," Marty answered. "No, Norma, I didn't know that. I'm sure Uncle Peter's aren't very happy."

"We shouldn't fight in war, should we?" Bobby asked. "Just like we shouldn't hit people in the face, right?"

"That's right," Marty answered with a wink at Norma.

Several months later, Norma got the sad news from Uncle Peter's that Joshua had been killed. He had been in France only a little over six weeks. How Norma grieved with the Brubacher family. Fun-loving Joshua had been just like a brother to her.

May 7 brought the good news that Germany had surrendered. Japan fought on. In August the U.S. bombed Hiroshima and Nagasaki. Several days later, Japan surrendered. The world rejoiced. On September 2, the war was officially over.

Bobby and Betty did their rejoicing by climbing up on the old wooden platform where the Shenks put their milk cans for the milkman to pick up. Using sticks they banged on the empty milk cans and shouted, "Uncle Art's coming home! Uncle Art's coming home!"

Harry Shenk had come to Marty in August. "I thought I should let you know that I'm planning to sell out, Marty. I sure have appreciated your help. Do you think you will be able to work for Ivan Martin again?"

"Yes, Ivan said he would take me back after the war. Thank you, Harry, for the job. I'll start looking for a house up that way. We'd like to move before Bobby starts back to school."

chapter thirty

When It Rains, It Pours

Pennsylvania 1945-1946

Shifting Dickie to her left arm and taking Betty's hand, Norma walked quietly into church and sat down. She smiled at her friend Anna, who pulled her little David closer to make room. Bobby followed Marty up the aisle on the men's side of the church. He was old enough to be trusted to behave while Marty had devotions. It was good to be back in church at Churchtown.

While living at Loag's Corner, they had attended Conestoga Mennonite Church sometimes, because it was closer. Now Marty had found half a house for rent in the little town of Goodville and was back working at Ivan Martin's stone quarry.

Norma joined in singing "Choose My Path, O Blessed Savior."

As Marty walked up to conduct the devotional, her heart welled up in praise. "Thank you, God, for my path—the joys and duties." She squeezed Dickie to herself, and putting her arm around Betty, she turned her attention to Marty.

The congregation at Churchtown had been good for both of them spiritually. The sound Bible teaching and the emphasis on mission work added purpose and meaning to life.

Norma enjoyed the little town of Goodville even though the four-room apartment they were renting was small. It was a friendly neighborhood.

Erma had moved to Pennsylvania and was living in an apartment in nearby Blue Ball. What a glad day it was to meet her at the bus station when she moved from Michigan. Now she rode the bus to Lancaster and worked as a waitress.

Winter came, and with it Magdalena's wedding. Susannah would miss her help, and so would Norma when the new baby came in the spring.

Just a few days before Betty's fifth birthday, little black-haired Erma Naomi joined the family. "How Mom would enjoy seeing this little one!" Norma thought. "Especially since she carries the name Erma and the name Naomi, which was baby Elenora's middle name." In order to keep the Ermas apart, little Erma Naomi was called Naomi. Later she was called Nonie until her teenage years, when she chose to be called Erma.

Erma happily took off from her waitress job and came to help take care of Norma and her namesake. As usual, Dr. Martin recommended ten days of bed rest for Norma.

Norma lay in bed cuddling baby Nonie when she heard Bobby and Betty saying, "Daddy's home! Daddy's home!"

Marty came straight into her room and sank wearily into a chair. The children happily began to pile on top of him, but he put up his hand to stop them. "Not now," he said, dropping his head into his hands.

The children fell back disappointed, and Norma asked in concern,

"Marty, what is wrong? You don't look good. Are you sick?"

"I guess I'll have to see the doctor," Marty answered. "I'm feeling sicker than a dog. I have a terrible sore throat."

"Dr. Martin plans to stop soon to check up on the baby and me. I'm sure he can check you then too." Norma turned to Bobby. "Take Betty and Dickie out to play and ask Aunt Erma to come here."

Bobby had been standing there with concern on his face. He moved quickly to obey. His big, strong daddy was never sick. Marty moved to the next room and flopped wearily on Bobby's bed.

Dr. Martin breezed in sometime later and efficiently checked Norma and the baby. "Everything looks good, Norma. You have a fine little girl. Now you have help, don't you?"

"Yes, my sister Erma is here, so I'll be good," she said, smiling. Sobering quickly, she asked, "Could you check Marty out? He's in the next room. He's really looking sick."

Norma could only partly hear Dr. Martin's probing questions. She thought she heard Marty give a low moan. Whatever could be wrong? She heard Erma starting up the steps about the same time Dr. Martin came to the doorway of her bedroom.

"Norma, you have a sick husband. It's a little early to tell for sure, but it looks very much like scarlet fever.

"Now then, he should come through all right," he added, noticing the alarm in Norma's face, "but he will be a very sick man for a while and will need to be quarantined."

Norma and Erma looked at each other in dismay. The small house had only two bedrooms. "I'll run over to Barbara and see if she can lend us a bedroom on her side of the house," Erma suggested.

Barbara was more than willing. Soon the door between the two apartments was opened, adding a third bedroom to the Reed side.

Dr. Martin looked at Erma. "I'll help you get him situated, then I suggest if he's in the children's room now, that you change that bedding and air out the room. Anyone who goes in his room will have to gown up, and they'll have to disinfect when they come out. We must do our best to protect Norma and the children, even though children don't usually get scarlet fever. In a day or so, he'll break out in a rash if it is for sure scarlet fever. Do you know anyone who can give shots? He's going to need them regularly for a while."

Erma blushed slightly. "My boyfriend Ronald was a medic in the military. I'm sure he'd help us out."

"That sounds good," Dr. Martin said. Then he grinned mischievously. "It probably won't be hard to get him to come. I'll be back tomorrow. If he can come, I'll show him how. Meanwhile, I'll put up the quarantine sign. It will be good if you have a little extra help around here, Erma. Norma, you relax and take care of your baby. We'll take care of Marty."

"Erma, I don't know what we would do without you!" Norma said later when Erma came in to check on her. The children's room was cleaned and aired out. They were fed and tucked into bed.

"Norma, you have been a wonderful sister to me. I'm glad I'm here to help. That's what sisters are for." She gave Norma a quick hug. "I guess I'll gown up and go check on Marty now."

The next day confirmed Dr. Martin's suspicions. Marty did indeed have scarlet fever. Bobby raced up the stairs to talk to Norma just as the door opened to Marty's room. He stopped in his tracks. Inside, he saw his daddy roll over in bed, groaning in misery. Daddy was going to die! Whatever would they do then?

Slowly he walked into Norma's room. "Mama, is Daddy going to die?" he asked, biting his trembling lip. "He's really sick!"

Norma reached out and put her arm around his shoulder. "Daddy is very sick, Bobby, but the doctor says the medicine will help to make him better after a while. You just be a good helper for Aunt Erma. Try to keep Betty and Dickie happy so she can get the work done."

"I'll try," Bobby said bravely. "But Betty acts like she's kind of sick, and Dickie is fussy. I wish I could go over to Anna Weaver's to get the eggs and asparagus, but Aunt Erma says we must stay home because of that quarantine."

"That's right, but it will only be for a while."

"Oh, Mama, did I tell you what Anna calls a paper bag? She says she's going to put the asparagus in a 'tut'!" Norma and Bobby laughed together. "And, oh Mama, Aunt Erma has her bike here, and I'm learning to ride it in the lane."

"Well, you be careful, and you better go now, Bobby, and check on the children."

Bobby bounded down the stairs. As long as Daddy was going to get better, everything would be okay.

But Betty was lying on the couch. "My head hurts," she complained.

Erma carried a fretting Dickie. "Here, Bobby, can you show him a book? I need to take drinks upstairs."

When Erma's boyfriend, Ronald, arrived, Erma was putting a cool washcloth on Betty's forehead. She held Dickie in one arm. She looked at Ronald despairingly. "I think you better ask Dr. Martin to come. These children are sure acting sick."

Ronald stopped by Dr. Martin's office on his way home. "How soon can you get down to the Reeds? Erma has her hands full. The children are acting sick now too."

"All of them?" Dr. Martin asked in concern.

"I'm not sure. I think Bobby was still acting okay," Ronald replied.

Dr. Martin hurried to Goodville as soon as his office closed. "Well, well, what do we have now?" he questioned Erma.

"I don't know, but Betty says her head hurts, and Dickie's been fussy. They both feel a bit warm."

"They haven't been near Marty, have they?"

"No, we are being very careful," Erma replied.

The doctor examined the children and took their temperatures. "Hmm," he said quietly. "Low fever, swollen glands, no coughing, baby's eyes are a bit red... Oh, what do we have here?" he said peering closely at Dickie's face and neck, where a fine rash was beginning to spread. "It sure looks like German measles to me."

"Measles!" Erma exclaimed. "What next!"

"How about you, young man?" the doctor asked, turning to Bobby.

"Oh, I'm fine!" Bobby said quickly. He really had been feeling kind of tired, but—

"Let's check you out, just in case," the doctor said. "Open your mouth. Let's take your temperature." Expertly he felt the glands in Bobby's neck and checked the thermometer. He looked at Bobby sharply. "Kind of tired?"

"Well, yeah," Bobby answered, "a little bit."

Dr. Martin turned to Erma. "It looks like we have three cases of measles here. Double reason for that quarantine. How are you holding up?"

Erma smiled wearily and said, "Kind of tired too, but I already had the measles."

"Well, that's a good thing!" the doctor replied. "Dickie's eyes are a bit reddened already. We should get them to their bedroom and darken the room. How about if I carry this little lady upstairs?" he said, carefully lifting Betty off the couch. "I might as well check your other patients while I'm here."

"I don't want to go to bed now," Bobby protested mildly.

"Get some books and toys and come," Erma said. "It sounds like you'll soon be glad that you are there."

Betty settled into her bed with a sigh. Dickie was soon asleep, and Bobby was surprised at how good his bed felt.

Marty was still too sick to be concerned about the sick children. Dr. Martin stopped at Norma's room. "Well, Norma, I'm glad you have such an efficient little nurse here. You know they say, 'When it rains, it pours.' I hate to tell you this, but I'm afraid your three children have the German measles."

"Measles! Measles yet too! Whatever are we going to do?"

"We are going to get through this," he answered kindly. "You, young lady, are going to rest and take care of that new baby. There are plenty of helpful people around. I'll be by regularly to check up on all of you."

After the doctor had left, Norma looked at Erma in dismay. "Erma, you are already worn ragged. How are you ever going to manage?"

"People are already helping, and they will help more, I'm sure," Erma answered. "We will get through this. Harry Oberholtzer said he will deliver groceries to the front porch. Anna Weaver dropped off a pot of soup with the eggs. Ronald will help some, when he stops by. At least we have three bedrooms on one floor, thanks to Barbara."

"Erma, how can I ever thank you enough?" Norma said tearfully.

"Sis, you have been looking out for me from day one. Now it's my turn. If you have that letter you wrote ready, I'll take it down and iron it like the doctor said, to kill the germs. Ronald will make sure it gets mailed. You know," she added, "it doesn't take much cooking these days, and the children are sleeping right now. Even Bobby, who didn't think he was sick."

"Norma, try not to worry," Erma added, stroking baby Nonie's soft, dark head. "You just get your strength back. You'll have plenty to do when you are on your feet again. Marty is a little more comfortable today. I better go. I thought I heard someone on the porch," she said, gathering up a load of laundry and hurrying down the stairs.

Soon Erma was back. "Here, Norma, is a note from George's wife, Elizabeth. She dropped off a jug of cold tea and a pot of chicken soup."

Even though others helped where they could, the quarantine kept them at home. Norma couldn't help but see Erma's weariness. Up and down the stairs she went—bringing cold drinks from the hand pump on the back porch, a cracker for Betty, clean diapers for the baby, medicine for Marty. Sometimes she was comforting and rocking Dickie.

Gradually, the children started to feel better. They laughed at each other's speckled faces. Dickie sometimes came to lie on the bed beside Norma. Finally, Norma's ten days were up, and she could go in to see Marty. He smiled at her weakly.

"How's the new mama and baby?"

"Oh, Marty, we are fine, but how are you?" Norma asked, noticing his thin, flushed face.

"I'm a lot better than I was, but not as good as I could be," he answered. "How are the children? You all had quite a time out there, I understand."

"Oh, they are feeling better, but pretty speckled yet. Bobby can't wait to get outside again. I can't wait until I can send Erma for a nice, long rest."

"She's been amazing, hasn't she?" Marty said. "That Ronald sure knows how to give shots. I can't even feel them."

After several weeks, the children had fully recuperated and Norma had taken over her own housework again. All through April and well into May, Marty slowly regained his strength.

One day he stood by the window looking into the back yard, where his lime truck was parked. "A man can't pay the bills when the truck sits idle," he muttered to himself.

"Oh, Marty," Norma said, coming over to stand next to him, "you'll get there. A couple weeks ago, you were too sick to care. You are doing better all the time. Let's just thank God for that."

"You're right, I know. It's just that I get so tired of sitting around."

"Well, that's a good sign," Norma replied.

"All right, at least I can be a good babysitter for you," he said, reaching for baby Nonie. "She just doesn't pay me for my services." The old twinkle was back in his eye.

At last the day came when Marty drove his truck out the lane. Finally life was getting back to normal, and there was plenty of lime hauling to help pay the bills. Marty bought a 1938 Ford dump truck with spreader attachments for spreading lime. They were still hauling lime for the government. Sometimes the government was slow to pay. Ivan Martin regretfully asked his employees to hold their paychecks until the government check came. Marty was making fifty-six cents an hour. He also got paid for overtime, and there was plenty of it. Things were looking good for Marty and Norma. They thanked God for bringing them through.

chapter thirty-one

Dream Come True

Pennsylvania: 1946-1947

Norma stood at the front window, looking out across the street. Two houses down the street stood Anna Weaver's house. Wouldn't it be wonderful to have a house like that for their growing family? Tall maple trees shaded the long front porch. At the back door was another large porch. There were four rooms downstairs, four rooms upstairs, an attic, and a cellar. That house was more than twice as big as the apartment they lived in now! There was room for a big garden.

Suddenly Norma stopped her dreaming. Yes, Anna was selling her house, but it was not good to get her hopes up. Probably a lot of people would be interested in a house like that, and unless Marty could get a loan from Wayne Martin, the house would not be theirs. Even with a loan, a person never knew how a public auction would go.

"Imagine—a home of our own! No more renting and moving." Norma stopped herself again. She turned to pick up six-month-old Nonie. Resolutely she began singing, "Choose my path, O blessed Savior…"

The screen door slammed. One look at Marty's face, and she knew he had *not* gotten a loan.

"Sorry, Norma, but Wayne said there is no money on hand to loan out right now. The auction is just two weeks away. We just need to pray."

"I know, it's hard not to dream," Norma answered. "Even if we got the loan, someone could outbid us."

The day for the auction drew closer. Marty and Norma committed the situation to the Lord. The morning of the auction, Wayne Martin walked down Water Street and knocked on Marty and Norma's door.

"Well, Marty," he said, "someone just brought money in. I brought ninety dollars with me for a down payment. If you are still interested, we will work out the rest."

"We sure are!" Marty answered. "What an answer to prayer! The auction is today!"

Wayne smiled. "Just in time. What are you thinking you would pay for the house?"

"Well, I've asked around a bit and thought I wouldn't go above $5000. What do you think?" Marty asked.

"That sounds about right to me. I wish you the best." And Wayne was gone.

Marty hurried to the kitchen. "Norma, would you like to go look at the house? That was Wayne. We can get the money."

"Really? Marty, what an answer to prayer! Oh, I'm so excited. When can we go?"

"I'd say as soon as we can before there are too many people there. I'd like to look the place over once more."

They looked at the property. The house stood at the end of a row of houses. The property was not as deep as the other properties, but it was twice as wide. One side was bordered by an orchard belonging to the neighboring farm. A barn-like garage stood at the end of the lane. Norma had never been through the house. She waited eagerly until Marty was ready to step inside.

An old hand pump stood on the back porch. "No well," Marty observed. "Just a cistern. I'd want to drill a well soon."

Norma was looking past him into the large dining room. French doors separated it from the living room. Eagerly she moved to the kitchen and looked around at the gleaming white painted cupboards. "Maybe just a dream," she reminded herself. They looked into the living room and small parlor downstairs. Then they toured the two large and two small bedrooms upstairs. Bobby and Betty were fascinated by the attic.

While Marty checked the roof and structure of the house and Norma dreamed of all the storage room, Bobby and Betty looked out the little attic windows. "There's our house over there," Betty said excitedly.

"We're up high," Bobby observed. "We can see the people coming to the sale."

Marty and Norma mingled with the crowd as the household auction progressed throughout the morning. Then it was time to sell the house. Norma prayed. Marty's hands grew cold and his pulse quickened. He didn't hesitate, though, to enter into the bidding.

"All-ll right folks, it's a good, sound house we have here. Who'll give me 3000, 3000, 3000. I've got 3000. Who'll give me 3500, 3500." The bidding continued. "I've got 4800. Who'll make it 4900, 4900." Marty bid. "I've got 4900. Who'll make it 5000, 5000, 5000. I say who'll make it 5000. I've got 5000. Who'll make it 5100." Marty was at his limit, but he had not made the last bid. "5100, 5100. Do I have a bid?" Marty nodded. "I've got 5100. 5200, 5200 anybody give me 5200? It's going, folks. Anybody give me 5200? Sold! To Martin Reed."

Norma glanced at Marty. His face was white. Marty fingered the lone quarter in his pocket. The house was theirs!

"It's a nice house you have there, Marty," his brother Daniel remarked.

"I'm going to have to spread a lot of lime for this one," Marty answered.

Marty signed the papers and paid the down payment. The crowd thinned out. Norma walked back inside to take a look at her kitchen. Now she could dream.

"Daddy bought the house, didn't he, Mama?" Bobby asked.

"Are we going to live here?" Betty wondered.

"That's right," Norma answered. "Daddy bought it, and we are going to move here."

"It's a pretty big house," Bobby observed. "I can't wait. When can we move? Oh, look, we will have our own phone now," he said, pointing to the crank phone hanging on the wall.

Marty came walking over and looked at Norma above the excited children. "Well, my little wife, I guess your dreams came true."

Norma looked back at him, her eyes shining. "It's a miracle, Marty. We only got the loan this morning. Just think, a home of our own. This is quite a step up from the tent we lived in the first summer we were married, isn't it?" They laughed together.

"Boys, I'm going out to look at the garage. Do you want to go along? I think Mama wants to dream over the house some more."

"Look, Mama," Betty said. "I like this little step by the window. I can play church here with my dolly!" The stair steps came down to a landing and then turned the corner with two steps in the dining room.

"That will be nice," Norma answered, shifting baby Nonie to the other arm. Norma was trying to imagine their few pieces of furniture in this big house.

Marty came back into the house. "Norma, I forgot to tell you that Daniel told me Father is sick. That's why he and Mother didn't come to the auction. The doctor says typhoid fever."

"Typhoid fever!" Norma looked shocked. "That's a dangerous disease, isn't it?"

"It is, but Dr. Martin is treating him with penicillin and sulfa and talks positive. Father will likely be sick for months, and they will be quarantined, of course. It's going to keep Aaron busy with only thirteen-year-old Irvin to help on the farm."

"It's good most of the field work is done," Norma commented. "We thought scarlet fever was bad, didn't we?"

"Father will be sick longer than I was," Marty agreed. "Daniel said he's sure Father will have to downsize his farming operation."

"Maybe they will move closer to us," Norma dreamed.

This time Norma thoroughly enjoyed moving! Marty enjoyed watching her delight. Norma loved her kitchen. It was not big enough for the kitchen table, but the table was placed in the center of the roomy dining room. The kitchen table was to become the center of family and social life for years to come. The children explored the new house and yard. Bobby and Betty each claimed a bedroom and were happy to share with Dickie and Nonie. There was even an extra bedroom left!

The bedroom wasn't empty for long. Art was home from the war

House Marty bought in Goodville, PA

and needed a place to live. Gladly Marty and Norma opened their home to him.

Bobby was quite fascinated by their telephone. He watched while Marty cranked the phone and then asked the operator for Ivan Martin's stone quarry. Six or seven other families shared their party line. Each family's ring was different. When they heard one long ring, Bobby knew it was for them.

It wasn't so fascinating when the phone rang in the night. Neighbor Johnny Hurst had a trucking business. His ring was one long and one short. He got calls at night from his truck drivers.

It was possible to pick up the phone and listen in on someone else's conversation. Sometimes a telltale *clink* when you were on the phone told you a nosy neighbor was doing just that.

Norma was glad for the fact that they could now phone Wilson and Susannah to see how Wilson was doing or to ask advice from Susannah. Wilson was convalescing well, but he knew now that he would not have the strength for the heavy farm work that he had done before. So the farm was put up for sale with plans to move in the spring.

As the farm work petered out and Wilson could do more, Aaron, Marty's brother, decided to work for Daniel hauling lime for Ivan

Marty and lime truck

Martin. He needed to live closer to the job, so Marty and Norma offered him a place to stay. With Art and Aaron both living there, mealtimes were filled with lots of friendly discussion. How those two liked to argue!

Finally Norma looked at them. "Whatever are you two going to do if one of you gets married?"

They looked at each other and grinned. "I guess we'll get together and argue," Art answered.

One day Norma and Art sat talking at the dining room table. "I talked to Walter recently, Norma. He has lots to say about his friend Edna. Sounds like they're getting married. He seems happy.

"He sees Mom occasionally and said she's still doing housework here and there for folks. Sometimes I wonder how long that will last."

"I've wondered too," Norma answered. "Do you ever hear from Raymond or Dad?"

"Actually, I just talked to Raymond. He and Dad are both working at a Studebaker plant. It sounds as though he likes his work. I'm glad at least one of us can have some kind of relationship with Dad. I feel like I hardly know the man."

"I know what you mean," Norma sighed. "Walter told me one time that he felt like Dad just kicked you and him out when he took you up to Brutus to work. It wasn't unusual for boys your age to work away, but it was so far away. Then our home fell apart and there was nothing to come home to. That's what made it hurt."

"Well, I sure appreciate you and Marty giving me a place when I couldn't stay at Uncle Joe's anymore."

"We're glad too. You should have heard Bobby and Betty rejoicing when they knew you were coming back from the war."

Just then loud crying came from the back yard. "Sounds like a war in the sandbox," Art joked as Norma hurried outside to settle the squabble.

Marty had dumped a big pile of sand in the back yard for the children to play in. The sand pile was an attraction to the neighborhood children as well. Often several of them would come and spend the afternoon.

When winter came, Water Street was the gathering place for sledding. On a good sledding day, the sledders got a long, gradual ride from Main Street down past the Reeds' house and on around the corner at the neighboring farm. Bobby was old enough to sled with his friends from the little red schoolhouse on Main Street. When Nonie was napping, it wasn't unusual for the neighbors to see Norma out sledding, with Betty and three-year-old Dick on her sled. They made snowmen and snow angels. Norma was not much past her own girlhood. Memories of an absent mother made her want to give her children what she had missed.

As soon as possible, Marty had a well dug and brought running water into the kitchen for Norma.

One day Marty came home and hurried to the kitchen to find Norma. "How would you like to have Father and Mother living right here on Water Street?"

"Where?" Norma asked. "Oh, wonderful! Which house?"

"Two houses up on our side of the street. It's for sale, and George and I just had a look at it. Father and Mother need to come see it, but it looks good, and the price is good."

"Oh, Marty, I've missed having them near us! That's almost too good to be true! When could they get in?"

"Well, Father wants to be off the farm by spring so the new owners can take over with spring planting. The house is available very soon, and spring isn't far away."

"Oh, won't the children be excited. We better not tell them yet in case it falls through."

Norma loved to work outside. So when the weather warmed up, she was soon busy planting garden. Owning their own property made it worthwhile to plant strawberries and shrubs.

There was a triangular piece of land behind the garage. It was all grown up in brambles. Marty bought a billy goat and staked it out to clean up the brambles. Once the ground was worked up, Norma planned to plant raspberries. Meanwhile, Bobby had fun with the billy goat.

A number of the neighbors were Old Order Mennonites who drove horse and buggies. Regularly Bobby watched the horse and buggies go past the house. Then he got an idea. Finding a few ropes, he harnessed the goat to the wagon. What a ride he would have! Norma watched from the clothesline where she was hanging up wash.

Much to Bobby's dismay, the goat was more interested in eating the soft grass in the yard than in going forward. Bobby sat in the wagon thinking. Norma smiled to herself, but offered no solutions. She knew Bobby would figure something out. She went back into the house to get another load of wash.

She was just ready to come out again when she heard the screech of brakes. Dropping her wash basket, she ran. A truck was stopped in the middle of the road. In front of the truck was Bobby, the wagon, and the goat. Bobby looked scared, but otherwise he seemed to be all right. Newt Kramer, the driver, was laughing and wiping tears from his eyes.

"Bobby, whatever are you doing on the road?" Norma asked.

"Well, I—I—didn't know how to get it stopped," Bobby answered, looking sideways at Newt with a perplexed and uncertain look. "You see, I put a carrot on the end of a stick and hung it in front of the goat. He took off after the carrot and came tearing out the lane. I couldn't think how to stop when I got to the road."

"And then…" Norma stopped.

Newt took up the story. "I'm sorry, Mrs. Reed, for the scare, but I was coming down the street, and suddenly right in front of me is this goat running fit to kill, with a wagon rattling on behind and one scared-looking little fellow riding." He smothered another laugh. "I got stopped, and all ended well, but I don't know if I'll ever forget that one."

"I'm so sorry, Mr. Kramer, for your trouble, but we'll try to keep the goat off the road from now on." Norma grabbed the rope and led the goat and Bobby off the road.

When Mr. Kramer drove away, she found herself shaking. "Bobby, are you okay?" she asked.

"Yeah, I guess I'm just a little scared," Bobby answered. "That Mr. Kramer—the boys at school said he's a grouchy man. He doesn't want any of the boys to come close to his buggy shop. I was scared when I saw it was him. The boys say he's a poky driver too. They laugh and say, 'Tramp her down to thirty-five.'"

"I guess we can thank God that he is a slow driver, Bobby," Norma said, giving him a hug. "You could have been hurt badly. I can tell you too why Mr. Kramer doesn't want the boys at his buggy shop. He paints buggies, and he doesn't want anyone kicking up dust because of the wet paint. You see, Bobby, I think we learned two things today. Sometimes we get wrong ideas about people because we don't understand everything. The other thing is to plan ahead a little better— like figuring out how you are going to stop the wagon once you get it started. Now, go tie the goat up for today."

Wilson and Susannah bought the house on Water Street. Norma

Wilson Reed family
Back row: Magdalena, Daniel, Irvin, Aaron, Marty, Esther
Seated: Emma, Susannah, Wilson, George

helped Susannah clean the house and plant garden. "Oh, Mother," Norma rejoiced, "this is like old times. It is so nice to have you living nearby again."

"We're glad too," Susannah answered. "It was a little hard to give up the farm, but it would have come sooner or later anyway. I'm just so glad that Father is finally feeling better, and we will certainly enjoy living close to you, George's, and Daniel's."

As Norma tucked the children into bed that night, she thought, "What more could I want? I have Marty, four healthy children, and a home of our own. Marty has a steady job, and we have a church we are happy with. And now Father and Mother live nearby. Oh, I am so blessed!"

chapter thirty-two

I Didn't Know It Would Mean This!

Pennsylvania: 1947-1949

"Mama, there's an old man at the back door," Betty said quietly. "He looks kind of poor and scary."

Norma wiped her hands on her apron and hurried to the back door. Baby Nonie toddled over and hung on to her skirt. Dick stood nearby watching.

"Good morning, ma'am." The old man's grin revealed several gaps in his rows of crooked teeth. "I was wonderin' if you could spare a cup of coffee."

"Surely," Norma answered cheerfully. "Would you be glad for a sandwich too?"

"I'd be much obliged, ma'am. Do you mind if I sit here on the porch steps awhile?"

"That will be fine," Norma answered.

He settled down on the porch steps with his lumpy bags beside him. Marty had built a large covered porch at the door on the side of the house. Nearly all visitors showed up at that door.

Dick peeked out the dining room window as Norma hurried to the kitchen. "Here, Betty, you can spread mayonnaise on this bread while I make coffee," she instructed.

"Who is he, Mama?" Betty whispered.

"I don't know his name," Norma answered, "but he's a poor man who probably lives in a little shack and doesn't have a job. There seem to be quite a few people like him since the war. Some people call them 'tramps' because they tramp around and ask for food."

"We have enough food, don't we?" Betty wondered.

"Yes, we do, and we are happy to share with poor people. That's what Jesus wants us to do. Here, why don't you carry the sandwich, and I'll carry the coffee."

"I'm a little scared, Mama."

"It's all right, Betty. I'll go too," Norma answered.

"Thank you. Thank you, ma'am. God bless," the old man said when they handed him the food. "You got a good mother there, little miss," he said, looking at Betty and rubbing his stubby chin. Betty smiled shyly and nodded.

More than one tramp found his way to Norma's door. Betty soon learned that her mother always had a cheerful word, hot coffee, and food for each one.

Marty wanted his children to see the other side of life. He took the family for a drive up the Welsh Mountain. There Bobby and Betty saw ragged children running around tumbledown shacks. Years later he took his family to see the slums of Chicago. This wasn't for the sake of idle curiosity, but rather out of compassion for the less fortunate. When the Churchtown church began summer Bible school at a little community church in nearby Cambridge and began bringing children from the Welsh Mountain by the carloads, Marty and Norma threw

Left to right: Nonie, Dick, Betty, Bobby

themselves into the work. They helped to pass out invitations, hauled children, and taught summer Bible school classes.

One day Susannah sat at the dining room table talking to Norma about Marty's oldest sister, Emma.

"William and Emma are having some financial difficulties. Daniel is offering William work hauling lime, but we just don't know where they will live if they come from Michigan. I'm just not sure that Father could handle it with five children at our house. He still needs his rest at times."

"They are looking for a new little one in December, aren't they?" Norma asked.

"Yes, I'm worried about Emma," Susannah answered. "It was just a year and a half ago that her twins were born and died. They need to get in here to Pennsylvania before the baby comes, but I doubt if they can afford to rent until William works for a while."

"Well, Mother, maybe we could turn our parlor into a bedroom temporarily," Norma answered. "We could sleep some of the children upstairs and some in the living room. I'll have to talk to Marty."

"Oh, that would be a relief," Susannah answered. "It's a good thing your house isn't bigger, Norma, or you would just fill it up!" she said laughing. "I'll help out wherever I can."

"You know, Mother, people gave me a home when I needed it. I want to do the same for others."

And so the Ebys settled in with the Reeds temporarily. In December Dr. Martin hurried to Marty and Norma's house. This time it was to welcome little Danny Eby into the world.

The following summer Marty and Norma again helped out with the summer Bible school work at Cambridge. The needy children reminded Norma of her own childhood, the tarpaper shack, and tattered shoes. With a deep sense of satisfaction, she reached out to these children.

When Bobby and Betty started school in the fall, Betty had a secret. Mama had told her that the front parlor was going to be turned into a bedroom again, and God was going to give them their own baby this December.

Early in December Larry Lee made his appearance. When the children gathered eagerly around to see their new little brother, Marty teased, "Well, Bobby, this little fellow looks so much like you that we might get the two of you mixed up." With the exception of his deep dimples, Larry did look a lot like Bobby, with his round face and head of tight curls.

Norma's hands were full with two children in school and three preschoolers, but she happily cooked and cleaned and kept her treadle sewing machine busy making dresses and shirts and pants. Marty occasionally took one of the children along on the lime truck. Norma loved to see him playing on the floor with the children.

In the fall they worked together raking the leaves from the big maple trees in the front yard. In spite of all her busyness, Norma played in the snow with her children and took time to play simple board games around the table. She taught them games from her childhood like "Jing Hands Up" and "Hide the Thimble." When summer came, she put Larry to sleep in the baby coach, and they all planted garden together.

Then one day Norma got a phone call from Michigan. It was Abe

Sauder's wife. "Norma, your mom's been working and living here and there. It's not been going too well. I think maybe you better come get her and take care of her."

Norma was silent for a moment, then she replied, "Thank you for calling. I'll discuss it with my family." Slowly she hung up the receiver and stared out the window. "Take care of Mom? Mom is only fifty-five. I am busy with my family. How would Mom fit into our happy home?" Memories of childhood hurts threatened to choke out the happiness. Norma groaned quietly, "Oh God, what do you want me to do? Marty and I agreed that we want to have our home open to others, but I didn't know it would mean this!"

Marty and Norma discussed the idea. Marty was not opposed to bringing Mom to Pennsylvania. But his main concern was Norma's feelings and workload. They both knew that if Mom didn't find a job in Pennsylvania that worked out for her, everything would fall back on Norma.

Norma searched her own heart. "Am I being selfish? I don't want anything to spoil our happy home. Why do all the childhood hurts surface now? Mom wasn't there for me most of my life. Am I obligated to her now? Have I forgiven?" Norma prayed. She opened her Bible. There it was—"Honour thy father and thy mother." It didn't say, "if they have been good to you." That meant Mom. God would take care of the rest. Norma surrendered it all to God, and she was at peace. Then she talked to her siblings. Marty discussed it with his parents. Everyone agreed something needed to be done.

"You know I can't keep Mom right now," Erma said. "But I might be able to help find her a job."

"Are you sure that you want to do this, Norma?" Art asked.

"It's the right thing to do, Art," Norma answered.

"Then I'll go get her when you're ready," Art offered.

"Sis, are you sure you will be okay with this?" Walter wondered.

"God will help me, Walt," Norma answered.

Raymond's only comment was, "Norma, you have a good heart."

Wilson and Susannah were supportive. One neighbor who also came from Michigan looked at Norma. "Why would you take care of her when she didn't take care of you?"

Norma looked at them calmly and said, "Because she is my mother."

Art made the trip to Michigan. What if Mom wouldn't consent to come? But she came willingly enough. Times were hard, and when her marriage had ended, she was financially unable to maintain and furnish a home of her own. For almost twenty years, she had moved from place to place where she found work.

It had been six years since Norma had seen Mom. Bobby was the only one of the children who had faint memories of "Grandma Brenneman." Norma reflected over this as she and the children sat on the back porch shelling peas. Bobby, Betty, and five-year-old Dick were pretty good at the job. They all took turns popping the shells open for three-year-old Nonie to pick the peas out. Larry toddled about, putting everything into his mouth.

"You know, children," Norma began, "Grandma Brenneman did not spend her life serving God like Grandmother Reed did. Sometimes it will be fun having her here, and sometimes it might be hard. If we are kind and patient with her and pray for her, maybe she will decide to give her heart to Jesus."

"Will she live with us always?" Bobby wondered.

"Not necessarily, Bobby. Your Aunt Erma is going to try to find a place where she can live and work."

"Will she go to church with us?" Betty wondered.

"I hope so, Betty, " Norma replied. "We'll invite her along anyway, won't we?" Betty nodded.

"I don't know her," Dick said uncertainly, "but I like Grandmother Reed!"

"We like having Grandfather and Grandmother living nearby, don't we?" Norma said, smiling at him.

"Is there a Grandpa Brenneman too?" Betty wondered.

"Yes," Norma said slowly, praying for wisdom to answer. "He and

Grandma don't live together. When I was a little girl about your age, they stopped living together."

Bobby and Betty both looked at her in surprise. "Then what?" Bobby wondered. "What happened to you then?"

"I wouldn't like if you and Daddy did that!" Betty said soberly.

Norma sent another prayer heavenward as she looked into the faces of her innocent children. She reached over and gave Betty a hug. "You don't need to worry about that, Betty. My mama and daddy were not serving God. Daddy and I love God, and God helps us to always love each other. My daddy took me to a different home to live. It was a sad time for me, but he took me to a happy home to live where I learned about God."

"I'm glad you learned about God, Mama. Then you can teach us about Him," Betty said.

"I'm glad too," Norma said.

Betty enjoyed helping to get Art's room ready for the grandma that was coming. "Uncle Art doesn't need this room anymore, does he?" Betty asked.

"No, he's married now. He won't live here anymore, but we can go visit him," Norma answered.

"Do you think Grandma Brenneman would like if I picked some flowers for her?" Betty wondered.

"Oh, that would be nice!" Norma replied. "You can pick some roses and sweet williams if you want. We'll put them here on the stand." Even though a bit of apprehension lurked, Norma looked forward to showing Mom her house and children.

Alzina arrived, bag and baggage. She seemed genuinely grateful to Marty and Norma for giving her a place to live. She enjoyed meeting her grandchildren and exclaimed with delight over the flowers in her room. "Roses! How did you know I liked roses?"

"Betty picked those for you," Norma said.

"Why thank you, Betty! I really like flowers!" she exclaimed. Betty smiled shyly.

Mom

Bobby was happy to find out that Grandma liked to shell peas. The buckets and buckets of peas to shell didn't look so bad with Grandma to help. Willingly she washed dishes and hung up laundry for Norma.

When Sunday came, Norma asked her, "Will you go along to church with us, Mom?"

"Well, I think I might just do that," she answered. Norma rejoiced when her mom continued to attend regularly with them. Mom enjoyed the singing, and occasionally Norma would hear her singing snatches of song as she hung out the laundry.

Then Erma found a job for Mom, and she moved to Lancaster near Erma. Mom was doing housework for the owners of Moen's Buick Dealers. No one really knew what all had gone wrong for Mom in Michigan. How would Mom do on this job?

chapter thirty-three

And the Phone Rang

Pennsylvania: 1950-1951

"*Ring...*" Norma pushed toys aside with her foot and hurried to answer the phone.

"Norma, this is Marty. I'm down here at the shop. I need someone to bring the lime truck down here. I guess Father is gone, isn't he?"

"Yes, he and Mother went to Downingtown."

"I was afraid of that. I'm just not sure what to do. How about if you drive it here, and then I'll run you home. You probably have Esther there, and she could watch the children."

"Oh, Marty! Esther is here with us, but—Marty, I can't drive that lime truck!" Norma objected.

Marty chuckled. "Oh, I think you can. You know how to shift. It's not much more than a mile down here."

"But Marty! I never drove a big truck like that."

"You can do it, Norma. I really don't have any other way to get it here. None of the other men are here right now, and I need to get back to the quarry. I don't have time to walk home."

"Well, all right then," Norma said, "but you better pray for me."

Marty smiled to himself as he hung up. Norma was a plucky little wife. She'd get the truck here just fine.

A few minutes later, Norma climbed up into the lime truck. The children stood in the yard watching. Mama was going to drive Daddy's big truck!

"I think I could probably drive it down there," twelve-year-old Bobby offered.

"You have to have a driver's license, silly," Esther informed him.

Norma was glad Marty had turned the truck around facing the road. At least she didn't have to back it out. Gripping the steering wheel tightly, she stretched her foot to push the clutch in. Then she turned the key, and the truck roared to life. She released the brakes. Panic almost took over when she remembered that she was starting out at the *bottom* of Water Street. Perching on the edge of the seat, she strained to hold the clutch in and still see over the steering wheel. Carefully she eased into first gear. She was off! Slowly she started up Water Street. Now it was time to shift. With only a little grinding of gears, she made it into second. Oh dear, now she was at the stop sign. There was no traffic in sight, so for the first time in her life, Norma purposely ran a stop sign. As she turned onto Main Street and went past Harry Oberholtzer's store, she thought, "I hope no one is looking, or I will be the talk of the town."

Now it was time to shift again. She pushed the clutch in and tried to shift into third gear. *K-k-k-k. K-k-k-k.* Where was third gear anyway? Carefully she tried again. *K-k-k-k. K-k-k-k.* Well then, the only thing to do was go the rest of the way in second gear. *Chug. Chug. Chug.* She went out through town, and down the long hill to Frogtown.

When Norma chugged into the shop, Marty was waiting for her with a grin. "I knew you could do it!"

"Oh, Marty! Never again! I couldn't even get it out of second gear!"

"Sorry, Norma, but you are here, and I really appreciate it. Now I'll run you home on my way to the quarry. Unless, of course, you wanted to drive," he added mischievously.

She gave him a reproachful look and climbed up on the passenger side of the truck. She waved at George's children playing in the yard. George and Elizabeth lived by the truck shop. "How is Elizabeth? Did George say anything?"

"She's really not doing too well. The older girls are trying to keep things going," Marty answered.

"I should take them a meal and maybe bring little Irene over for a while to help them out."

"Thanks again, Norma," Marty said, stopping in front of their house. "I expect to be home for a late supper."

It was April when the phone rang again. This time it was Wilson's voice. "Norma, I have sad news. George just called here. Elizabeth passed away. Mother and I are planning to go over there."

Norma gripped the phone. Dear, sweet Elizabeth—and now seven motherless children. What would George ever do?

"If you and Marty want to come over too," Wilson continued, "Esther could come down and watch the children."

"We'd appreciate that. I'm sure Marty will want to be there for George. Thanks for calling, Father."

The next few days were a blur. Neighbors and friends surrounded the family with help and support. George wanted to keep his children together. Norma offered to occasionally take three-year-old Renie to come and play with four-year-old Nonie. The little cousins were happy playmates.

George's two oldest girls, Dorcas and Anna Mary, were twelve and fourteen. They would manage the best they could, as they did when their mother was sick. Norma and Susannah didn't live far away, and they helped where they could.

When this year's summer Bible school came at Cambridge with its record attendance, Norma wasn't busy hauling children to Bible school. Little Wilmer Wilson arrived in the middle of June. He was a dainty, fine-featured baby. Susannah said he should have been a girl, but Wilson was obviously very pleased to have a namesake. The five siblings vied for a turn to hold the new baby.

The phone rang again in August. "Hi, Sis! This is Walt. How's that new baby?"

"Oh, he's doing fine. He doesn't lack for attention."

"I'm sure of that. Well, we have good news for you. We have the prettiest little baby girl in Michigan. She's just a couple hours old, but I couldn't wait to call you. We decided to name her Norma Jean after a very special sister of mine."

"Why, thank you. I feel honored."

"You've been a wonderful sister, Norma."

"How are Edna and the baby doing?"

"They are just fine. I'm having a little trouble, though. Seems my shirt buttons want to bust. I never knew how proud a papa could feel. I sure hope I can be a good dad to her, Norma. I don't want her to get hurt like we were."

"I think you'll be a wonderful dad, Walter. You got a lot of practice by being a good big brother."

"Thank you, Sis. You take care now."

"Thanks for calling, Walt. Give that baby a hug for me, and give Edna my regards."

Alzina had made out reasonably well on her new job, but as time went on, the situation wore out. She had made friends among various people in the city, and not all of her friendships were desirable.

One day the phone rang. Norma laid baby Wilmer down and hurried to answer it. It was Erma. "Norma, could you and Marty come and get Mom? I talked to the Moens. She's packed up and moved out of there. They know where she is. It's not a good situation. You will probably be glad if Marty comes along."

Once more, Esther came to stay with the children, and Marty and Norma drove to Lancaster. Mom was very quiet on the way home. She moved back into Art's old bedroom.

Norma's heart was heavy. If only Mom knew the Lord. While she could be very pleasant, there were times when she snapped at the children or complained about their noise. Norma prayed for grace. At least when Sunday morning came, Mom went along to church.

One day Betty found Norma in the basement doing laundry. "Mama, Grandma says I took her pocketbook, but I didn't. I saw in her pocketbook once when she opened it. It's just papers and hankies. It smells like powder. I wouldn't even want her pocketbook."

"I know, Betty," Norma sighed. "She probably misplaced it. I'll go help her find it. Just pray for her, Betty. She's getting older, and she needs Jesus."

Norma found the pocketbook hidden under the bed pillow, where Grandma had put it to keep anyone from taking it. What had there been in Mom's life that made her so afraid of people taking her things? Norma realized there was much of her mom's life that she knew nothing about.

One evening, Norma sat in church as the preacher clearly and plainly explained salvation through Jesus. Norma felt overwhelming gratitude for the gift of salvation. "Thank you, God, for forgiveness and peace and joy." Bobby and Betty had recently given their hearts to the Lord. Marty and Norma rejoiced together to see their children choosing the right. Quietly Norma opened the songbook as the preacher pleaded with the audience to make their peace with God.

"If you are tired of sin, won't you come to Jesus and let Him take your burden away? We are going to sing an invitation song. If you are ready to lay your burden at the foot of the cross, just stand to your feet until we acknowledge you. We will pray with you after the service."

Reverently the song began. "Just as I am, without one plea, but that Thy blood was shed for me…"

Out of the corner of her eye, Norma saw someone standing—it was Mom! A tear rolled down Norma's cheek. She wiped it away unashamedly. Mom had made a choice for God! "Oh thank you, thank you, God," she whispered.

After the service, Norma handed baby Wilmer to Susannah and went with Mom to the prayer room. Freely Mom confessed her life of sin and selfishness. Her prayer was a simple one, but the peace of God shone from her eyes when she rose from her knees. The next morning Norma heard Mom singing, "What can wash away my sin? Nothing but the blood of Jesus…"

Norma was busy ironing. Steam irons being unknown to her, she took another shirt out of the plastic bag. The night before, she had sprinkled the clothes with water, rolled each one up, and put them all in a bag so they would be damp and easier to iron. Bobby, Betty, and Dick were in school. Larry and Nonie played on the floor with baby Wilmer. Mom came and sat down on a chair nearby.

"Norma, I would like to wear a head covering like you do. Do you think you could help me get one?"

"Why sure, Mom. I'd be glad to if that's what you want."

"I think it's the right thing to do, and do you think you could sew me a plain dress like yours too?"

"Mom, I'll gladly do that for you, and if I can't find time, we can get someone else to sew for you."

"Well, Norma, I think I want to be part of your church, but do you think God really forgave me for all the things I've done in the past?"

"I'm sure of it, Mom. The Bible says, 'If we confess our sins, He is faithful and just to forgive us our sins.'"

"But Norma, do you think I can be good enough to be a part of your church? Do you think I can keep on doing right?"

"Yes, Mom, with God's help, you can. When we stumble, we go to Jesus and ask Him to forgive us, and He does."

"Norma, I'm so glad that you brought me here to Pennsylvania."

"I'm glad too, Mom."

Mom and Norma

It was March when the phone rang again. It was Erma's husband, Ronald.

"Really!" Norma exclaimed. "Did everything go all right? How is Erma? What a surprise! Wait till I tell Mom!"

Norma turned from the phone to her questioning family. "Ronald and Erma have twin girls!"

"Twins!" Alzina exclaimed.

"Oh, when can we go see them? What are their names?" Betty wondered.

"Their names are Kathleen and Eileen, and they are identical."

"Is Erma doing okay?" Mom wondered.

"Yes, they are all fine," Norma answered.

"Now Linda has two babies to play with," Naomi said. "She and Ronnie won't have to take turns like we do."

"Aunt Erma's going to be busy," Betty observed. "I can't wait to tell Esther!"

Norma noticed how Mom enjoyed her grandchildren as babies. Arthur's second son was born soon after the twins. Mom made out well with the twins.

Norma came home from grocery shopping one day to find Dick sitting on the porch step crying softly. Naomi was trying to comfort him. "Grandma got upset because we children were running around the kitchen table. We were just having fun, but Grandma got angry. She took the broom and came after us. It was scary, and Dick can't seem to get over it."

Norma sighed to herself. Mom just didn't seem to know how to relate to the children when she was alone with them. "Where is Grandma now?" Norma wondered.

"She went into her room and slammed the door," Betty answered. "When Dick started to cry, then Larry cried too, and it was awful!" Betty unloaded. "We ran outside and hid behind the barn for awhile. I'm glad you are back."

"I'm sorry, Betty. Really, you children are not to be running in the house, you know. You can do that outside. But I'll talk to her."

There were times when Alzina went to stay at Erma's house for a while. One day Norma overheard Erma's Linda talking to Betty and Naomi. "Mom and Dad were both working, and we were home with Grandma. I don't know what Ronnie did, but Grandma came after him with a broom. He ran as fast as he could for the back door. When he got to the screen door, it was locked. He was so scared he jumped right through the screen."

Norma took the girls aside and explained to them, "Grandma is getting older, and she isn't used to having children around. You will need to try not to do things that upset her."

Norma purposed in her own heart to try not to leave Mom in charge of the children, but one day she was called away unexpectedly on a short errand. With a few quick words of admonition, she left. Returning a short time later, she found the children in a huddle and all visibly shaken. Mom was nowhere in sight.

Bobby was indignant. "Mom, you won't believe what Grandma did! She actually chased us with a kettle of boiling water!"

That was the last time Mom stayed alone with the children. Through it all, Norma tried to help the children respect Grandma where they could. "You know," she explained, "Grandma has not been serving God for very long, and there are still a lot of things for her to learn about following God."

Marty was concerned about the emotional load that Mom placed on Norma. Sometimes Arthur came and took Mom to an appointment. Other times, she would go and spend several days with Aunt Sarah's Mandy. While there were times that Norma had to pray for grace to relate to Mom, there were also times that Mom could be very pleasant and helpful. Coming into Mom's room and finding her happily reading her Bible was all the reward that Norma asked for.

I'LL SEE YOU IN THE MORNING

chapter thirty-four

Changes

Pennsylvania: 1952-1956

"Spam again!" Bob muttered.

"Well, I like Spam!" Dick said, eagerly eyeing the supper with the hungry eyes of a growing nine-year-old.

"I think Mom knows more ways to fix Spam than anyone else!" Bob continued. "Spam gravy, diced Spam mixed with macaroni, Spam sliced, breaded, and fried, Spam ground up with pickles and eggs for sandwich spread…"

Marty was lifting Wilmer into the high chair. "That's enough, Bob!" he said. "Be glad your mother can work miracles with a little can of Spam. A lot of people in the world would be glad to take your place."

"Where's Larry?" Norma asked, coming from the kitchen with a bowl of steaming potatoes.

Everyone looked around. Larry's stool was empty.

"Who left all those boots by the back door?" Betty asked with the exasperation of a big sister. Her question was answered by a muffled giggle.

"I know where Larry is," Dick said, running over and pulling open a little door in the wall. There sat Larry in a little cubbyhole that used to be a woodbox in the days of a woodstove. Wood could be thrown in from the back porch and then taken out of the woodbox from inside the house. Now it was used for boots.

"There you are!" Marty laughed. "Now you go and wash your hands for supper."

After prayer, Marty watched Bob load his plate with potatoes, Spam gravy, and buttery corn. As he put a big spoonful in his mouth, Marty said, "It's pretty good, isn't it, Bob?" Bob grinned sheepishly.

"These potatoes are sure better than the ones Grandma made," Dick said, laughing. Everyone joined him, including Grandma. "Daddy's face looked so funny when he tasted them," Dick added.

"I sure thought I had oil when I fried them," Grandma said. With no indoor bathroom, hair washing was often done at the kitchen sink. Grandma had grabbed the shampoo by mistake!

"I talked to Raymond today," Norma said, spooning food into Wilmer's mouth. "He called from Indiana. He's happily married, and they found a house in South Bend. I'm so glad for him."

"It sounds like we'll have another wedding here soon," Marty said. "George told me today that he and Anna Weaver are planning a wedding."

"I'm so glad for him!" Norma responded. "And glad for the girls— they have carried a heavy load since Elizabeth passed away."

"Uncle George is getting married?" Betty wondered.

"Is he getting married to the same Anna Weaver that used to live in this house before we did and sold us asparagus in a paper tut?" Bob wondered.

"That's right," Norma answered. "I think she will make a wonderful mother for George's children. I'm so glad that George has found such happiness again."

"Well," Marty said, "tomorrow is church. Bob and Dick, you carry dishes to the kitchen. Betty, you start washing dishes. Mama has baths to give, and I need to study for devotions." Marty had been Sunday school superintendent since Cambridge had organized Sunday school a year ago.

The little mission congregation was holding services every Sunday morning now. James Sauder had been ordained minister, and a year later, Marty's brother George had been ordained deacon.

One morning Norma was doing laundry. She shook out a pair of little overalls and pinned it to the clothesline. Before reaching for another pair, she paused to watch a cardinal at the bird feeder. As she continued to hang up wash, she overheard Bob and Betty talking in the nearby garden where they were hoeing corn.

"I'd sure much rather be driving a lime truck than hoeing garden," Bob was saying. "Next year this time, that's what I'll be doing."

"Do you think Daddy's going to let you drive a truck as soon as you're sixteen?" Betty asked.

"I think so. I heard Dad and Grandfather talking...I can hardly wait! I guess then you'll have to hoe corn by yourself," Bob added with a mischievous grin.

"Well, I like working outside, and Dick can help some. Erma's going to be eight. I hoed corn by that age, I'm sure. I wouldn't want to drive a lime truck anyway," she returned.

Norma looked at her children. Bobby was growing fast, and it was hard to believe that he would soon be driving a car. Betty at twelve was such a big help!

One day in early November, Norma got her wish. The children crowded happily around their new little sister. Betty and Naomi were thrilled.

"What are we going to call her?" Naomi wondered.

"We were thinking of naming her Patricia and then calling her Patty.

We thought maybe Patricia Diane," Norma answered.

Bob sat cuddling his little sister. "Diane! I don't want her to die yet!"

Marty and Norma both laughed. "We also thought of Patricia Ann. Do you like that better?" The older children all nodded their agreement.

Betty stroked her little sister's soft cheek. "Oh, Mama, it will be so much fun to dress her up. I think she's going to have curly hair like Bob and Larry."

There was the sound of running feet across the porch. It was Esther, all out of breath. "I came to see the new baby. Mother always makes me wait two hours after she sees the doctor leave. She said you have a little girl. Oh, Betty, won't you have fun! May I get in line to hold her?"

As baby Patty grew, changes came to the Reed household. One morning in late spring, Norma stood at the dining room window looking out over the back yard. A robin took his early morning bath in a puddle in the driveway. A chickadee flitted to the bird feeder, and the sky turned shades of pink and gold as the sun rose to meet the new day. Norma loved sunrises. While other things changed, God did not.

It was a strange feeling to see her firstborn off to his first job. Bob was driving a lime truck. He was happy and confident. She felt a tug at her heart since she knew the boyish immaturity that her capable sixteen-year-old still had. Her prayers followed him out the door.

Betty was becoming a young lady and dreaming of going to Lancaster Mennonite High School. When fall came and she left Monday morning to stay in the school dorm until Friday, Norma missed her help very much. Esther was married and no longer available to give a hand. Naomi was learning to help, but she was only ten. So Norma worked harder herself.

She always made sure her children had time for carefree, childish play. Mom was still living with them, and she helped with dishes and laundry. There were still occasional clashes with the children to deal with.

Then there was Dick. Dick's childhood sickness had left its effect.

He struggled in school. The doctor had said that his sense of judgment and mental maturity would in some ways never pass a ten-year-old level. That was becoming more evident. With Betty in a Christian school, Norma and Marty wished for something better than public school for their other children, especially Dick. So in the fall of 1956, Norma began driving the seven miles twice a day to Morgantown so their children could attend Conestoga Christian School.

Marty decided that Norma's plate was too full. Besides this, they were anticipating an addition to the family in December. "Norma," he announced one morning. "I think with Esther and Betty gone, it's time I head up to New Holland and get you an automatic washer. If we put it here in the dining room, it would save you running up and down the cellar steps with laundry and just make your workload a little easier."

"Oh, Marty, that would be wonderful! Can we really afford that?"

Marty smiled at her enthusiasm. "As busy as you are, we can't afford not to."

Neither Marty nor Norma knew just how needed that washer would be in the weeks and months ahead.

Norma helping Dick make a snowman

chapter thirty-five

Not My Brother!

Pennsylvania: 1956

"Let's make a big, big pile to the top of the fence!"

"I want you to cover me up!"

"Here, Dick," Norma instructed. "Fill these baskets full of leaves and dump them on the pile. Larry, you help him. Don't jump on the pile yet, Wilmer. Wait until it gets bigger."

The crisp fall air whipped color into the children's cheeks. Big yellow maple leaves floated down from the tree. Norma and Naomi raked industriously, and little Patty toddled around picking up a leaf here and there and carrying it to a basket.

"We're going to get a pile higher than the fence!" eight-year-old Larry exclaimed excitedly.

"All right, boys," Norma said, "now let's make a hole in the middle."

"Me first! Me first!"

"Me too! Me too!" Patty echoed.

"Larry and Wilmer, you get in. Here, Larry, let Patty sit beside you. Now cover them up. Oh dear, where are my boys?" Norma said. "Dick, did you see the boys? Where's Patty?" A giggle came from the pile of leaves. Suddenly the pile exploded.

"Here we are," Larry and Wilmer said together.

"Again! Again!" Patty begged.

"Let's give Dick and Naomi a turn now. Larry and Wilmer, you help to pile the leaves that you scattered."

"Here, Dick, you can hold Patty. Now cover them up." A growling noise came from the pile of leaves. And then with a roar, Dick and Naomi burst from the pile.

Norma was just covering Larry and Wilmer again when she heard the phone ringing. She hurried into the house to answer. A strange voice greeted her. "Are you the sister of Arthur Brenneman?"

"Yes, I am."

"I am calling from the Arlington Hospital in Virginia. We have Arthur Brenneman here. He has been in a very serious accident. He gave us your number to call."

"Oh, no," Norma said, her mind in a whirl. "Is he going to be all right? How serious is it?"

"Ma'am, the accident was very serious. His truck caught fire, and he is badly burned. I suggest any close family members should come at once. He told us that you would notify his wife."

Norma sat down weakly on a chair. "Yes, sir, yes I will. Could I have the name and address of the hospital again and also the phone number?"

"Certainly!"

Norma scrambled for a pencil and paper. "Thank you, sir."

"Yes, and ma'am, I repeat, any close family members may want to come at once."

Norma hung up the phone. Her hands were trembling. Art! Her mischievous, fun-loving brother. Art, with five little sons and another baby on the way. "Oh, and I must tell Art's wife, Esther. It's too bad Marty's sister Esther isn't here to help us anymore!"

Betty came from the kitchen where she had been baking. "Mom, what is it? What happened?"

"Oh, Betty, Uncle Art was in a bad accident. I'm so glad it's Saturday and you are home from school. Will you watch the children? I must go out to the garage and tell Daddy, then I must go up to Aunt Esther."

"Is he going to be okay?" Betty wondered.

"I don't know, Betty. I'll tell you more later."

Norma found Marty in the garage fixing one of the children's bikes. "Marty, what shall we do?" she asked pouring out the news.

"Why don't you drive up to Esther and tell her. Then bring her and the boys here. I'll call my brother Aaron and see if he'll go along to take Esther to Virginia. As close as he and Art are, I'm sure he'll want to go. Are you okay with that?"

"Yes, Marty. Could you call Erma, Walter, and Raymond too? I'm afraid I'll be busy with Esther and the boys."

Norma drove the short distance to Arthur's home along Main Street. "Esther has her hands full," she thought. "She has boys at the age of one, two, three, four, and six." Norma found her in the kitchen, canning peaches. Two-year-old Billy held on to her skirt, sucking his thumb. Little Jimmy came crawling to Norma. The other boys were playing in the back yard.

Esther took one look at Norma's face. "Norma, is something wrong?"

"Sit down, Esther. We need to talk."

Esther took a chair at the kitchen table, but not before she looked outside to make sure the other three boys were okay. "Has Butch been up to something?"

"No, Esther, it's Art. I got a phone call from Virginia. He's had a bad accident. They said you should come."

Esther's hands went to her mouth. "How bad?" she asked.

"Bad, Esther," Norma's voice trembled. "The truck caught fire. He has bad burns, but he must be talking, because he gave them our number. They said any close family should come."

Esther's head dropped into her hands. "What am I going to do, Norma?"

Norma forced herself to be calm. "Let's turn off the peaches and gather up the boys and some clothes. I'll take them to our house. Marty will take you to Art. I think Aaron will go along too."

Just then the door burst open, and Butch, Davy, and Arthur Jr. came in. "We're hungry." They stopped short. "What's wrong, Mom?"

"Your daddy had an accident and he's in the hospital," Norma answered. "You boys go find yourselves each a pair of shoes. Butch, you help me find some clothes. You are all coming to our house."

"Okay!" the boys agreed. Davy looked at his mother with concern and then went off to find his shoes.

"Esther," Norma said, "can you pack a bag for yourself? You could be staying awhile."

Esther nodded and moved toward the bedroom.

Norma grabbed diapers and pajamas. Someone would have to come back later to take the diapers off the clothesline and get more clothes. Quickly she loaded the boys into the car and made sure the gas burner under the peaches was shut off. By the time she got home, Marty and Aaron were ready, and Esther was off. Norma carried Jimmy inside while the other boys ran to jump in the leaves.

The phone was ringing. Norma set Jimmy on the floor and went to answer it. It was Aaron's wife, Julia. "Yes, Julia," she answered, "I have the boys here, but there are things to be done at their house. If you take down the wash on the clothesline and try to find extra clothes for each of the boys, I'd appreciate that. I'm pretty sure there will be other offers of help. I'll get someone else to take care of the peaches Esther was canning."

She had no more than hung up the phone when it rang again. It was Erma. "Norma, Raymond called me. He and Dad heard the news and are on their way here from Indiana! Did you hear anything more since Marty called me?"

"No, Erma," Norma answered. "I'll let you know. I'm glad Raymond is coming—and Dad. But Erma, Mom's here, and Art's five boys are here, and I'm not sure I can handle Dad and Raymond coming, with everything else that's going on."

"I'm sorry, sis. I'll try to entertain Dad here and spare you that."

Norma had her own youngest five children and Art's five all tucked into bed when Marty called. Bob and Betty sat waiting to hear more.

"Norma," Marty began. "It's really bad. You'd never recognize Art. I could hardly believe it when we walked into his room and he said, 'Hey, Mart!' It's really that bad, Norma, that the doctors haven't done a lot except try to control the pain. They are afraid if they start working on him too much, he will go into shock and die from that. They said it's a chance in ten million that he will survive, and then he won't live long."

"Oh, Marty! How is Esther?"

"She's amazing, Norma!"

"Tell her the boys are here and all tucked into bed. Marty, does anyone know what happened?"

"Yes. Art told the emergency crew that he had just filled his tanker truck with fuel and was headed home. The last while he had been having trouble with his lights. The trucking company knew about it and had worked on it several times. He said he had just come to a corner when his lights went out. He hit a metal bridge. It sliced the truck apart, and it burst into flames. Art said he crawled out and his clothes were on fire, so he rolled and rolled on the ground to put out the fire. When the ambulance came, they looked all around and didn't see Art. They said, 'Where's the man? Where's the man?' Art answered, 'I'm right here.'"

"If he's talking like that, Marty, do you think maybe he will make it?"

"Actually, Norma, we know he is a determined man and has five boys to live for, but really, the doctors don't give any hope. If you'd see him, Norma—I'm glad you didn't come here in your condition."

Norma was silent.

"Are you all right, Norma? Yes, I plan to come on home tonight yet. Aaron will stay here for now."

"I'm very glad you are coming home. I have twelve children right now, you know! I have them all in bed."

"There was an old woman who lived in a shoe..." Marty began.

They both laughed. It felt good to laugh in the midst of everything.

"I'll hurry home, Norma."

"Take care, Marty." She turned to Bob and Betty, who waited expectantly. They listened soberly as she filled them in on details.

"You know, Mom," Bob said, "Art is more than just an uncle to us. He's like a big brother since he lived with us so much. How much do his boys know?"

"Not much. They're too small. They know their daddy's hurt, but we'll let Esther tell them what she wants to tell," Norma answered. "I think they'll catch quite a bit from all the adult talk. Your Grandpa Brenneman and Uncle Ray's are coming Monday."

"Really!" Bob exclaimed. "I only have faint memories of them both."

Norma was busy tending children on Monday when there was a knock at the door. It was Raymond and his wife and four-year-old Raymond Jr. with Dad. Norma came to the door carrying Jimmy and greeted them warmly.

"Well, well," Dad said, looking at the children who had gathered around to see who came. "You're going to have to tell us which are yours and which are Art's. At least I know the girls are yours."

"Norma, I didn't know you ran an orphanage," Raymond said with a chuckle.

Norma introduced the children, and then Dad was soon ready to go. "I'll leave Raymond's here with you, and I'll be back tomorrow." It was only then that Norma realized that Dad's second wife was waiting in the car. With a heavy heart, she waved goodbye as they headed back to Lancaster.

Raymond enjoyed his nieces and nephews. He soon had them clustered around him watching him draw. "Draw an airplane," someone would say. As if by magic an airplane would appear on the paper. "Draw a dog." And a dog would appear, much to the children's delight.

Little Ray enjoyed all the new playmates. In spite of her handicap from polio, Raymond's wife offered to make her native Hungarian goulash for supper. Norma accepted gratefully.

Dad arrived early the next morning. Norma had been apprehensive

Art and Raymond

at the thought of Mom and Dad meeting after all these years. She need not have worried. When Alzina came downstairs, they greeted each other matter-of-factly. "Hi, John." "Hi, Alzina." And that was it. Dad seemed to enjoy his grandchildren. He had brought gifts for the children and smiled at Nonie's obvious delight at the new dress he had bought for her.

Art hung onto life. He had confronted the doctor: "It's been three days since my accident. I have five little sons and another baby on the way. You better get busy and do something for me, because I plan to live." Amazed, the doctors began to make plans for treatment.

Dad and Ray left to go back to Indiana after a few days. Norma had kept Art's boys for ten days before Esther came back and took her boys home. The next day Walter, his wife, and their six-year-old Norma Jean arrived from Michigan with Uncle Joe and his wife, Myrtle. Several days later Marty took them and Esther to Virginia. Norma kept all the children, including Norma Jean.

The phone rang, and it was Aunt Sarah's Mandy. "Norma, I'm sure everyone is calling to see how Art is. I'm interested in that too, but I'm calling to see how you are. You have Arthur's boys, all your own work, and lots of company besides."

"Actually," Norma answered, laughing, "today I have Walter's Norma Jean besides Art's boys, but Esther came and took them home for a while. Am I ever glad for the automatic washer Marty got me. We have it here on the main floor, and I keep it going steady."

"Norma, I want to help out. I'd like to have all your company back here for dinner and—what about your mom—how's she doing?"

"Well, Mandy, it gets a little difficult at times. Mom doesn't handle all this fuss very well. Art's going to be in the hospital a long time. As soon as Walter's are gone, I'm going to have a talk with Erma. With all this and a new baby coming, Mom's going to need another place to live."

"Your mom's welcome to come stay here for a couple days if you need a break. I'd like to do more, but we have my parents to look after too. I know what else we could do! You can send Butch to us. Aaron and the boys would keep him busy."

"Thank you, Mandy. You are like a real sister to me. I know you're busy too. We just might take you up on that sometimes."

Several days after Walter left for Michigan, Norma had a talk with Erma. "Something has to change, Erma. Esther's going to be needing help for a long time. The neighbors are being very helpful, and so is Marty's family. Several of them have taken a turn to drive Esther down to the Arlington Hospital. The problem is Mom. She can't handle having this many children around, and Art's boys are busy boys. The other day I couldn't find Butch, Davy, and little Art. We finally found them at the creek, a mile away! They must have gone across the fields. I was about frantic. I spanked all three of them."

Erma snickered. "I guess they found out they better listen to Aunt Norma. Really, Norma, I know what you mean about Mom. That's why I couldn't keep on having her this past spring. Then especially when I started working at Schick's. I don't see how you do it, Norma, with a baby on the way—helping Esther and keeping Art's boys, plus out-of-state company! What do you think we should do?"

"Well, I've checked out the Good Samaritan Home on Welsh Mountain. They have an opening. We could still have Mom here for Sunday or even for several days, but at least she could have her own space, and I could get a break."

"That sounds good, Norma, but will Mom consent?"

"I have suggested the idea to her. I'll talk to her, Erma."

"Then how about if I come to your place tomorrow, since it's Saturday, and we move her to the home," Erma said. "I think for your sake it can't be too soon."

"Thank you, Erma. I'll see you then." Norma was relieved that although her mom had mixed feelings about moving, she went along agreeably enough the next morning and exclaimed pleasantly over her nice, sunny room. Norma promised to be back to pick her up in about a week so she could go along to Cambridge for church and spend the day.

Norma's load also lessened when Marty's brother George offered to take several of Art's boys the next time Esther was gone. Besides Mandy's and George's offers, other neighbors and family helped to babysit or take Esther to the hospital.

Art held determinedly onto life. The doctors operated on his arms and hands, then his eyes and head. When he could, he got the nurse to put a call through for him so he could talk to his boys. Esther continued to make regular trips to Virginia, and Norma helped where she could—babysitting, doing laundry, mending, and ironing.

In early December others pitched in more to help with Esther and the boys. Norma was cuddling her own little boy. Keith Eugene was enthusiastically welcomed by all the little Reeds.

"Look," Nonie said, stroking the baby's fine hair. "He has lighter-colored hair than most of us."

"He gets that from my mother's side," Marty said.

"I don't care what color his hair is," Wilmer said emphatically. "I'm just glad for a little *brother*."

It was February by the time Norma made the trip to see Art in the hospital. Nothing could have quite prepared her for his changed appearance. But it was Art, and he greeted her happily. "How's the new little fellow?"

"He's doing real well, Art. I'm glad you understand why I didn't come sooner."

"I sure do, Norma, and Esther has been telling me about all you've done for her. I can't tell you how much it means. I know you'll take good care of her when the baby comes. Looks like I'll be here awhile yet."

"Don't you worry, Art," said Norma, laying her hand on his bandaged arm. "We'll give her the best of care."

"Thanks, Sis," Art said huskily. "Thinking of my boys goes a long way in helping me through all of this."

"We're praying too, Art."

"Thanks."

This milk truck crashed into an abutment at the Difficult Run Bridge on Route 7 in Fairfax County this morning, police said, when the driver, Arthur H. Brenneman, 37, of Goodville, Pa., fell asleep at the wheel. The truck caught fire. Mr. Brenneman, his clothes ablaze, managed to jump out and roll in grass. He's in critical condition in Arlington Hospital, with third degree burns over half his body.
—Photo by Francis Peal

Art's family: Davy in back
Left to right: Art Jr., Esther holding Billy and Jimmy, Butch

New Era Photo

Arthur H. Brenneman holds his youngest son, Joseph, while Mrs. Brenneman looks on.

Fight for Life Costs $23,000

Burned Goodville Man Returns From 13-Month Hospital Battle

Expenses of keeping a Goodville truck driver alive during the 13 months since he was involved in an accident have passed $23,000—and there will be many future medical bills.

Arthur H. Brenneman, father of six small sons, returned from Arlington, Va., Hospital last night. His hospitalization period was two days shy of 13 months, and physicians said he was on the brink of death at least three times.

Spirits Excellent

His spirits were excellent today as he resumed the business of being a father. He had nothing but praise for the treatment he got at Arlington.

"The people at the hospital were wonderful to me," Brenneman said today. "You can't imagine how much they did for me."

Some indication of the care giv-

penses:

$9,923.07 for room and board and laboratory expenses.

$434.80 for bathing solutions.

$2,466.30 for drugs.

$13,000 for nurses.

This totals $23,634.17. And this is exclusive of the physicians' bills, which are not part of hospital records.

Only Portion Paid

How are these bills being paid? The hospital isn't sure if and how it will collect. So far, insurance has paid $9,610.79 of the expenses, besides a portion of the nurses'

[handwritten diary excerpt:]

jesse someone, ... for a while.

15, Arthur had a terrible accident. Marty and Ann took Esther to Virginia. She was canning peaches when I went to tell her. I brought the children down here,

Excerpt from Norma's diary

chapter thirty-six

A Trip Back

Pennsylvania: 1957-1960

Norma stared in dismay. Fluffy yellow chicks lay scattered here and there, their heads twisted at odd angles. None of them moved. "What happened?" Nonie wailed, dropping to her knees beside the fallen chicks. Wilmer stood rubbing his eyes. Little Art and Davy looked uncertainly at their Aunt Norma.

"We buthered them!" little Art said matter-of-factly.

"Boys!" Norma exclaimed. How did a three- and a four-year-old manage such havoc before someone caught them?

"Here," Larry announced, coming into the garage cuddling a little chick. "Somebody must have let the chicks out— Whatever!" he exclaimed, stopping short and looking at the scene on the floor.

Nonie began counting the dead chicks. "They didn't get them all! Some got away."

Norma took Art and Davy by the hand and walked toward the house. "Auntie Norma, I'm sorry! I'm sorry!" Davy was sobbing by now.

The last little frightened chick was found late that night after all the children were in bed, but most of the sixteen chicks were gone.

The next day Esther came with many apologies and twenty-five little chicks to replace the lost ones. "A few extra for good measure," she said.

Norma was relieved that Butch was with neighbors Luke and Bessie Martin when he came down with the measles. Jimmy was at George's when he contracted the mumps. But it was Norma that Esther called at 4:30 one morning in May. Norma dressed quickly and drove Esther to the doctor and then on to the hospital where Joseph Ray was born several hours later. Then she hurried home to call Arthur and tell him of the safe arrival of his new little son.

When Esther came home from the hospital, she exclaimed in surprise at the cleaning and painting that had been done at her house. A new table and chairs graced the kitchen. Another neighbor gave a new baby carriage, and someone else gave a new chest of drawers. Norma had sewed new diapers. "I'm making a special call to Art to tell him about this!" she said happily.

Uncle Joe, who had given Art a home in his boyhood, had recently moved into a trailer on Marty and Norma's property. He was obviously pleased with a namesake.

Arthur continued his struggle for life. Sixty percent of his body was covered with third-degree burns. Several times his temperature went to the 107-degree limit and doctors gave up his case, but Art always fought back. He went through five major operations for skin grafting and countless minor operations while Esther continued to be at his side as much as possible. Nine months after the accident, he was walking unaided. The whole neighborhood rallied around to help where they could.

It was almost thirteen months before Art left the hospital in Virginia. Everyone was glad that he could spend Christmas with Esther and his boys. After several weeks at home, he went to Fort Howard Hospital in Maryland for more surgeries and therapy. The hospital trips were not as long now.

Norma rejoiced that Art took a more serious view of life. He was baptized and began attending church. No one guessed that Art would live to be ninety years old, enjoying not only his boys but his grandchildren as well.

Wilmer, Bob holding Keith, Dick, Nonie, Betty holding Patty, Larry

By the summer of 1959, Marty and Norma felt they could get away for a trip back to Michigan. What excitement and cheering when the children heard the plans! Bob and Betty weren't going along, but the last night of summer Bible school couldn't go fast enough for the six younger Reeds. They had already packed to go. After the service, they headed for Michigan. They planned to drive through the night.

"Daddy, aren't you glad they got the whole turnpike finished now?"

eleven-year-old Larry asked.

"It will make traveling a lot easier," Marty answered.

"Daddy, will you wake us up at the tunnels?" Wilmer wondered.

"We'll make sure you don't miss them all," Marty agreed.

The children fell asleep to the faint *thumpety-thump* of the tires crossing the seams of the concrete road. Several hours later, when Norma woke the children at the tunnels, they chorused, "Toot, Daddy, toot." Marty obligingly blew the horn several times in the tunnel so the children could hear it echo.

The little Reeds were good travelers. When they pulled in at Mary Evelyn's at suppertime, two-year-old Keith said, "More and more bye-bye."

The next morning when they drove into the Brutus churchyard, memories flooded Norma's mind. Picking up Keith and taking Patty's hand, she walked into the church with Nonie following her. Marty and the three boys sat across the aisle.

Many faces were different, but Clyde and Rosetta Kauffman, and Rosie Weaver still sat at their usual spots. When Clyde stood up to preach, Norma remembered the little girl who listened with interest as she heard for the first time of Jesus, the good shepherd. She glanced at Marty and remembered Dad sitting at much the same spot, staring uncomfortably at the floor. Then she thought of herself as a teenager eagerly drinking in the plan of salvation.

Rosie hurried to her after church, just as she had long ago. "Why, Norma, what a lovely family you have! I believe I count six, but none of these are Bobby or Betty."

"No, Bob and Betty are growing up and have their own things going," Norma answered.

"Would you have time to come over for a meal?" Rosie asked. "I'd love to have you."

"Thank you, Rosie. I'll talk to Marty. I think we probably could."

Clyde and Rosetta were waiting to shake Norma's hand. "Norma, it's such a blessing to see your family," Clyde said. "It's a real encouragement to us."

"Thank you, Clyde," Norma responded. "I will always appreciate how you and Rosetta have encouraged me."

"Marty, could we take time to walk to the graveyard?" Norma wondered as they were leaving the church house.

"Sure," Marty agreed.

Norma paused at Grandpa Brenneman's grave. She remembered his warm handclasp and his kindly hand on her shoulder. How she would have loved to introduce her family to Grandpa! He had probably never guessed what a stabilizing factor he had been in her life. Norma resolved to do the same to her grandchildren if she ever had any. She moved over to the simple marker at baby Elenora's grave. She told the children of the little sister she had grieved for long ago.

"Marty, Erma and I have talked about putting a real gravestone on Elenora's grave someday. It just looks so forlorn this way." So it was—years later, when finances allowed, Norma had her wish.

What a pleasure it was to show the children the places of interest and introduce them to old friends.

One day the family traveled across the new Mackinac Bridge to the northern peninsula. The bridge was two years old and was one of the largest suspension bridges in the world. What an improvement over the slow ferry of long ago. They stopped to watch several boats come through the boat locks that Marty and Norma had visited on their wedding trip.

The boys went fishing with Mary Evelyn's husband, Bert, and came home happily carrying thirteen fish from the clear waters of Lake Michigan. "Now that's fish worth eating!" Norma declared. She had always had a hard time enjoying the fish they brought home from the muddy creeks of Pennsylvania.

They took the children to see the old school at Woodland, Uncle Peter's farm, and the old Reed homestead. They shared a meal with Mose and Bessie and drove out to the dam where Marty and Norma had walked and dreamed of their future together. Marty smiled at Norma over the heads of the children and reached for her hand. "I'm glad you said 'yes.'"

"Oh, Marty, I'm glad too," she responded.

They visited various other friends and then drove east of Pellston past the Hamners where they had lived when Betty was born. Then they headed for Petoskey to see Walter.

They stopped for a drink at the artesian well along the road going out of Brutus, where Marty and Norma had walked on their dates. After supper at Walter's, they went to the nearby breakwater. The children clambered out across the rocks while Marty and Norma followed a bit more slowly, reminiscing.

"It's been a wonderful trip, Marty," Norma said. "Thank you so much for making it happen. It was good to revisit all these places, and it was so relaxing."

"I think it was high time for you to get away and relax. Ever since Art's accident, you have been carrying a heavy load."

"I know, but we'll just thank God that Art seems to be coming through."

The sun was setting as they headed back to Walter's. As they gathered around in Walter's yard, Nonie asked, "Where's Dick?"

Everyone looked around. No Dick.

"Did he come along back with us from the breakwater?" Marty asked.

"Yes, I walked beside him," Wilmer answered.

Everyone spread out looking for Dick. Walter went inside to check the house. Marty walked down toward the lake. Larry and Nonie walked around the old Indian church next to Walter's house. Norma prayed, fighting down fear. Dick was fifteen now and sometimes had a mind of his own, but he was still her special one that took a little more care and looking after.

After two and a half hours of frantic searching, someone said, "He's here!" and brought Dick out of the shadows. "He must have wandered off towards town."

"Welcome back, Dick," said Marty. "Do you have any idea what time it is? It's 10:30 at night." Marty told him some more things that not everyone heard, and Dick was still quite subdued as they headed south for Indiana the next day.

It was good to see Raymond again on their stop in South Bend.

On Sunday morning, Norma followed Katie into church. Although it was a different church than long ago, sitting next to Katie brought back more memories. Words weren't needed. They smiled at each other happily.

Marty and Norma were glad for their good little travelers as they started the hot trip home.

Alzina met them at the door. "Welcome home!" she called out cheerfully. Marty had curtained off a section of the girls' big bedroom, and Mom had been living with them again. During the weeks they were gone, she had spent the time at Erma's but was back to welcome them.

Betty and her boyfriend, Dave Myer, drove in the lane. "It sure is good to have you all back again," Betty greeted them. Keith ran and threw his arms around Betty.

"Betty is becoming quite a young lady," Norma mused. Betty had stayed at home working at Rubinson's Department Store and dating Dave. Now she was making plans to teach summer Bible school in Alabama. How thankful Norma was that Betty's teenage years were much different from her own unguided, lonely ones.

When fall came, Marty and Norma decided Dick's school days would end. School had been a struggle for him. Besides taking him to a new doctor to get help for his nerves, they found a job for him working on a chicken farm for Charlie Gehman. Dick was pleased. He was not so happy about the fact that Marty would not consider him getting his license now that he was sixteen. Marty knew Dick could not handle that responsibility. Dick voiced his disappointment various times over the next few years, but then seemed to resign himself.

One blustery, snowy day, Norma promised Keith a sled ride. The night before, there had been over twenty sleds on Water Street—children, parents, and grandparents. But Norma had decided daytime was safer for a four-year-old who really should be in bed at night anyway. So today, down Water Street she and Keith flew, past Grandfather Reed's and then past home and on around the corner. To Keith's delight, they took not just one, but two long rides.

"Now, Keith, we are going to go see how Aunt Sarah is doing. Remember, she had a heart attack a few weeks ago."

Aunt Sarah's daughter Betsy met Norma at the door. "Norma, Mom's not good at all. She's calling for her sister Salome. We were trying to phone you. Will you go get Salome?"

"Sure," Norma agreed quickly.

Soon she was back with Aunt Salome. When they entered the kitchen, Mandy met her. "Norma, thank you for coming!" she said, squeezing Norma's hand. "You belong with us now. The doctor doesn't think Mom will survive the day."

Norma stood at Aunt Sarah's bedside. She gently took Aunt Sarah's hand in hers. "Aunt Sarah, it's Norma." Aunt Sarah squeezed her hand. With tear-filled eyes, Norma stroked her arm. Memories of a heartbroken little girl and Aunt Sarah's soothing touch, a shoulder to cry on, a gentle word of encouragement—Aunt Sarah had given it all. Stroking Aunt Sarah's cheek gently with the back of her hand, Norma turned to the kitchen and sat down quietly with Mary, Betsy, Mandy, Lydia, Uncle Peter, and Silas. Katie was coming from Indiana.

But Aunt Sarah lingered on. Norma visited whenever she could. It was three weeks later that Norma got a call that Aunt Sarah was gone.

Some days after the funeral, Norma stopped in to see Uncle Peter. He was up again after an illness and tending his chickens.

"Thank you for coming, Norma," he said in a quavering voice. "I've thought about you a lot."

"Uncle Peter, I want to thank you for all you and Aunt Sarah have done for me," Norma responded. "It changed the direction of my life."

When Norma left, Uncle Peter gave her two slips of white lilacs. She treasured those lilac bushes. Uncle Peter lived another nine years without Aunt Sarah, lovingly taken care of by his daughters.

chapter thirty-seven

Oh, Mom!

Pennsylvania: 1960-1961

"Good mornin', Sista Norma," the little black Mennonite lady said as she hurried up to Norma after church. "I want to gib dis fo da chillens." She handed Norma two small, very crumpled brown paper bags.

"Why, thank you, Sister Murray. Patty and Keith will like this!"

Standing at Norma's side, Patty smiled and nodded agreement.

"God bless yo day!" the little lady said, hurrying toward her waiting ride.

Norma smiled after her as she handed the bags to Patty. Sister Murray was a dear soul, and loved the Lord enthusiastically. This was a usual Sunday morning occurrence, but something was different. What was it? It was the strong smell of rose-scented perfume. Sister Murray did not usually smell like rose-scented perfume! She lived in a little shack on the Welsh Mountain and certainly rose-scented perfume had never been one of her priorities. Suddenly Norma remembered—Mom had rose-scented perfume. I wonder…

Patty and Keith waited until they were in the car to check out the contents of their bags.

"Peanuts as usual," Larry said, looking over Keith's shoulder.

"You better check them to see if they're too stale before you eat all of them," Betty warned.

"I got hardtack gum. How many candies did you get?" Patty wondered.

"I got three that are wrapped. Mama says we have to throw the others away," Keith answered.

"Are you going to chew that hardtack?" Wilmer wondered. "If you're not, I'll take a piece. It's not too bad if you chew it awhile."

"Mom," Norma asked later, "did you give Mrs. Murray a bottle of your new perfume?"

"Not exactly," Mom answered with a determined set to her chin. "She doesn't smell good, you know. So when we knelt for prayer, I sprayed some on her."

"Oh, Mom!" Norma exclaimed looking at her mom in shock.

"Well," Mom said defensively, "it seems I sit beside her every Sunday and I have to do *something* to help the situation."

"Mom, I really don't think you should do that," Norma said carefully.

"What then?" Mom asked in a huff.

"Well, I never really noticed that she had *such* a bad odor," Norma answered. "She can't help the way she has to live. Just love her soul."

"Humph!" Mom replied.

The next Sunday morning, Norma came into her mom's room to find her thoroughly saturating her hanky with perfume. She looked at Norma smugly. "Now I'll just put that in front of my nose when we kneel for prayer."

Norma sighed a bit to herself and then coughed from the overpowering smell. "Are you ready to go, Mom?"

"Pretty soon," Mom replied.

Norma tried to wait patiently while Mom moved slowly about her room, putting this and that away so "no one will get it while we are gone." Meanwhile, she heard the last of the children heading out to the car. Marty gave the horn a little toot.

Keeping Mom could be a challenge. One night Norma was sleeping soundly after a busy day when she heard a knock on the bedroom door. It was Betty. "I'm sorry to wake you, Mom, but Grandma has been fussing around. She even has Nonie and Patty awake. She says her leg hurts, and she can't find her gauze."

"Oh, Betty, I'm sorry. I'll come talk to her." Norma got out of bed and found some gauze in the bathroom cabinet and then went to talk to Alzina.

"Here, Mom, I have some gauze for you. Please try to be quiet. You have the girls all awake." (The curtained-off section of the girls' room was less than satisfactory.)

"But, Norma," Mom answered, "you just don't know how sore my leg is! I think we should see a doctor right now."

"Mom, it's three o'clock in the morning. If you would just lie down and prop your leg up, it would probably help a lot."

"You just don't understand. Now where is my liniment?"

"Please, Mom, calm yourself. I would like to go back to bed, and these girls need their sleep."

"Well, go then!" Alzina replied shortly.

Norma went back to bed, but she didn't sleep.

The next day, Norma called Art. "Could you come and take Mom to the doctor? She had us up in the night with her bad leg. She wanted a doctor in the middle of the night."

"Sure, Sis. I'll come," Art agreed.

"You know, Art," Norma added. "I'm afraid we're going to have to move Mom to the Welsh Mountain Home again. We are trying to get ready for Betty's wedding, and when Mom's unhandy like this, it's just too much."

"I agree, Sis," Art answered. "Let's talk to Erma and get things moving. If you say you've had enough, then I know it's time."

When Art came that afternoon to take Mom to the doctor, she objected. "But I don't want to see a doctor *now!*"

Art stood his ground. "Mom, I came to take you to the doctor and we are going."

Muttering to herself, Alzina started hunting for her pocketbook and got ready to go.

On the way home, Art took the opportunity to tell Alzina that she would be moving back to the Welsh Mountain Home. Alzina was not too pleased with the idea.

"Norma is getting ready for a wedding, and this is how it will be for now," Art stated. "We don't have room to keep you, and it's not a good time for Erma. The home will give you a nice room." Grudgingly

Mom goes to The Welsh Mountain Home

Alzina consented.

Now Norma and Betty were more free to enjoy all the shopping, sewing, and planning that goes along with a wedding. But ten days before the wedding, in the middle of the final planning, the phone rang. It was Mrs. Lefever from the Welsh Mountain Home. "Mrs. Reed, I'm sorry to tell you this, but we discovered this afternoon that your mother is missing. By all appearances, she has run away."

Norma gasped, "Run away! Do you know where she is?"

"She can't be very far away. She was in the dining hall for lunch, and she has to be on foot. There's no public transportation up here on the mountain, and I doubt if anyone would pick her up."

"Thank you, Mrs. Lefever. I'm sorry about this. My brother will come and pick her up. We'll let you know when we have her."

"One more thing, Mrs. Reed. I'm sorry to inform you that, given the circumstances, we cannot take her back as a resident here."

"I understand, Mrs. Lefever."

Norma turned from the phone. She closed her eyes and rested her head on her hands.

"What's wrong, Mom?" Betty asked in alarm. "Whatever is going on?"

"Grandma ran away from the home."

"Oh no, Mom! Where is she? Is she all right?"

"She's probably okay. I must call Art."

"Art, this is Norma. Mrs. Lefever called and said Mom ran away from the home."

"She ran away!" Art exclaimed. "When? Where is she? Well, I'll be—"

"She just left this afternoon. Can you go look for her? She's probably walking down off the mountain on those twisty mountain roads."

"I'll go right away, Norma. What shall we do with her?"

"Bring her here, Art. They won't take her back there."

"I'll bring her, and I'll talk to her. I'll call Erma too. Don't worry, Sis."

Art found Alzina walking rather slowly along the mountain road, clutching a brown shopping bag and her ever-present pocketbook. She climbed into his car willingly enough. By the time she got to Norma's, she was very subdued and went quietly to her curtained-off corner of the girls' room.

Art and Norma stood talking. "Sis, I told her a thing or two. I tried to be nice. She is my mom, I know. I called Erma. She will take Mom till after the wedding. She'll be here on Friday."

"Oh, bless her heart! We'll manage a couple days until she can get here. Thanks, Art."

"I'll take care of getting Mom's things from the home on Monday," Art offered.

"Thanks again, Art. I don't know what I'd do without you."

On October 1, the Reed home was a flurry of activity. Betty's close friend Vera was there to help with the last-minute details. Norma had always enjoyed having the happy group of Betty's friends in and out of their home. With everyone's help, the wedding went beautifully. George's son Harold preached the message, and before long Norma was seeing her oldest daughter off to a new life. She couldn't help comparing this day with her own wedding day. While that had been a happy day, she was so glad that Betty's was different.

The day after the wedding, Norma went to Erma's and brought Mom back. Marty built a more durable partition in the girls' room, and Mom settled in again.

Several days later, Norma heard Patty and Keith laughing. "Do it again, Grandma! Do it again!" Keith begged.

Norma looked into the dining room. Mom had taken her false teeth out and was squeezing her gums tightly together. Her large Roman nose seemed to almost touch her chin. Patty and Keith laughed again, and Mom joined them. Then she popped her teeth back into her mouth and said, "Now that's enough."

"Norma," Mom said, "these teeth need fixing. I'm afraid I cracked them when I dropped them in the sink. If we could go to Lancaster and get them fixed, maybe I could shop at Woolworth's. I really do need some things."

Norma looked at the jars of tomato juice and ketchup waiting to be canned. A basket of laundry sat waiting to be hung on the clothesline. There were red beets waiting to be canned and—the phone rang.

"Well, Bob, where are you?

"You got to Chicago at midnight? But you just left Harrisburg at quarter to ten in the evening.

"Really!

"These planes are amazing!

"You know how long it would have taken us to drive that distance. That's hard to believe. Thanks for calling. I'm glad you're there safely."

Norma turned from the phone.

"Norma, I really do need to go shopping today," Alzina persisted. "I must have some things."

"Mom," Norma responded, "I just can't take you today. I'm sorry, but I will try to get your teeth fixed soon. Maybe I can drop them off when I go to pick up Marty."

"But, Norma, you just don't understand. My leg hurts, and I must have medicine and gauze. I need some powder too."

"Mom, I'm sorry. I just can't do it now."

Alzina stomped up the stairs in a huff. Norma prayed for grace.

Some days Alzina could be quite pleasant. She enjoyed singing and had a good time with the children. The next day she minded their noise and got irritable. There were times she apologized, but often Norma's attempt at reasoning with her accomplished nothing.

"Norma," Mom said one day. "Are you sure that I've been forgiven for the things in my past?"

"Mom, you have given all that to God. His blood has washed away your sins."

"Sometimes I'm just not sure," Mom faltered.

Laying aside her ironing, Norma reached for a Bible. Sitting down beside her mom, she patiently pointed out verses of God's forgiveness. Later in the day, Norma heard Mom singing, "What can wash away my sin? Nothing but the blood of Jesus."

"Thank you, God," Norma whispered, "for forgiving my mother. Help me always to keep a forgiving heart toward her."

Marty and Norma enjoyed attending the George Brunk revivals when they were held in the area, but Norma soon found out it did not work to take Mom along. Over and over, Alzina would respond to the evangelistic invitation and again go over the sins of her past, seeking forgiveness. Norma found it easier to stay home with her to avoid unsettling her peace.

"You know, Marty," Norma said one day. "Keeping Mom makes me so thankful that God spared me from a life of sin. It's not just her struggle for assurance of salvation. There are so many Christian graces she never learned, and they are so hard to learn now. I am glad we took her in, but some days are so hard."

"Did you have a hard day today?" Marty asked sympathetically.

"Well, yes, I guess I did. She was fussing about this and about that and was irritable with the children. I tried talking to her, but—"

"Well, maybe I should talk to her," Marty suggested. "If that doesn't work, we better see if Erma can take her awhile again. I think you've had enough for now."

So Alzina moved to Erma's. The change seemed to make things go better for awhile. Sometimes Norma brought her back for the weekend.

Alzina was pleasantly surprised when Norma had Art's and Erma's family all together for her birthday.

"Thank you for getting this all together for me," Alzina said. "The cake and the flowers are all so pretty. You are so good to me, Norma."

chapter thirty-eight

They Have It So Good!

Pennsylvania: 1961-1963

"Mama, why did Vernon have to die?" Keith wondered, standing next to the sewing machine, his face troubled and his eyes teary. "I miss him. He was my friend. Is he in heaven, Mama?"

Norma put her arm around Keith. Remembering the many unanswered questions of her childhood, she patiently explained to Keith that his little friend had gotten very sick and so Jesus took him home to heaven. "Now Vernon is happy with Jesus, and someday we can go see him."

"Did his mama and daddy go to see him?" Keith asked.

"No, Keith, they went to another country to tell people about Jesus,"

Norma explained, laying aside the jacket she had mended for one of Art's boys.

"Why did they go, Mama? He was our preacher."

"James and Rhoda knew that God wanted them to go preach to people in a country called Honduras, so they went. Now we have Uncle George to be our preacher."

"You sewed dresses for them before they went, didn't you, Mama?"

"Yes, I helped sew for them."

"Who are you sewing for now?" Keith asked as Norma picked up a piece of fabric and set her treadle sewing machine whirring again.

"This is a dress for Mrs. Wilks because she doesn't know how to sew."

"I like Mrs. Wilks. She gives me cookies," Keith said. "At one time she didn't love God, did she?"

"That's right, Keith. Mrs. Wilks is an old lady, and we are so glad she decided to love God."

"Here comes Hannah!" Keith rejoiced as the back door opened.

"Good morning," Hannah greeted them cheerfully. "Sewing again? Mind if I run a load of laundry?"

"Help yourself," Norma agreed.

"Read me a story! Read me a story!" Keith begged as Hannah arranged her laundry in the washer and started it.

"You never get tired of stories, do you?" Hannah said laughingly as she and Keith settled down with a book.

After Uncle Joe had spent some time living in a trailer at the edge of the Reeds' property, he had moved away. Hannah, a young single lady who attended Cambridge Church, had moved a trailer onto the same spot. She quickly became part of the Reed family and was a favorite aunt to the children and a very close friend to Norma.

Norma laid aside her sewing and went to put on the coffeepot. She and Hannah sat visiting at the table.

"So did Nonie and Renie have a surprise this morning?" Hannah asked with a chuckle.

"Did you hear the fuss?" Norma wondered.

"Well, I heard screaming, and I looked out and saw their tent was down. What happened?"

"Oh," Norma laughed, "Larry and Willie had to get up early to dig some ditches for the plumber. They knew the girls were sleeping in the tent, and they decided to have some fun and drop the tent on them. The girls didn't think it was fun. It was high time for the girls to get up, so I wasn't too hard on the boys."

"That explains why I saw the boys over by the grape arbor, and it looked like they were laughing," Hannah said.

"Changing the subject, Wilson keeps on improving since his stroke, doesn't he?" Hannah asked.

Cousins
Back row: Larry, Nonie, Dick, Linda (Erma's), Ronnie (Erma's)
Middle row: Art Jr., Kathleen (Erma's twin), Patty, Eileen (Erma's twin), Billy (Art's)
Front Row: Wilmer, David (Art's), Jimmy (Art's), Butch (Art's), Ray (Raymond's)

"Yes, we are so thankful. For a while we didn't know if he would ever walk again. I'm glad for Susannah that he can work again. He wouldn't make a very good invalid. He was out in the garden when he still needed the hoe to lean on."

"It's sure nice Erma has your mom right now."

"It's a blessing—"

There was a pounding of feet on the board porch and a clatter of lunch boxes. The schoolchildren were home. Larry, Wilmer, and Patty gathered around the table eating leftovers from their lunch boxes.

"Mom, can we go pigeon hunting with the neighbor boys tonight? They're getting fifty cents a pigeon at Green Dragon farmer's market right now."

"No school work?" Norma asked.

"Nope," the boys answered together.

"Well, ask Daddy when he gets up. He's going out on the chicken truck tonight, so he's sleeping now."

"Menno and I want to set some muskrat traps," Wilmer interrupted. "Can we go Friday night?"

"I'm not going," Larry said. "It's my turn to go with Daddy on the chicken truck."

"And there's a yard to mow and a garden to weed," Norma added. "I think Grandfather Reed could use some boys' help too."

"I hope he doesn't come down here early Saturday morning after I've been on the chicken truck and call up the stairs 'cause he can't find his tools," Larry said.

"Larry, Grandfather won't remember that you were on the chicken truck. He's used to starting his work early, and if he can't find his tools, he remembers that sometimes you borrow them."

"I know, I know," Larry answered. "But I hope he waits to lose them until I'm not trying to sleep in."

"What else is there to eat? I'm still hungry," Wilmer stated.

"Me too!" Larry agreed. At eleven and thirteen, the boys always seemed to be hungry.

"Here," Hannah said, reaching into her otherwise-empty wash basket. "I brought you some apple snitz."

"Oh, yum! Don't take so many, Larry—I want some too," Keith pleaded.

"Children, what do you say?" Norma chided.

"Thank you, Hannah. Thank you, Hannah."

In the middle of all the chatter, Norma looked at her happy, growing children. "They have it so good. They don't know how good they have it." She thought back to some of the lonely scenes of her childhood.

Bob and Betty were both married now. Nonie was in high school, and Dick was working at Weaver's Chicken, but he had problems relating on the job. Recently he had been laid off a week for not cooperating. Yes, Dick too could be difficult at times.

"Let's go ride our bikes," Wilmer suggested.

"Boys, before you go play, I want you to do some cleaning up in your room so we can sweep it. Wilmer, you can carry some of your wood projects up to the attic. And Larry, it's almost impossible to sweep with all those wires strung around."

July 3, 1962, brought a very special day for Marty and Norma. "Twenty-five years of marriage—isn't it hard to believe?" Marty asked.

"Twenty-five wonderful years, Marty!" Norma answered.

They were on their way to Betty and Dave's house for supper. Betty had the touch for serving a meal with elegance—candles, flowers, and homemade raspberry ice cream, but the big surprise was a large poster with the number 25 spelled out with silver dollars!

"Now, Norma, we are going to do something special with that money," Marty planned. "What would you say if we put this toward an indoor bathroom?"

"Oh, could we? That would be wonderful!" Norma exclaimed. "Where would we put it, though?"

"I think we could take a piece off the parlor and put a door into the kitchen," Marty answered.

Twenty-Fifth Anniversary

Half a year later, the Reeds thought they were living in luxury when they had a bathtub and an indoor toilet.

August was a busy time for Norma. She had much of the canning done—jars of pickles, cherries, tomatoes, ketchup, jams and jellies, and peaches sat waiting to be carried to the basement. They totaled 198 quarts. The corn was done—75 quarts for the year. There were apples and red beets to do yet.

Norma took one more swoosh across the porch with her broom. "Done!" she said, going to put her broom and bucket away. The dining room was washed and waxed, the living room and parlor swept, the bathroom cleaned, and the supper dishes washed. Marty and Larry had gone to Green Dragon. Patty was visiting at Betty's, and Nonie was on a trip to Canada. "Come, Keith, let's go sit on the neighbor's porch. I'm tired, and I see John and Lydia over there. Maybe Hannah will join us. Sure enough, here she comes now." Norma and Hannah crossed the street and settled into rocking chairs on the porch.

John and Lydia sat on the porch swing, gently swinging back and forth. "Here, Keith, I think we have room here for you," John invited. Keith smiled and found his spot on the swing beside the kindly grandfather.

"You've had a big day, haven't you, Norma?" John asked. "You have visitors and neighbor children in and out of your house all the time. I saw you out there scrubbing your porch and walk."

"Yes," Norma said. "This rocker feels pretty good."

"Is your mom with Erma right now?" Lydia wondered.

"Yes," Norma answered. "We take turns. Erma especially tries to take her over my busy times."

"Here comes Grandfather," Keith said.

Wilson was coming down the street, and seeing the neighborly gathering, he came over and joined them. Dick and Wilmer, who had been playing catch, came and flopped in the grass. "Well, boys," said Wilson. "How did you make out with your pigeon catching?"

"We got a total of 108 pigeons, and got paid twenty-seven dollars at the Green Dragon."

"Twenty-seven dollars!" John exclaimed. "Wilson, I think you and I should go in the pigeon catching business, don't you?" Everyone laughed at the idea of the two grandfathers climbing the rafters of the barn to catch pigeons.

"Quite a storm we had the other night, wasn't it?" John commented.

"It was kind of hard on my cherry trees," Wilson agreed. "Norma, you folks almost had your tent blown down at the meetings, didn't you?"

"I'll never forget that!" Norma agreed. Turning to John and Lydia, she explained, "We were having revival meetings in a big tent near

Honey Brook. The storm came so suddenly that we didn't think to dismiss the service. Of course we didn't know how bad it would get."

"I wouldn't want to be in a tent in a storm like that one," John said. "What did you do?"

"Well, it got so noisy in there," Norma continued. "It was raining hard. The tent was flapping. Our evangelist, Paul Ebersole, quit preaching. Men and women were holding the tent poles down. We sure thought the tent would go. A chain tore, and a section of the tent started filling with water. The men were soaked, and the tent poles were jumping. The canvas was snapping, and some of the children were crying. Most of us were huddled in one spot praying, especially when one of the men shinnied up one of the big poles to disconnect something electrical. We were afraid that he would get shocked from lightning, but he was trying to make it safer for all of us."

"I cried too," Keith admitted. "But God took care of us, didn't He, Mama?"

"That's right!" everyone agreed.

"So how are you making out with your next-door neighbor?" John wondered.

"We try to keep peace," Norma answered. "The fence line keeps getting pushed our way." Sylvester and Susie[1] lived in the house between Marty's and Wilson's properties. More than once, Sylvester was found helping himself to Wilson's cherries. At times weeds were thrown over the fence on Marty's property. Angry words and accusations were thrown at them too, but still the Reeds on both sides tried to return kindness.

"Did you boys get your baseball back?" Wilson wondered.

"Yes," Wilmer said. "We were afraid to run across their yard to get it. Susie took it inside, and then later she threw it out of their attic window. She wrote all over it, 'Keep your ball at home!' and things like that."

"Poor Sylvester and Susie. They can't be happy," Norma said. "Boys, here come Daddy and Larry. I think it's time for us to head for bed."

[1]Not actual names.

Some time later, Hannah and Norma sat at the table playing a board game after most of the children were in bed. "Say, Norma," Hannah said, "I've been catching little hints here and there that there might be some special interest between the Reed and the Allgyer families. You know both families are like family to me. Maybe I'm just imagining it, because I always thought Nonie and Wil Allgyer would make a good couple."

Norma laughed. "You're pretty sharp. Actually, I meant to tell you. He's coming to see her for the first time this week."

"Really! That is so nice. I'm glad for them. So your mom's coming back again?"

"Yes, for several months. Erma and her family need a break. I'm not so busy now, so I feel like I can take a turn again. Did I tell you about Erma's surprise?"

"No, what now? I hope it's a good one. She's had her difficulties."

"Oh, we all think it's good once we got used to the idea. The twins are as excited as twelve-year-olds would be to have a new baby in the family."

"Really! That is a surprise! No wonder you are taking your mom back. When will this be?"

"This fall—October, I think."

"Now, Norma, what other surprises are you hiding from me? First it's Wil and Nonie's friendship, and then it's Erma."

"I really did plan to tell you both of those things, and you already know that I'm going to be a grandma this fall."

"Yes. How is Betty doing?"

"She's doing fine. We are all so excited, but it's going to take me a while to get used to the title of 'Grandma.'"

The beginning of August, Dave and Betty's little Greg joined the family. Erma and Ronald's baby, Lisa, arrived in October.

Norma sat cradling her new grandson. She looked into his little face and was thankful that he had parents who truly loved each other and two sets of grandparents who were serving the Lord.

chapter thirty-nine

A Long Night and a Long Day

Pennsylvania: 1964

"Look at all that snow! It's supposed to snow and blow all day! How am I going to get to work?" Dick worried.

"Don't worry, Dick," Norma consoled him. "We have good snow tires, and Daddy will take you to Weaver's, and Nonie to Rubinson's Store."

"I hope we leave early. Nonie, better be ready. I don't want to be late for work."

"No school today. Yippee!" Wilmer rejoiced. "Come on, Larry, let's eat breakfast fast and get out there."

Larry didn't need any urging. The boys were soon bundled and out the door. The snow continued to fall fast.

At 10:30 the phone rang. It was Nonie. "It's snowing so hard there's hardly anyone coming into the store. If you come for Dick, you can get me early too."

Norma had the washer running—Monday was washday, rain or snow. "Marty, do you think if I finished up this wash, you could drop me off at the laundromat to dry these clothes when you go to New Holland for Dick and Nonie? It would be a lot nicer than hanging the wash around in the house or hoping it will dry on the porches."

"Sure," Marty agreed. "Why don't we start soon after lunch."

"You might need to do some shoveling to get up Water Street," Hannah stated. "The snowplows haven't gone yet." She had just come home from work in the storm. "I'll stay here with the children while you go."

Piling baskets of wet laundry and snow shovels in the car, Marty and Norma started out. Slowly they crept up the hill. About three-fourths of the way up, they spun out. Marty looked at Norma with a grin. "I guess the only way to get up this hill is to shovel."

"Sure," Norma agreed, reaching for a shovel. Side by side, they shoveled their way up the road to Main Street. Then backing up for another run, they slowly crept up the hill. It had taken half an hour to get up Water Street. Instead of fifteen minutes, it took another half hour to get to the laundromat. "I'll shovel a path to the door, if you carry the heavy baskets of wet laundry in," Norma offered.

Then Marty went for Dick and Nonie. "Here you are!" Dick greeted Marty. "I thought you'd never come!" Coming back, they left the car parked on Main Street and carried the baskets of clean, dry laundry down the hill to home.

Larry and Wilmer had shoveled the drive and walks at home and for Wilson's. Now they were helping some of the neighbors.

By evening, Water Street was swarming with sledders. "Come along sledding, Mama," Keith begged.

Marty had gone to bed early, expecting to be called to work before morning. Norma and Hannah sat at the table relaxing with a game of

"Sorry."

"Sure, let's go," Hannah urged.

"All right," Norma agreed, "but the younger children will have to come in soon."

Keith rejoiced. "Ride with me, Mama! If my sled is heavier, we will go faster."

Soon Hannah and Norma were part of the happy group of sledders. When Norma had the younger children all tucked into bed, Hannah sat at the table reading the newspaper.

"How about a couple more rides?" Norma suggested.

"Sure," Hannah agreed.

"Here comes Mom," Dick rejoiced as they joined the sledders on the hill again.

"You can ride with me, Auntie Norma," Art's little Jimmy offered. "I like when you come sledding. Moms don't usually come."

Norma and Hannah stood at the top of the snowy hill, giving the children big pushes for a fast send-off. "Susannah's not feeling too well, is she?" Hannah asked.

"No, she's not. I've been going to Wilson's now in the mornings to brush Susannah's hair and help with housework. Her neck is sore. She has a lump that we are concerned about."

"Norma, you are busy helping everyone!"

"Well, Hannah, you know Susannah has been so good to me—like a mother I never really had. I don't think I could have a sweeter, more gracious mother-in-law. I'd do anything for her."

Susannah continued to have problems. Then the doctor diagnosed her with a goiter, and she was scheduled for surgery. The day before she went to the hospital, the phone rang.

"Mom, this is Nonie. Did you hear the news? Rubinson's Store is burning!"

Norma gasped, "Are you all right?"

"Yes, Mom, everyone got out, but the whole store is burning. It's terrible, Mom," Nonie said tearfully.

"I'm so glad you are all safe. I'll be up there as soon as I can drop some clothes off at the laundromat."

"Okay, Mom. I don't want to leave yet. We are all watching the fire."

The phone rang again. "Mom, this is Dick." Norma could tell he was upset. "Did you know Rubinson's is burning? Is Nonie okay?"

"Yes, Dick, I just talked to her. Everyone got out okay. Don't worry," Norma comforted him. "She's fine."

"I'm so glad," Dick said. "Now I can work again."

Dick could get so unnerved, and it seems his life went in cycles. Sometimes he couldn't sleep. Of course, that meant sleepless nights for Norma and times of comforting and consoling him as he worried over his own and others' spiritual condition. Marty talked and prayed with him. In his somewhat limited way, Dick had given his heart to the Lord and been baptized.

There were days Norma prayed for grace as Dick talked nonstop. Then he would enter a sleepy cycle when he slept just about any time he sat down. Marty and Norma doctored and prayed. There were times Dick faithfully worked at a routine job and seemed content. Other times he chafed at his limitations. Marty tried to take Dick with him when he could.

One evening when Marty was at work, Norma planned to be gone for several hours with friends. Dick had been difficult the day before. Now she was relieved to find him swinging on the porch swing with neighbor John. He seemed happy to just stay at home. John was a patient listener to Dick's chatter. Several hours later, Norma returned.

Larry said, "Mom, where's Dick? Didn't he go with you?"

"No, he was on the porch with John when I left. He's probably in bed," Norma answered.

"Nope, he's not up here," Larry called a moment later from the boys' room.

Norma glanced out the front window. John's house was dark. The elderly couple had gone to bed. The children fanned out, looking all over the house from attic to basement. Wilmer ran up the street to see if he was at Wilson's. No Dick.

Norma called Marty at work. Soon he called back. "Ira Nafziger says he saw Dick walking to Blue Ball and picked him up. Dick told him he wants to work in the egg room at Weaver's for a couple hours. But I checked; Dick isn't in the egg room."

"Norma," Marty continued, "let's keep praying, and I'll be home soon. Maybe we'll just have to report him missing to the police."

The whole night was spent hunting and praying. At five in the morning, Norma and Hannah lay down to rest. Marty sat by the phone in case Dick would call home.

At seven o'clock, Marty went back to Weaver's Chicken to see if Dick had shown up. Maybe he had gone with one of the chicken-catching trucks and would be riding back in on one of them. But no one knew anything of him. So Marty reported him missing to the Ephrata state police.

Around noon, the phone rang. "This is Jesse at Weaver's Poultry. I just got a collect call from Dick. He said he's in Maryland—south of Baltimore, and he wants off for vacation now."

"Maryland! Oh, Marty, now what do we do?" Norma exclaimed.

"Just keep praying," Marty answered. "The Pennsylvania police will contact the Maryland police, and they will be looking."

Norma called Betty, and she soon came home to join the vigil. Then the phone rang again. "I got another collect call. Dick wants his check sent to Frederick, Maryland, to the Key Chevrolet garage."

Marty notified the police, while Norma prepared to leave for Maryland. It was 6:30 in the evening. As they traveled south, Norma's thoughts went back to a very snowy day twenty-one years before, when she and Marty had struggled to get their very sick baby to the hospital.

Three and a half hours later, Marty and Norma were with the city police in Maryland. Then they saw Dick. He stood in a cell with his hands on the bars, looking out. Norma wiped tears and Marty blew his nose. Very willingly, a subdued Dick came with them. It was a quiet trip home. They arrived at 2:30 a.m.

Dick hadn't really seemed to know where he was headed. After Marty explained the dangers and the worry that he had caused, Marty was quite sure Dick would not run off again.

Perhaps Dick had felt threatened by his younger siblings maturing past him. Nonie was dating. Larry and Wilmer often went away with friends. But over time, Dick seemed more satisfied with his place in life. He enjoyed playing games like crokinole with his Grandma Alzina when she was there, and he thoroughly enjoyed his nieces and nephews. He thought the world of Grandmother Susannah.

"Mom," he said one day when Norma had asked him to carry a basket of clean laundry to Susannah's house, "I think Grandmother Reed is one of the nicest people I know."

"I think so too, Dick," Norma agreed. Norma continued helping Susannah until she was up and about again. Dick willingly walked to the store for bread or whatever Susannah needed.

Dick needed extra comfort and understanding when neighbor John was injured in a farm accident and died several days later. John had been a very special person to Dick.

The talkative and sleepy cycles continued on throughout Dick's life. As Norma prayed for grace, she knew that in her heart this child held a very special spot.

chapter forty

Two Hospitals

Lancaster General Hospital

Pennsylvania: 1965-1966

"How do you like it, Marty?" Norma asked glancing with satisfaction at the dining room with its white, ruffled Priscilla curtains and recently painted light green walls.

"I think it looks pretty good," Marty said. "You put a lot of hard work into it, didn't you?"

"Yes," Norma agreed. "But now I'm tired. How about a cup of cold tea out on the porch swing?"

"That sounds good to me, especially if you join me." The front porch was a pleasant place to rest. High shrubs surrounded the porch on three sides, allowing a view of the nearby road without being easily observed. Two big maple trees in the front yard added their shade.

"You know, Marty, I'm so glad that the people from the Mennonite church near Erma's have taken an interest in Mom," Norma said. "I don't feel so pressured to get her here for church. It's been a blessing to Erma that Mom's friends, John and Lois, have brought her out here to visit several times. Lois even helped sew dresses for Mom."

"Erma's been pretty faithful in keeping your mom over the last couple years. Do you think it might be wearing thin for her?" Marty wondered.

"I'm afraid it might be. Mom at least has her own room there, but she has problems relating to Erma's children too. She enjoys little Lisa, though, and is actually good at watching her for Erma."

Norma laughed, saying, "You know how Mom uses so much powder. I heard Ronnie telling our boys that their stairs to the second floor where her room is has powder footprints on them."

Marty chuckled, then asked, "Did you talk to your dad since the tornadoes in Indiana?"

"Yes, I called him, and he said he is fine, but he seemed to appreciate my concern. He said the storms were south of him." They swung in silence. A horse and buggy clip-clopped down the road.

"I sure appreciated J. Paul Graybill's message on Sunday," Marty began. "After all the turmoil we've had at Cambridge with Paul Hartz leaving, the message on baptism just laid it out so simply and plainly. We needed that after Paul's ideas about baptism. I appreciate J. Paul so much," Marty continued. "His kind, fatherly way reminds me of Clyde Kauffman at Brutus."

"I thought his sermon was wonderful too," Norma agreed. "This whole upheaval has been so hard. I'm really going to miss Joyce Hartz and Hannah—oh, Marty!"

"Yes." Marty put his hand over Norma's. "I know that's hard for you. You and Hannah have been as close as sisters. She seems to be the only one going along with Paul Hartz's ideas."

Norma sighed. "I hardly see her anymore. She talked to me the other day about moving her trailer away. That will leave more than just an empty spot in the yard."

"Do you think," Marty wondered, "that a trip back to Michigan this summer might be a good thing for all of us? I've always wanted to take the children to Mackinac Island."

"That would be very relaxing," Norma agreed.

"The children are at the age where they would enjoy renting bikes and driving around on the island," Marty planned. "You know they don't allow cars on the island, just horses and wagons and bikes."

"Wouldn't Dick be thrilled with a trip like that!" Norma agreed. "Let's do it early enough that it doesn't run into our preparing for Nonie's wedding."

"How about July?" Marty wondered. "They are planning for a September wedding, aren't they?"

"Yes, and the other thing, Marty. You know we could hear from the Children's Bureau sometime soon. We should go before then."

"I hope we're not biting off too much," Marty said. "This idea of getting foster children really appeals to you, doesn't it?"

"Yes, it does. The added income will help us, but really, Marty, you know I was a foster child too. I always wanted to give some troubled child a little of what Aunt Sarah gave me."

"You have a big heart, Norma," Marty said, squeezing her hand. "I just hope it's not too much. You know, not every foster child is a good little girl like you were," he teased.

"I know, but I'd like to do it at least once. It helps me that Larry is working at Weaver's and can take Dick along to work. I don't have to run as much. Your mother offered to keep Mom up there sometimes when Erma needs a break."

"I'm glad Mother is up to that," Marty said. "It took her a while to get on her feet again after surgery."

It was a happy group of travelers that headed for Michigan, from nine-year-old Keith to Nonie and her fiancé Wil Allgyer.

They were only home a few weeks when the Children's Bureau called. Norma made a quick trip to Lancaster. The children cheered when she returned with two-year-old Lena and four-year-old Grace. But Grace could hardly stop crying. Norma remembered Aunt Sarah's arms around her as she held Grace close. Gradually the tears subsided. The girls were grubby, and to Norma's dismay had head lice. A bath, clean clothes, and a careful delousing of their soft, short curls, and they were two very beautiful little girls. Patty, at eleven, thought it great fun to have two little sisters.

Grace turned out to be a handful. Numerous times Norma had to punish her for trampling through the flowerbed to the bird bath, slopping around, and carrying water back to the sandbox. Finally she learned that when Mrs. Reed said 'no,' she meant it. While Grace was hard for others to handle, she loved Mrs. Reed.

The wedding came and went, and then Norma was ready to share the secret that she and Marty had been keeping. Ten years after Keith and several months before her forty-sixth birthday, there was going to be a new little Reed! Except for being a little more tired, Norma felt good. There was no time to pamper herself. Marty was right about the fact that Erma needed a change from keeping Mom. Mom was having continued trouble with a sore leg that wouldn't heal. Susannah's offer of a room at their house for Mom to sleep occasionally when she was with Norma seemed to be the answer.

The Reed house was full. Wil and Nonie had moved in after their wedding. They were busy preparing to go to Portland, Maine, in I-W service. Susannah often had Marty's sister Esther's little girls. They liked to come to Auntie Norma's too, where there were cousins, foster girls, and neighbor children.

There was all the cooking and laundry that goes with having busy teenagers. Larry and Wilmer were going to high school at LMS; Norma needed to take her turn in carpooling; Patty and Keith were going to Conestoga School.

Norma and Erma were talking on the phone one day. "Don't feel bad, Erma," Norma said. "You have certainly done your part. You've had Mom most of the time for the last three years."

"But, Norma, how can you take Mom?" Erma objected. "Your house is full. Then with the baby on the way, you have to take care of yourself."

"Well, I did talk to the Children's Bureau and told them I can't continue to keep both girls. Grace is transitioning to go to the home where her older brother is. She seems fairly happy with that. Lena's easier to keep."

"But what will we do, Norma?"

"I'll talk to Susannah and see if Mom can move into one of their bedrooms on a permanent basis, but first, Erma, we have to get some help for Mom's sore leg. Dr. Martin would like to admit her to the General Hospital and try to get it healed up. It might take skin grafting."

"If he thinks so, I'd be in favor of that," Erma agreed. "If she's at Susannah's, that means a lot falls on you, Norma. She'll be at your house during the day a lot of the time."

"I know," Norma answered. "But Mom spends a lot of time puttering around in her room. I think it will work, but let's get her into the hospital first. Then we'll talk to Susannah."

Toward the end of October, Alzina was admitted to the hospital. About the same time, Marty was doctoring for discomfort in his chest. Dr. Martin sent him to a doctor in Philadelphia. Dr. Drew suggested X-rays. Meanwhile the hospital decided to go ahead with skin grafts for Alzina. Marty went for X-rays and the diagnosis came back—a spot on the lower outer tissue of his lung. Marty was scheduled for surgery in Lancaster the next week.

"Two hospital stays," Norma said to herself. "That's two too many." Soberly she packed a bag for Marty's hospital stay. The next morning when Norma got up, the boys were already in the dining room talking with Marty, who had just come home from work. A shadow hung over the family. Marty prepared to be laid up for awhile. He changed the tires on the car and went for a haircut.

On Sunday morning, Marty and Norma came home right after Sunday school and soon were on their way to Lancaster Osteopathic

Hospital. "Norma, you know all we can do is commit this to the Lord. I'll be well taken care of, and I'll understand when you can't get in to see me. I don't want you any more overloaded in your condition."

"I guess I should drop in on Mom at the General Hospital after you are admitted," Norma planned. "I'm glad that at least both hospitals are in Lancaster. Mom seems to have come through her surgery pretty well. At least in the hospital she doesn't have access to all her concoctions that she likes to put on her leg. I hope they keep her long enough to get it well healed."

"Marty," Norma began and then paused. "Did Dr. Martin say for sure that the spot on your lung is tuberculosis?"

"Yes, he's quite sure it is, but he's very optimistic about treatment. He didn't promise, though, that I won't be a sick man for awhile."

When Norma went to bed that night, instead of listening for Marty's truck to go through town, her thoughts were at the hospital.

The day of the surgery, Norma kept vigil at the hospital. The surgery went well, but the following days were hard ones. Sometimes Marty was too sick to care if Norma was there or not, but gradually he began to recover.

Norma was having her own troubles. Several of the children were sick, the washer broke down, and the repairman took several days to get there. Laundry piled up. One day the clothesline broke, dropping clean laundry to the ground. At the same time, Norma was doctoring for a blood clot in her leg.

Marty was feeling better, but Mom, who had been taken to the Wetzler Home from the hospital, had only lasted about a week there. Now they wanted her removed. Norma spent time on the phone trying to find a place for Mom. Susannah wasn't sure she could handle her. Finally it was agreed to move her to Susannah and Wilson's. They had a spare room. One of the neighbor ladies would come in and help.

After two weeks in the hospital, Marty was discharged. Just having Marty home, even though he was still recuperating, put Norma's world to rights.

"Your mother is gracious," Norma told Marty, "but there comes a time. The neighbor helping to care for Mom told me that Mom ripped the bandage off her sore leg."

"Maybe it's time for a family council," Marty replied. Soon Ronald and Erma, Art and Esther, and Marty and Norma gathered around the table to discuss the problem.

"My mother has not said that she can't keep Alzina," Marty stated. "But I'm afraid if we don't lay down some guidelines, it will come to that."

"We all know she's not easy to keep," Ronald said. "Norma and Erma know that better than anyone. Different people are bothered by different things. It could be anything from her false teeth clacking to—well—I understand that Marty, here, doesn't appreciate when she starts clearing off the table before he's done eating."

"Mom does have those little irritating habits that we can't change," Norma began.

"We all have some of those," Art interrupted with a laugh.

"I think," Norma went on, "what bothers Susannah is that Mom doesn't know her boundaries. Susannah agreed to give her a room, not the whole house. Susannah needs the kitchen to herself—she's giving Mom meals. She can't have Mom slopping around in her kitchen. I already told Mom that she is not to go into their bedroom even to water the plants on the windowsill."

Erma gasped.

"If Susannah has no place for her own privacy, she'll wear out fast," Esther stated. "Especially when Alzina's having a bad day and is irritable."

"Amen," Art agreed.

Erma said, "Norma, didn't you say Mom has something she's putting on her leg 'cause it itches from healing, and the stuff is irritating it again?"

"Yes," Norma agreed. "And she won't listen to anyone who tells her to quit."

Finally it was agreed that Norma, Erma, and Art should go talk to Susannah and Alzina together and have an understanding. Norma and Erma should also take the anti-itch medicine away.

As the three started out the door to Wilson and Susannah's, Ronald said to Marty, "You know, Marty, it amazes me how they stick to their mom after the way she let them sit in their childhood."

"It's the right thing to do," Marty answered. "It's called forgiveness."

"I will say this," Ronald answered. "In spite of all her faults, there are times when I actually enjoy having Alzina around. She has her own sense of humor and can be quite pleasant. She loves to entertain babies. That helped Erma out a lot with Lisa."

"I know what you mean," Marty answered. "We've been pretty negative today, haven't we? But you know it had to be said."

When her three children came to talk to her, Alzina took it seriously. "I know, I know," she said. "I understand. I'll try."

Susannah was relieved. But several days later, Norma was hanging up laundry when Mom came down the street. Norma sighed to herself and prayed for grace. It was obvious that Mom was carrying a chip on her shoulder.

"Mom," Norma began carefully but firmly.

Soon Mom was apologizing. "Norma, I'm sorry. I know I shouldn't be like this. I'm so glad for all you and Susannah do for me."

Norma's heart went out to her mother. It was so hard to break lifelong habits! "Mom, you are forgiven. Remember, Mom, God forgives too, and He will help you."

Norma took another basket of laundry out to hang on the back porch. Soon she heard Mom inside singing, "When the Roll Is Called Up Yonder, I'll Be There."

chapter forty-one

A Place for Mom

Pennsylvania: 1966-1970

"What a snowstorm!" Norma said, looking out the kitchen window. Boots stamped on the back porch, and the door burst open.

"I'm frozen!" Larry announced. "Daddy got up the hill, but we boys stood on the back bumper to weight it down. He barely made it. You should see Main Street! It's only one lane, with turnouts for cars. Oh! Fresh cookies! Can I have some?"

Norma turned from the oven with a pan of hot cookies. "Yes, after you hang up your wet clothes. Where's Wilmer? Oh, here he comes."

There was more stamping of boots, and Wilmer came in red-cheeked and snow-covered. "Cookies! Yum! It's terribly windy out there," he announced, pulling off his gloves and sending a shower of snow across the room. "There's a big snowdrift higher than the Chevy. In fact, it's half buried. There's another one as high as the grapevines."

"I wish I could go out," Keith interrupted.

"You'd freeze!" Larry said.

"Look out the front living room window, Keith," Wilmer suggested. "There's a snowdrift as high as the porch."

Norma put fresh pans of cookies in the oven. "Boys, get yourself warmed up, and then I have another adventure for you."

"What?" Larry and Wilmer said together.

"Harry Sauder's phoned here," Norma answered. "They said the milk truck can't get through. Their containers are all full, and they are dumping milk. If you get dry clothes and really bundle up, you can walk out there and get milk for us, for Grandfather's, and maybe some of the other neighbors. You *must* bundle up, though; it's quite a walk to their farm."

"That sounds like fun," Larry said, holding his hands over the kerosene stove.

"Sure," Wilmer agreed. "Do I have dry gloves somewhere, Mom?"

"I want to go out too," Keith insisted.

"No, Keith, you have to wait until the wind dies down," Norma

Snowstorm of 1966

Big drift at front porch

answered. "There will be snow out there for a long time yet."

When the boys came back with four gallons of milk on the sled, Norma hurried them off for hot showers and dry clothes. Then she busied herself making pudding to go with the cookies. By the end of the day, there were thirty dozen cookies tucked into bags for future use, and Norma was tired.

Since the boys had no school the next day either, Norma put them to work moving furniture. The parlor was turned into a downstairs bedroom in preparation for a new little arrival.

Finally the storm blew itself out. All the neighbors on Water Street emerged from their warm houses and shoveled their driveways. Then they worked together to shovel the street up to the main road. Snowbanks rose too high to see over.

"Marty, doesn't it remind you of a good old Michigan snowstorm?" Norma asked.

"It sure does," Marty agreed. "I'm just glad you're not needing Dr. Martin right now."

For two Sundays, church had been canceled. Finally came a Sunday morning when they could go to church. Coming to an especially snowy stretch of back road, Marty slowed down. "Everybody up back," he announced to the children. Happily they tumbled over the seats into the back of the station wagon.

"Go for it, Daddy!" Wilmer said as Marty started into the snowy stretch. The extra weight in the back was what it took, and soon Marty said, "Okay, back in your seats."

Several weeks later, Dr. Martin came to Goodville one more time. It had been ten years since he hurried there to welcome Keith, and twenty-eight years since Marty and Norma had welcomed their firstborn Bobby. Norma was soon cuddling a healthy, black-haired baby boy. Baby Donald Jay was as warmly received as Bobby had been. Donny just missed Marty's fifty-first birthday by four days. Norma was nearing her forty-sixth birthday. They laughed together and treasured their little son when Marty told Norma he had overheard several people in town talking—"Did you hear about that old couple at Goodville that had a baby boy?"

The boys cheered for another brother. Patty was used to being surrounded by brothers and was just glad for a baby in the family. Betty hurried home to help her mother, then took Lena along home to play with her Gregory.

When Donny had fussy days, Mom willingly entertained him while Norma went out to the garden or hung up a load of laundry. "Mom, I really appreciate your help. I don't know how I'd get my work done when he's so fussy," she told her mother gratefully.

"Norma, I'm just glad I can help you," Mom responded. "You do so much for me. We get along just fine, don't we?" she said, smiling at the baby in her arms and giving him a little squeeze. Alzina was still boarding at Wilson's, but regularly walked down the street and spent the day with Norma.

One stormy summer evening, Wilson's went away and Alzina came down to Norma. Marty was on the truck, and the older boys had gone to help set up the tent for revival meetings. Patty was at Betty's house, and the younger boys were in bed. It was just Norma and Mom.

Crash! Boom! The lights flickered. Rain beat against the windowpane. Flash. *Crack. Boom!*

"Norma!"

"Yes, Mom, God is with us."

"I know—but—" Mom began, and then the lights went out.

"I'm getting a candle, Mom," Norma said calmly. As the candle flickered and grew bright, Norma began to sing, "Be not dismayed whate'er betide, God will take care of you." When she got to the chorus, Mom joined in, "God will take care of you, through every day, o'er all the way…"

When they got to the end of the song, Alzina started another one. "Thou thinkest, Lord, of me…" she sang. Norma joined in.

Before too long, the lights blinked back on. "I think the rain has let up. Mom, come over to this window and look at the sky," Norma exclaimed. A beautiful rainbow arched against the golden sky.

"Oh, Norma. It's beautiful!"

"Isn't our God so mighty," Norma said.

"He sure is," Alzina agreed.

"Mom how about if I walk with you up to Wilson's?"

"I'd really appreciate that!" Alzina agreed. "I need to get my rubbers on. There's water everywhere!"

So, shielding her with a big umbrella, Norma walked her mother up the street to bed.

One cold, windy morning some time later, Norma hurried to get her laundry started. Keith was home from school with a bad sore throat. She was expecting grandchildren. Nonie's Sherry and Betty's second boy, Jeffrey, were coming for the day. They were close in age to Donny, and the three were great playmates.

"Keith, Grandmother is just right up the street. I think you will be fine while I run to New Holland," Norma said. "I need to go meet Betty and get Jeffrey."

"Sure," Keith answered. "Probably Grandma will come down anyway."

Sometime later Norma was back with the three toddlers. It was time to get Sherry to bed. There were still breakfast dishes to wash and laundry to hang up. Why was Keith smiling and acting so mysterious? Tucking Sherry into bed, Norma hurried to the kitchen. She stopped in surprise. The dishes were all washed and dried and put away. The counters were sparkling clean. "Keith, did you do this?" It didn't look quite like a ten-year-old boy's work. Keith put his hand over his mouth to stifle a giggle. Just then Norma saw Mom hiding around the corner. Keith and Grandma burst out laughing.

"Grandma really surprised you!" Keith exclaimed.

"Why, thank you, Mom!" Norma said. "What a nice surprise on a very busy day. Now, Mom, I have a surprise for you. That money you were waiting for finally came."

"Well, well. I thought I never would really get that money," Alzina

Mom and Donny

exclaimed.

"You have $371.30 from your brother's estate," Norma said. "I think we should save most of it, but how about if you and I go shopping in a couple days."

"I'd sure like that!" Alzina responded. She loved to shop. Now she could even buy toys for the children.

For many years Norma had known very little about her mother's relatives in Alberta. After Bob was born, she and Erma had written to their Grandma Ruffert. Then contact died out. Norma often wondered about her ancestors, but Mom had little to say. Then there had been a phone call from a cousin in Calgary whose name was also Norma. She wanted to know about her Auntie Alzina's children. She and her husband traveled to Pennsylvania, and the two cousins met for the first time. Now Mom's brother had apparently mentioned her in his will. Norma's curiosity was again stirred about the family she had never known. But there was no time for research.

Mom's sore leg still hadn't healed right. In fact, now it was worse. Susannah faithfully dressed the sore. But one day she called Norma. "Norma, I think your mom is having problems. She seems kind of weak and thick-tongued. I wonder if she had a stroke."

"I'll be right there!" Norma answered.

Susannah was right. Mom could hardly talk. She would start saying something and couldn't finish. Neither could she walk alone.

After the doctor assured them that Mom's condition was stable, it was time for another family council. Norma and Marty sat at the table with Erma and Ronald. Norma made coffee and put out shoofly pie. "Marty and I have been talking about this. It is too much for Susannah. We think the thing to do is move Mom into our parlor. We don't have any girls of dating age and don't expect to need the room for any more babies."

"You never know," Ronald teased. Erma poked him with her elbow.

Marty laughed. "You have quite a record yourself, having Lisa so far on behind."

"I know, I know," Ronald agreed.

"Norma, are you sure you can handle that?" Erma wondered.

"You got to do what you got to do," Norma answered. "I think I can get several of the single neighbor ladies to help me if I need it."

"I'll be home tomorrow, so I can help set up the bed and move furniture," Marty offered.

"It's nice you have that room right off the kitchen if Mom's going to need more care," Erma observed. "I'll help you where I can."

"Art will do his part too," Norma said. "Erma, you *did* have Mom for about three years. You know, though, I will be glad to see more of you. It seems like we've both been busy in our own worlds."

"I know. I've missed you, Sis," Erma agreed.

Alzina was content to settle into the little room near the kitchen. At times she was happy and singing; other times she cried. There were days when she was very confused and needed to be watched continuously. Others pitched in and helped—Art and Esther, neighbor ladies, Susannah, and Norma's children. Erma came when she could. One of the hardest times for Norma was when Mom's confusion took her into her past life. Then Norma prayed for grace and forgiveness.

Gradually Mom improved. Her breathing and walking were better.

Mom, Erma, and Norma

Then Wilson's health began to fail, so Susannah and Norma shared burdens. Susannah came and dressed Alzina's sore leg. Norma in turn took over the outside work at Wilson's.

She sorely missed Larry's and Wilmer's help. Larry was married, and Wilmer was working at Rutt's Kitchens. But Keith at thirteen was a good helper.

Then one day, Norma got word that Uncle Peter had died. Once again she joined Uncle Peter's family. Together they grieved the loss of a dear father. For Norma he had been the best father figure she had had. Willingly he had taken in three abandoned children and loved them like his own.

July 3 came. Marty and Norma sat at the table. The house was quiet. The children were all in bed. "It's been a wonderful thirty-two years, Norma," Marty said, putting his hand on hers. "And will you say 'yes' for the next thirty-two years?"

"Oh yes, Marty. I've never been sorry." He gave her hand another little squeeze.

"So where were you hiding this blueberry pie?" Marty asked, reaching for another piece.

"Oh, I have lots of hiding places," Norma said with a smile. "I knew it was your favorite. I'm sorry I couldn't manage to go out to eat like you suggested."

"Really, that couldn't have been better than this—just you and me—and a blueberry pie."

"I think I like this better too. Oh, Marty, I'm so excited about the new kitchen cupboards. If Willie weren't working at Rutt's Kitchens, we never would have had an opportunity like this. They are beautiful cupboards. Solid oak should last a long time."

"I'm glad, Norma. You deserve the best. It's sure good Nonie's husband knows how to take a circular display kitchen and make it fit our kitchen. You know I'm not a carpenter. I guess we'll have to have at least one cupboard made for the corner. The boys are planning to move the bathroom upstairs soon. That will give us more space for the kitchen."

Norma laughed and said, "It's a good thing you didn't run Dave's car into the outhouse the other day. We might have to go back to using that for awhile."

Marty chuckled. "I barely missed it. I was just trying to move the car, and suddenly the brakes quit.

"Changing the subject, Norma, sometimes I wonder what we should do about church. It seems like things are really slipping. Church rules are not being enforced. It reminds me of the Brutus church when we left. Now look where Brutus is. We don't want to lose the basic doctrines of the Bible, but I'm afraid that's where it will end up."

"I know, Marty. I agree. I'm glad we found a better school for Patty and Keith."

"Let's keep praying about it, Norma," Marty answered.

A year later, after much prayer, Marty and Norma changed their church membership to a church that they felt was holding on to Scriptural teachings.

Norma knew her mom loved surprises, so when her seventy-sixth birthday came, Norma baked a cake for her. After supper Arthur, Esther, Susannah, and several of the neighbor ladies came for cake and ice cream. With them was Cousin Katie from Indiana, who was visiting in the area. Mom was delighted.

Norma was planning to spend the next day quilting with Aunt Sarah's girls. "Katie, will you spend the night here?" Norma asked.

"Sure, if you have room," Katie responded.

"Well, Marty's gone on the truck for a couple days. Do you think you and I could still share a bed?"

"Well, why not?" Katie said laughingly. So for the first time in years, Norma and Katie lay talking into the night.

"Your mom is quite a care at times, isn't she?" Katie asked.

"Yes, she is, but she's changed some since her stroke. She's more often confused, but not so irritable. I think too that maybe she's more at rest since she has a permanent home with us. The poor woman has moved around most of her life. We did put her temporarily at Tel Hai Home this summer when we took a family trip to Michigan."

"Norma, you needed that!" Katie said emphatically. "I don't see how you do it. Wilson's had another stroke too, I heard."

"Yes, and Susannah is aging too," Norma answered.

"What about your dad, Norma?" Katie wondered.

"Oh, Katie, it's so sad. Erma and I took a trip to see Dad. He was so glad to see us. His second wife, Nora, was not. I thought maybe we shouldn't stay at Dad's overnight, but he insisted. The next morning Nora stayed in her bedroom. I had prayed that we'd get a chance to have a good talk with Dad. We did, and we were all in tears. In fact, after we left, Erma and I had to stop by the side of the road and have a good cry before we could go on. Dad had regrets, Katie. It was so hard!" Katie reached for Norma's hand.

"At least Dad knows we are not holding anything against him."

"Norma, I'm so glad that you could show your mom a better life, even if it's hard at times."

"Oh, Katie, I am too. I know that Mom has made her peace with God."

chapter forty-two

Reunion!

Pennsylvania: 1971-1979

"Well, Dad, what a surprise!" Norma exclaimed, holding the door open and welcoming him warmly. "I didn't know you were in Pennsylvania."

Erma followed him into the house, saying, "He surprised us both."

With a chuckle Dad said, "I decided it was time to come and see my children. Nora is in a nursing home now, you know, so I just packed up and headed for Pennsylvania."

"You drove from Indiana by yourself?" Norma asked in surprise.

"Well, yes, I wanted to see my children, you know. I had a few troubles, but I'm here now."

"He had a few troubles, all right!" Erma said quietly.

"Here, Dad, have a chair," Norma said. "Sit down, Erma. I'll put water on for tea, and Dad can tell me about his adventures."

"Tea sounds good," Dad said, pulling out a chair by the table. "I started out just fine—nice roads, good weather, and all. I left Indiana and got through Ohio fine, but when I got to Pittsburgh, I had a little accident. The car was done up pretty bad, but nobody was hurt. I'm not quite sure what happened. Might have got my wheel off the edge a bit and lost control. So I had the car towed to a truck stop, and the police took me to the bus station. I got a bus for Lancaster. Must have dozed off or something, because when I got to Lancaster, some character had relieved me of my wallet."

"Oh, Dad!" Norma exclaimed. "What did you do then?"

"Well, I had some money stashed away inside my coat pocket, so I got me a motel for the night. This morning I got a cab and showed up at Erma's door and gave her a good surprise."

"What a trip for an eighty-six-year-old man!" Norma thought. Aloud she said, "Oh, Dad. I'm so glad you are here safely!" She looked at Erma. Her eyes were brimming with tears. Norma knew they were both thinking the same thing. Dad—*their* dad—wanted to see his children that badly.

When Mom came out of her room to see who had come, Dad got up stiffly and went and shook her hand matter-of-factly. Norma and Erma exchanged meaningful looks.

Dad stayed a little over a week, spending time with Erma, Art, and Norma.

Marty had recently had several rooms and an attached garage added onto the house. Now there was a second bathroom downstairs, a small room which was to be a sewing room, and, best of all, a laundry room. Norma had been thrilled to get a dryer—no more trips to the laundromat on wet and snowy days. The small sewing room now served well as a bedroom for Dad.

Norma tried to sort out her own feelings. It felt good to have her parents together. It was what she had always wanted, and yet it was not, because the relationship between them was gone.

Others cared for Mom while Norma took time for her dad. Together they visited Uncle Peter's girls—Betsy, Mandy, and Lydia.

"So, Norma," Mandy asked, "how is Susannah doing since Wilson is gone?"

"She's doing as good as can be expected. It's almost a year now since Wilson passed away. We try to stay close to her. She's aging too, you know."

"You sure have your hands full, Norma. If you need to get away sometime, I'd be glad to take your mom for you."

"Thanks, Mandy. You are a true sister. It is less stressful since Wilson is gone. He lingered quite a while, you know. The children took turns spending nights there. At times we put our phone in the stairway in case they needed us at night."

"I'm sure that was a strain on Susannah. Just let me know if I can help you, Norma."

"I will. Thanks, Mandy."

When Sunday came, Dad went along to church. Norma prayed that some truth would touch his heart. She had been surprised and saddened when Dad told her he did not attend church anywhere.

Dad enjoyed his grandchildren, and the children found it interesting to learn to know the grandpa they had seldom seen. When Dad treated them with candy, Norma noticed that he walked to the kitchen purposely to give Mom a piece.

Then it was time for Dad to go. Norma had arranged a flight back to Indiana for him. With a heavy heart, she watched him leave. Would she ever see Dad again?

But in two months he was back. "I moved into a nursing home in Indiana," he said. "But a nursing home is a small world. So when Raymond and his wife asked me to come along to Pennsylvania, I said sure!"

"If only Walter could have come along too," Norma thought.

The next day Raymond's, Dad, and Norma sat visiting. Norma was serving him a cup of tea when Raymond exclaimed, "Well, look who's here!"

In walked Walter. "Walter!" Norma exclaimed. "How did you get here?"

"I drove all night, Sis—I couldn't stay away, so I got off work and came!"

Quickly Norma called Erma. "Hello, Sis, you know you and I have a birthday in three days. What are your plans?"

"I've been so busy, Norma, I haven't thought about it much."

"Well, Erma, you and I are going to have one of the best birthdays ever. Guess who came to celebrate with us?"

"Raymond's family is there, aren't they?"

"Yes, but Erma, Dad came with them and just now Walter drove in! Erma, do you realize that this is the first time we have all been together since Dad and Mom broke up?"

"Oh, Norma, it's too good to be true! That's over forty years, isn't it? Oh, Norma!"

"Can you come Tuesday for supper? Patty wants to make the birthday cake."

"Norma, I still can't believe this. Yes, of course we'll come. What shall I bring?"

"Don't worry about that. I've got extra help here—just bring yourself."

Tuesday evening they were all there—Dad, Mom, Walter, Arthur, Raymond, and Erma. Norma wrote in her diary that night, "What a wonderful birthday—my family."

The next four days were filled with family time. They laughed, they cried, they visited, and the men went fishing together.

Raymond pleased Mom by taking her shopping. Walter bought her a new upholstered chair. Donny was greatly amused when they threw Grandma's old, well-used chair on the burn pile. A big puff of talcum powder billowed up from the chair.

Norma savored every moment she could have with her dad. He was

Back row: Walter, Arthur, and Raymond
Front row: Norma, Mom, Erma and Dad

Our family — Mother, Dad, Walter
Arthur, Raymond & Erma are all
together first time in 40 years or
at least since I was 9½ —
We couldn't get Ralph to come to take
pictures So we took seven flash
snap shots —
What a Wonderful birthday my family
I was 9:30 all every one A.F.

Excerpt from Norma's diary

certainly declining.

Then they were all gone. What a memorable week it had been!

Several months later, when Norma tried to call him at the nursing home on his birthday, he wasn't well enough to come to the phone. Marty was in Indiana on the truck. He stopped to see Dad and then called Norma. "Your dad is bedfast and doesn't look good, Norma."

Once again Norma and Erma hurried to Dad's side. He seemed glad to see them but was too sick to talk. Norma held his hand as tears streamed down his face. Gently she wiped them away. Poor Dad. Did he have regrets? Did he make his peace with God? Reluctantly, Norma and Erma pulled themselves away and traveled home to their families. Several weeks later, they got the message that Dad was gone.

As the family gathered to lay Dad to rest, Norma was a bit surprised to find herself struggling. Many old memories came back to her. Suddenly she was a little girl again, hiding her doll from Dad's anger. Then she was cowering under the covers, trying to shut out Dad and Mom's fighting. Next she was trying to get Dad to pick up Mom at Kingsley, and soon she was crying in Aunt Sarah's arms. She saw Dad taking Raymond and Erma away. "Please, God, help me to forgive again," she pled. Then peace came.

Mom had stayed with Mandy while Norma traveled to the funeral. She took Dad's death calmly. Mom's health continued to fluctuate. At times she was very confused, and other times she sat happily pasting pictures in scrapbooks or singing.

Norma had several visits over the years from her cousin Norma, who lived in Calgary, Alberta. She told Norma, "Your mom has several sisters who are still living. I wouldn't be surprised if they would consider coming to visit your mom."

"Wouldn't that be something," Norma replied. "They haven't seen each other since I was a six-month-old baby and my parents moved away. I better not say anything to Mom, or she will get her hopes up."

"Mom," Norma announced sometime later, "I got a very special phone call today."

"Oh?" Mom asked.

"You are getting company from Alberta," Norma answered. "You'll never guess who."

"Your cousin Norma?" Mom guessed.

"No, Mom, it's someone you haven't seen in a long time. Your sisters, Erma and Edna, have plane tickets to come."

"My sisters!" Mom was speechless for a moment. "My sisters! Why, I haven't seen them in years! When are they coming?"

"They expect to be here next week."

"My sisters! Why, Norma, they must be old ladies by now. I didn't see them since they were young girls."

"That's right, Mom. If I calculated right, it's been fifty-five years."

"Norma, I'm so excited, but I still can hardly believe it. They are coming all that way to see me!"

"Yes, Mom. I'm so glad that you have been feeling better lately. We'll have to show them around Pennsylvania, won't we?"

"That would be nice," Mom agreed.

Aunt Erma and Aunt Edna arrived, and so did the newspaper reporter that someone had notified. Mom, who had always enjoyed reading the newspaper, was surprised to see her own picture on the front page, along with her sisters.

It was the middle of canning season, but Norma took her aunts sightseeing. They had never seen an open market like Green Dragon. They toured Hershey Chocolate and a local buggy shop. They marveled at the tall cornfields and big maple trees. Going to church with Marty and Norma was the first they had visited a Mennonite church service.

Evenings were spent talking and looking at pictures. Norma was able to piece together some of the skimpy information she had about her ancestors.

Mom was doing so well physically that Norma and Erma planned another surprise for her the following year. Mom had no idea why Norma was rushing around and setting the house in order. In fact, she didn't seem to notice at all. The rest of the family knew, and everyone

Alzina and her sisters, Erma and Edna

could hardly wait to tell Grandma. The children crowded around her bedroom door to watch her expression when Norma decided it was time to tell.

"Mom, Erma and I have been talking. Since you are good enough to take a trip, we decided to take you to Indiana to see Raymond and then on up to Michigan to visit Walter."

Mom's eyes opened wide, and her mouth dropped open. "Oh, Norma, do you really think I can? That would be wonderful!" Mom's happiness was touching.

It would be the first time Mom was back in Michigan in twenty-seven years. By the end of the day, she started to have doubts. "Norma, do you really think I can make such a long trip?"

"Mom," Norma reassured her, "it will just be you and me and Erma and Lisa. We will stop and rest sometimes." Then Mom was happy.

Two days later, they were on their way. Mom traveled well. "Are we really going to Indiana to see Raymond?" she asked.

"We sure are!" Erma responded.

"It's just so hard to believe," Mom said. Then she entertained herself by counting blue cars—all the way to Indiana. She counted seven hundred and fifty. That evening at Raymond's house, she said, "Well, I'm at Raymond's house. That wasn't so bad. Now I'm in Indiana."

After spending several days at Raymond's and visiting with Katie, who lived nearby, they headed north to Michigan to see Walter. Raymond's traveled with them. Mom could hardly believe that she was going to see where Walter lived too.

Mom was in for one more surprise. Norma had contacted her old friend Mary Evelyn. With her help they arranged to have a cottage by the lake. Mom just loved it! She sat in the cottage looking out across the lake. She could see Raymond by the water, fishing. "Oh, Norma, this is too good to be true!"

Norma and Erma smiled at each other. "Aren't we glad we brought her!" they agreed.

Walter, Norma, Raymond, Erma, Arthur

"Come on, Mom," Walter said, coming into the cabin. "I'm taking you fishing." Mom laughed at what she thought was a joke. "Really, Mom, wouldn't you like to go fishing?" Walter asked.

"Now wouldn't that be something," Mom responded.

"Come on, Erma, bring that chair, and I'll walk Mom out to the dock." Soon Mom was sitting in a chair on the dock. Walter cast the line in and handed the rod to Mom. "You pull her in, Mom. Now mind, you get a big one."

Everyone hoped Mom would get a fish. But when her last try came in empty, she said, "Never mind. I've had the time of my life!"

Then there was visiting to do. They looked up various ones of Mom's old friends. Then they visited the Gregorys and the Sniders and Mose and Bessie, who were in a nursing home. They drove through Brutus, past the school, the church, the huckleberry marsh, Uncle Peter's house, Grandpa Brenneman's house, Wilson's house, Abe Sauder's house, then out past the dam. Mom loved it all. Her dream had been to once more shop in the stores in Petoskey. To her disappointment, the stores in Petoskey just didn't have what she said she "was sure she could find in Petoskey." The stores had changed too in twenty-seven years.

Then it was back to Indiana, stopping at Raymond's again for a break. The trip from there to Pennsylvania was a happy time. Norma and Erma spent time singing. Mom counted cars. It had been a good trip, and one that Alzina would never be able to make again.

The next fall, Marty and Norma began toying with the idea of moving. They had not wanted to move away from Susannah, but now Susannah had moved into a trailer on Marty's brother Aaron's property because of failing health. With the outside work done for the season, they began to look in earnest. Their home of thirty years held many memories, but when they found a house at Bowmansville, Norma was enthused.

"Look, Marty, this can be our bedroom next to the bathroom, and Mom's room will be just across the hall. That will be so handy."

"What I like," Marty said, "is this living room. Somebody added this onto the house and put all their dreams into one room." The sunken living room, with a built-in brick planter, fireplace, and sliding glass doors to the backyard, was very appealing. "I think this fireplace is just the thing for an old couple like us," he said, winking at her.

"I like all the fruit trees and berry bushes. With plenty of garden space, we won't have trouble keeping Donny busy. And Marty—the view. Without neighbors' houses all around, I can look out over the field and see the sunrise. I love it, Marty!"

"You are easy to please, Norma. I'd like to add a garage with more living space above it."

Before they were moved into their new house, Susannah passed away quite suddenly. Norma grieved the loss of a very close friend and influential mother figure in her life. God had always had someone there for her in her mother's absence. First that person had been Aunt Sarah, then Bessie, and next Susannah. She remembered how Susannah had welcomed her into the Reed family with a wedding meal and her favorite lemon meringue pie. They had worked together, moved to Pennsylvania together, and shared each other's burdens. Susannah's godly life had been like a guiding light for Norma over the years. And yet she could not wish her back. Susannah was enjoying a well-deserved rest.

Mom had her difficult days, but there were good ones too. Norma remembered the time they had taken her to the zoo. Using a wheelchair, Donny had enjoyed pushing her around to see all the animals. Norma and Erma had taken her several hours away to Longwood Gardens to see the flowers.

One evening the rest of the family had gone to church while, Norma stayed home with her mom. She put two chairs by the fireplace. The record player was playing songs of heaven. Soon they were both singing along, "I'll meet you in the morning at the end of the way, on the streets of that city of gold...."

"Norma," Mom said, "I'm so glad you brought me to Pennsylvania.

I don't know where I would be if you hadn't."

"I'm glad too, Mom." Norma knew that her mother very likely would not be singing songs of heaven if she had continued to live the life that she had been living in Michigan.

"You know, Norma, the other night I woke up and I just couldn't get my breath. I really thought I was going to die, so then I prayed and I felt better."

"Aren't we glad that we can pray, Mom?"

"I sure am," Mom answered.

One warm spring evening, Mom felt good enough to go to church.

Mom

The church service was mostly singing. Norma's heart was blessed as she watched her mom singing her heart out. She remembered that other times she would find her mom sitting in her room, copying Scripture verses.

But Mom was having trouble with high blood pressure and shortness of breath. More and more, she complained of pain.

"Marty," Norma said one day, "I'm so glad Mandy could keep Mom so we could get away for awhile. That trip to Canada was so special."

"I know you needed that, Norma," Marty agreed. "It seems your mom has mellowed, but I know you still have difficult days when she is hard to please."

Visiting Cousin Norma at Calgary had been a special treat, but most of all Norma enjoyed being taken to visit the old homestead where her mom grew up. There was the bay window that Mom said had been filled with red geraniums. She tried to imagine her mother as a girl living and working there, and then Dad coming as a young man to claim his bride. Visiting Calgary had been a long-wished-for experience.

Although Mom had more pain, she still liked to go away sometimes. Norma took her shopping in a wheelchair. It was after a pleasant evening of going away for supper and visiting with friends that Mom sat talking to Norma in the kitchen. Finally she said, "Yes, well, I best be going to bed. I'll see you in the morning," and with a little wave of her hand she left the kitchen.

The next morning, Norma stood at the kitchen window admiring a glorious sunrise. With it came thoughts of heaven and those gone before. Then she wondered how it would be with Mom. Would she linger bedfast as Wilson had? That would be hard. "But, God, I know you'll help me through. It's so good to know that Mom is ready to go," she prayed quietly.

The sunrise faded, and she turned away to get breakfast ready for the family. It would be awhile until Mom was up, so meanwhile she busied herself with other housework. Sometime later she went to check on

Mom. Knocking gently on the door, she opened it. Mom was sleeping peacefully with her hand tucked under her cheek. But something was different. Suddenly Norma realized with a start—Mom was gone!

Stepping closer, Norma gently pulled the covers up around Mom's face. How peaceful she looked. Tears filled Norma's eyes. What had Mom said last evening? "I'll see you in the morning."

"Oh, yes, Mom," Norma whispered. "I'll see you in the morning—that glorious morning over there."

At Ninety-Four

Norma sat by the fireplace with her hands folded on her lap. Her walker stood beside her chair. Visitors were coming from a distance, and everyone was busy. It was nice to sit back and let someone else do the work, and yet still get to enjoy the company.

Her eyes were alight with interest as company arrived. She gave a special smile to a little girl who stood looking up at her.

As the family was introduced to Norma, Brother Nevin took her hand. "God bless you, Norma."

"And He does!" Norma answered quickly and emphatically, as she usually did. Nevin felt drawn by the fervent response of this frail old lady.

As the visit progressed, Nevin placed a chair by Norma's side. "Norma, I understand you have a story to tell, and I'd like to hear it," he suggested.

"Yes," Norma responded, "I do. My life was not always easy, but God is very good to me." Several others moved closer to listen. Then she told of her parents' separation, of her time at Uncle Peter's, and her lonely teenage years. "But the Lord gave me a wonderful husband. Marty and I were married almost 68 years. We had our disappointments and sorrows, but God saw us through."

"How long is Marty gone now?" Nevin wondered.

"He died in May of 2005. I sure do miss him. He was so good to me. When my mother needed a place to live, Marty agreed to giving her a home. That wasn't easy either, but she gave her heart to the Lord. I'll never forget her last words, 'I'll see you in the morning.'

"Some years later, Marty and I moved to a house in Blue Ball. We only had Dick at home anymore. Then my Uncle Joe, Dad's brother, needed a place to live. He was in his nineties, so we took him in. We were in our seventies, but he was so easy to keep. Joe had left the church like my dad. His last year, when he was ninety-nine and bedfast, he asked for our preacher to come. He wanted to clear some things up with God and be baptized into the Mennonite church. It was such a blessing to see him at rest and ready to go."

"Ninety-nine!" Nevin exclaimed.

"Yes. It was such an encouragement to never stop praying. Some of my own children have needed extra prayer. I couldn't gather them in my arms and make their choices for them, but I could still take them to the Lord."

"Did Marty pass away before Dick?"

"Yes, Dick lived a few years longer. I used to worry because Dick was always a special boy and depended on me a lot. I wondered what he would do if I died. But God is faithful. Dick passed away first.

"I've been so blessed. I could work out in my flowerbed and drive to the grocery store until I was ninety-three. Then I fell and broke my hip,

Norma praying

and a lot of things changed. It was hard to leave my home and most of my family in Pennsylvania, but I'm very contented now living with my daughter here in Washington state. I get to church every Sunday. And my friends didn't forget me. My children phone me, and most of them have come to visit me. I was so surprised on my ninety-fourth birthday. I got over one hundred birthday cards!"

"One hundred cards!" Brother Nevin echoed. "Your life must have touched many other lives. I'm so glad you shared your story with me, Sister Norma." As he stood at the door to leave, he raised his hand and smiled at Norma. "I'll see you in the morning."

Journey's End

At ninety-four, Norma enjoyed helping around the house, doing little things like folding laundry or washing breakfast dishes. Congestive heart failure made her tired. Although her physical heart was wearing out, she still had a heart for people.

One day a young woman with a difficult background was visiting. Norma knew she was trying to serve the Lord. Getting out of her chair and using her walker, Norma walked slowly over to her. Looking kindly into her face, she said, "I made it, and you can too." Then she went back to her chair, most likely praying as she went.

One morning Norma sat on the edge of her bed. She wanted to make sure Betty was taking care of her finances and all the children knew where she was (she was forgetful and had to be reminded of their visits). "Well, then," she said, "I'm ready to go." A week and a half later, she slipped quietly away.

Significantly, God had taken her home on Thanksgiving morning to spend eternity thanking and praising Him. Someone had once suggested to Norma that one thing she could still do was count her blessings. "Oh, no, I can't," she replied quickly.

"Well, why not?"

"Because," she responded, "I have too many blessings to count."

The Way She Chose

Patty Martin

Why did we all love her? What made her so dear
That she was so special to everyone here?
She was thankful and loving, unselfish and true;
She was spunky and cheerful and fun-loving too.

How did she become what we knew her to be?
What gave her this spirit, so loving and free?
What was it about her that made her life shine
With wisdom and love and a spirit so fine?
  She made choices.

When heartache and trouble came early in life,
And home life was filled with much trouble and strife,
She gathered her siblings protectively near
And tended and loved them through many a tear.
  She chose a selfless life.

Deserted by parents with folks she didn't know,
Her sad heart was warmed as she felt their love flow.
Through quiet observance, she made up her mind,
"I want what they have; I'll be one of their kind."
  She chose godliness.

When sent out to work at a tender young age
With no one to guide or direct at this stage,
The dance hall nearby held allurements for all.
Her heart, though so lonely, chose heeding God's call.
  She chose God.

When Marty came courting and asked for her hand,
Though others objected, they both took their stand.
She said, "Yes, I trust you and I'll be your wife."
Then she faithfully loved him for all of her life.
     She chose faithfulness.

A home of her own with her family around—
Let nothing destroy all the love she had found!
Then her mother came knocking: "May I have a place?"
Though it was not easy, she leaned on God's grace.
     She chose forgiveness.

Many others came also to draw from her store
Of compassion and love—she turned none from her door.
Her arms opened wide, and she took them all in—
Foster children and neighbors and much of her kin.
     She chose compassion.

Of beauty around her she always took note,
From the sunrise at morn to the poems she could quote.
The birds and her flowers she tended with care.
She saw good in people; their faults she did spare.
     She chose a good thought life.

Her Bible was precious; she marked it with care.
Every evening would find her with head bent in prayer
For children and family and each needy soul.
She asked God to help them to reach heaven's goal.
     She chose devotion to God.

Of her love for her church there was never a doubt.
She was there when she could, so as not to miss out.
She faithfully served and supported in prayer
Her leaders and others in missions elsewhere.

      She chose loyalty.

Her heart was so full as she spent her last days
In praise and thanksgiving for all of God's ways.
"My blessings too many to count if I would,
I only can say that my God is so good."

      She chose thankfulness.

When life's days were closing, she truly could say,
"I'm glad for the choices I made every day."
You and I can enjoy what her life showed to all
If we make the right choices and heed to God's call.

      Written for Norma's funeral

Background History of John and Alzina

John Wayne Brenneman was born in the year 1888. He was the son of Henry and Mary Isura (Selner) Brenneman. John's mother died leaving three small children: Sarah—age five (Aunt Sarah), John—three, and Mertie[4] (baby). Two years later, Henry married Sarah Berky, who was the mother of Joseph, Salome (the brother and sister who kept Art), and Amanda.[5] John's stepmother, Sarah (Berky) Brenneman, died when he was fifteen. Two years later Henry married Lydia Buehler (from Ontario). Shortly after this marriage in 1905 the family moved from Indiana to northern Michigan. They traveled slowly by covered wagon, stopping to spend a summer in central Michigan. John was a boy of sixteen or seventeen when they made this move.

[4]Mertie married Solomon Reist, moved to Oregon, and died at age 34.
[5]Amanda married Amos Gregory and died in childbirth.

Henry had bought forty acres of timber from the Bogardus Lumber Company. History indicates that Henry may have traveled as a teenager to northern Michigan with others to encourage the church there. Sometime after arriving in Brutus, Henry was ordained minister. He served the Old Order Mennonite congregation at Brutus as long as he lived.

John Brenneman spent the next few years very likely helping his father clear land and set up a homestead. The lumber company had taken what they wanted and then sold the land cheap. Clearing the land of stumps and timber was no small job. When Alberta fever went through the area, John caught it. Alberta was called the "last best west." The treeless plains of Alberta sounded exciting. Besides, John was twenty-one and the government was offering a good deal in 160-acre homesteads to develop land along the proposed railroads. Several men from Brutus traveled to Alberta and bought land near Youngstown, Alberta, going by the recommendation of the local storekeeper and not even viewing the land. They returned to Brutus to bring their families back to Alberta in the spring of 1910. Excitement ran high and John was young. On March 2, 1910, John, Aaron Detweiler, Solomon Reist (who later married John's sister Mertie), and James Buzzard left for Alberta. More people followed them. Little is known about the trip to Canada. John mentioned having a big tent, which would indicate they possibly did not go by train.

When they arrived, John and Aaron Kilmer put up a crude shelter and covered it with tarpaper. They had a stove in the center for warmth. They piled straw along one side. Everyone put their blankets on the straw to sleep. The shelter was shared with Owen Kilmer's, Noah Brubacher's, and Dan Burkhart's, who followed later. Then they built homes until everyone had a place to live. History says this group of pioneers came with few resources and only primitive equipment. They plowed their fields with one-bottom riding plows and oxen. The sandy soil plowed easily, but it was very vulnerable to erosion. When the wind and heat came, the fields began to show some ugly scars.

Eventually a school was built, which later became the meetinghouse for Clear Water Mennonite Church. A Sunday school was organized, but services were very irregular since there was only the occasional visiting minister until 1914.

In 1914, crops were a complete failure. Noah Brubacher's family at Brutus chipped in to help the family move back to Michigan. John Brenneman, Jonas Brubaker, and Owen Kilmer decided to strike out for something better. There were Brutus, Michigan, people who had relatives at Mayton, Alberta. So that fall they headed northwest.

John recounted to his daughter years later how they piled a few things on the horse-drawn wagon. They drove several cows along that provided milk for them. They would stop, milk the cows, put the milk in a tin bucket and hang it on a tripod over a fire. The ladies had made a fifty-pound bag of biscuits. They put some of these biscuits in the warm milk, and that was their meal. At night they slept in the covered wagon.

It was 180 miles to Mayton, and the roads were very primitive. One time they had a snowstorm and had to lay over for a couple days. Mercifully, the Lord provided an empty farm with a house and barn. There was hay in the barn which they fed to the cows and horses. They found and attended a Mennonite church at Mayton. That is where John met Alzina Ruffert. John was twenty-six years old, and Alzina was nineteen. Henry Ruffert, her father, said that John needed to work for him for two years if he wanted to have Alzina. On February 20, 1916, they were married in Henry Ruffert's home at Mayton.

Alzina's parents were Henry (1860-1917) and Veronica (known as "Franey" 1860-1947) (Hembling) Ruffert. They had moved to Alberta from Woolwich County, Ontario, where Alzina had been born. Information on the Ruffert family is very hard to find. Henry's obituary says that he joined the Mennonite church fourteen years before he died. He tried to live right until the day of his death. He died suddenly (possibly from a heart attack or stroke). His funeral was conducted by J.K. Lehman at the Mayton Mennonite church. He is buried in the

Mayton Cemetery.

The Hembling family is easier to trace (see attached family tree). Alzina was part of a family of at least ten children. She spoke very little about her family except for a story she told of being lost as a child when she followed her brothers into the bush (woods). John and Alzina were married by Noah Weber, who was the minister for the West Zion Mennonite church at Carstairs, Alberta.

The first home of John and Alzina was on a farm with the Ivy Wideman's. Walter Henry was born November 17, 1916. Arthur Harold was born almost two years later on October 1, 1918, at nearby Olds, Alberta.

The family then moved to an apartment in Calgary, Alberta. In less than two years they had moved 150 miles south of Calgary to Redcliff, Alberta. This is where Norma Frances was born June 26, 1920.

Alberta wasn't all that John had hoped it would be. He had had his adventure and found a wife. Now he was ready to move back to Michigan. They left Canada in February 1921. Norma was seven or eight months old. Four-year-old Walter was put in a wheelbarrow for the walk to the train depot. The family moved east of Woodland in a little shack by Bert Lake. Later they moved in with Aaron Kilmer's at Alanson, where Raymond was born September 19, 1922. Again the family moved to Brutus. There baby Elenora was born. This is where our story began.

Brenneman Family Tree

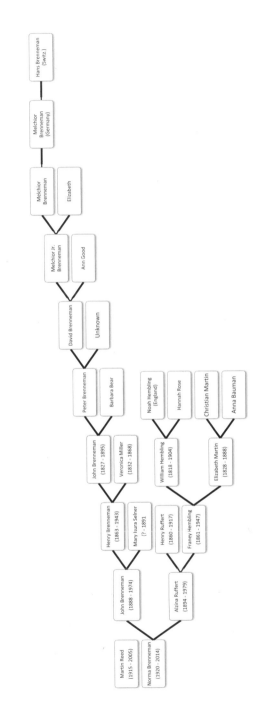

- Hans Brenneman (Switz.)
- Melchior Brenneman (Germany)
- Melchior Brenneman — Elizabeth
- Melchior Jr. Brenneman — Ann Good
- David Brenneman — Unknown
- Peter Brenneman — Barbara Bear
- John Brenneman (1827 - 1895) — Veronica Miller (1832 - 1868)
- Noah Hembling (England) — Hannah Rose
- Christian Martin — Anna Bauman
- William Hembling (1818 - 1904) — Elizabeth Martin (1828 - 1888)
- Henry Brenneman (1863 - 1943) — Mary Isura Selner (? - 1891)
- Henry Ruffert (1860 - 1917) — Franey Hembling (1861 - 1947)
- John Brenneman (1888 - 1974) — Alzina Ruffert (1894 - 1979)
- Martin Reed (1915 - 2005) — Norma Brenneman (1920 - 2014)